in memoriam
Richard G. Shoup
George Spencer Brown

Chapters Volume I

Iconic Arithmetic

simple

sensual

postsymbolic

Volume II
SYMBOLIC and POSTSYMBOLIC
FORMAL FOUNDATIONS

William Bricken

Iconic Arithmetic

Volume II

Any comments, corrections, refinements or
suggestions you may have will be greatly appreciated.

You can reach me via email at
william@iconicmath.com

Thanks.

In this series, available from Amazon Books:

Iconic Arithmetic (2019)
  Volume I   The Design of Mathematics for Human Understanding
  ISBN: 978-1-7324851-3-6

Iconic Arithmetic (2019)
  Volume II   Symbolic and Postsymbolic Formal Foundations
  ISBN: 978-1-7324851-4-3

Iconic Arithmetic (2021)
  Volume III   The Structure of Imaginary and Infinite Forms
  ISBN: 978-1-7324851-5-0

Chapters Volume II

Chapter Map

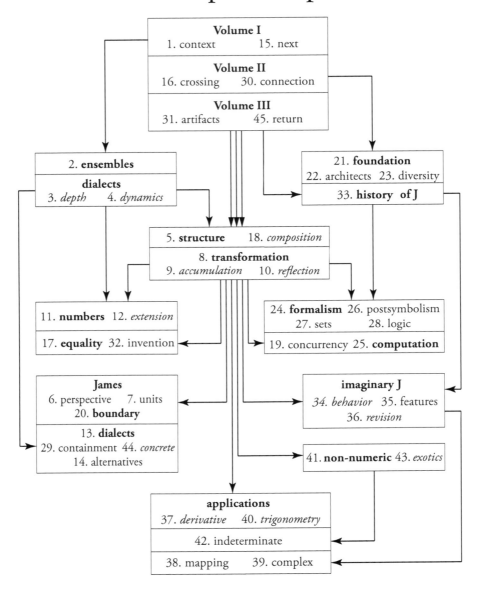

Arrows indicate flow of content.
Bold font indicates the focus of the block of chapters.
Italic font indicates a focus on demonstration of transformations.

Contents Volume II

Chapter 18. Composition   53

Chapter 19. Concurrency   73

Chapter 25. Computation   231

List of Figures

Cast of Characters

Visionaries

Aristotle
Gregory Bateson
John Horton Conway
Gottlob Frege
David Hilbert
Gottfried Leibniz
Giuseppe Peano
Charles Sanders Peirce
George Spencer Brown
Bertrand Russell & Alfred North Whitehead
Ludwig Wittgenstein
Stephen Wolfram

Voices

Alain Badiou
Paul Bernays
Richard Dedekind
Stanislas Dehaene
Solomon Feferman
Louis Kauffman
Jaron Lanier
Brian Rotman

Research and Perspective

Paul Benacerraf
Gregory Chaitin
Tobias Dantzig
John Derbyshire
Curtis Franks
Joseph Goguen
Mark Greaves
Verina Huber-Dyson
Stephen Kleene
Morris Kline

Donald Knuth
George Lakoff & Rafael Núñez
Rinus Plasmeijer & Marko van Eekelen
Hilary Putnam
Jean van Heijenoort
Francisco Varela
Fernando Zalamea

Colleagues

Art Collings
Graham Ellsbury
Jack Engstrom
Thomas Etter
Fred Furtek
Robert Horn
Jeffrey James
Louis Kauffman
David Keenan
Thomas McFarlane
Meredith Bricken Mills
Daniel Shapiro
Richard Shoup
Andrew Singer
William Winn

Special Thanks to

Paul Allen
Colin Bricken
Ian Bricken
Julie Bricken
Doug Emory
Jeffrey James
Louis Kauffman
Jaron Lanier
Ted Nelson
Daniel Shapiro
Richard Shoup
John Walker
Stephen Wolfram

Supporting Quotes and Concepts   *chapter*

Mentioned

Editors and Translators

(ed.)	*chapter*	(trans.)	*chapter*
W. Barfield	19	W. Beman	22, 23
J. Barwise	24	W. Ewald	27
J. Bendegem	23	R. Gaye	22
J. Bransford	26	G. Halstead	16
W. Brauer	19	R. Hardie	22
W. Disney	18	P. Mancosu	23
M. Donovan	26	I. Mueller	23
B. Engquist	17	L. Robinson	26, 28
B. Findell	26	D. Schlimm	28
T. Furness	19		
C. Hartshorne	29		
R. Hersh	28		
C. Janvier	26		
K. Ketner	26		
J. Kilpatrick	26		
D. Leivant	19		
B. Magnusson	26		
B. Meyer	26		
J-F. Perrot	26		
H. Putman	26		
C. Rollinger	19		
W. Schmid	17		
J. Swalford	26		
J. van Heijenoort	17, 22, 28		
I. Wachsmuth	19		
P. Weiss	29		

Preface

All fundamental questions can be settled
in a specifically mathematical way,
without having to rack one's brain about subtle logical dilemmas.
— Paul Bernays (1921)

When this project began, it was envisioned as an application of boundary techniques to numeric arithmetic, to be followed by a report on my twenty years of work with boundary *logic*. I thought that arithmetic would be a friendlier and more familiar introduction to iconic thinking than would logic. As the chapters of *Iconic Arithmetic* accumulated, it became clear that there were three relatively separable areas: basic iconic arithmetic, historical grounding and the exotics of imaginary and infinite forms. Each of these areas has taken a separate volume to explore, primarily to make the technical case for iconic math both structurally and computationally, and to provide a thorough description of historical modes of thought. Several major themes have emerged:

Comparative Theme: The concepts of elementary mathematics have evolved over millenia based on what seemed to be good ideas at the time. However *math is designed* and different designs lead to different ways of thinking about mathematics, about structure and about the world. This theme grew out of the recent evolution of computer programming languages.

Computational Theme: If mathematics were to be measured by how it is used, then *almost all math is silicon computation*. With the introduction of metamathematical concepts such as effective procedures, algorithmic decidability, finite resources and ubiquitous computation the focus of formal thinking has shifted from valid proof to computational feasibility. Wolfram's *Mathematica* has demonstrated that symbol processing is no longer within the domain of humans. This perspective reflects my choice of profession as a computer scientist.

Perceptual Theme: Many aspects of math are *visual and experiential.* The utter dominance of symbolic forms of math narrows our thinking and disenfranchises the majority of folks who are exposed to elementary math education. This theme grew out of my study of Spencer Brown's *Laws of Form* and out of Francisco Varela's approach to the embodiment of concept, as well as dozens of years teaching mathematical ideas.

Discovery Theme: Iconic arithmetic incorporates some *fascinating design features,* such as the pervasiveness of *void*, the dual nature of boundaries, the structural freedom of multiple dimensions, the natural parallelism, three elegant yet comprehensive axioms, and the surprising new methods of transformation. These features are reflected in new ways to think about structure and about reality. This theme was inpired by the work of Louis Kauffman and is a result of several decades of implementing formal iconic software tools.

Perhaps needless to say, I also learn by writing.

•••——————————————•••

I awoke one morning in 2015 to realize that my training in formal systems circa 1980 was, to say the least, antiquated. In the twenty-first century I was using a style of mathematical thinking from the early twentieth century, ignoring the fundamental evolution of mathematical perspective due to Grothendieck (algebraic geometry), Baez (n-categories), Chaitin (undecidability), Wolfram (universal computation) and others. I began to see that elementary logic and arithmetic are not determined, secure or natural. The iconic tools I had been working with for years have just as valid a claim to mathematical foundations as do the early explorations that led us today into set theory, Boolean logic and functional thinking. The bulk of the mathematical community still bases their formal thinking about numbers on Peano's axioms, while the modern evolution in mathematical thought appears to have taken place in the more rarefied atmosphere of the unification of advanced abstraction. Short of returning to school, I tried to leverage my antediluvian education to build what appear to be quite different systems of *elementary* mathematical thinking.

•••——————————————•••

Volume I of this series describes two alternative ways to conceptualize numbers. **Ensemble arithmetic** mirrors the evolution of numeric math for thousands of years prior to the symbolic dominance that took hold less than two hundred years ago. **James algebra** embodies iconic structure to open new perspectives on elementary arithmetic by reformulating the "laws" of algebra. And there are plenty of surprises, especially the unexpected appearance of **imaginary and infinite forms**, both of which constitute the content of Volume III.

This Volume II is focused on **comparative axiomatics**, comparing James algebra to our current formal foundations for the arithmetic of numbers. Three simple structural James axioms ground iconic transformations throughout the three volumes. From a computational perspective nothing is remote, complicated or indirect, given the narrow focus on elementary math.

Here we explore the potential of a postsymbolic math that injects our current formal foundations with multiple heresies while still respecting the formality of mathematics itself. To justify the imposition of new iconic forms and trans-forms, I've described and compared the approaches of several technically different fields including numeric arithmetic and algebra, predicate logic, set theory, computational pattern-matching, educational methods and iconic boundary mathematics. Not only is there no agreement across fields about the basic structures of arithmetic, there is also no communality across tools and objectives. Iconic math adds yet more enrichment through diversity.

Volume II feels quite different than Volume I, with deeper, more historical questions at the foundations of the current philosophies of mathematics. This is a necessary volume to address the many technical details about the structures, assumptions and thought processes that we now expect grade school teachers and students to grasp intuitively.

••• ———————————— •••

In reading the text, backward reference to Chapters 1 through 15 refer to Volume I. All structural necessities are included in Figure 16-1 of Chapter 16. Forward reference to Chapter 31 through 45 refer to Volume III. Figures 30-1 through 30-3 include all new structural forms introduced in Volume III. All references to online content have been verified as accessible during the latter half of 2018. The iconicmath.com website is the nexus for the content in these volumes and for forthcoming volumes focused more on computational logic.

The narrow side columns on each page hold handy illustrations and reminders in support of the text. In the case of formal transformation sequences, the rules being applied are listed line-by-line in the margins.

Aside from delimiting brackets that serve as unified iconic objects/operators, there are a few symbolic characters that have unusual roles.

I've used typographic delimiters, ( ), [ ], < > and others rather than Spencer Brown's spatial mark, ⌐ , for easier typography and to make available several different representations for types of spatial containers.

A fixed width Monaco font identifies mathematical forms and functions, while the linguistic content is printed in Cochin font.

The finger ☞ indicates a change in formal system, usually moving between iconic James forms and conventional string expressions.

The numeric unit represented by a round-bracket has two forms, ( ) and o.

The arbitrary James base is represented by #.

The quasi-token *void* is meant not to exist.

A *frame* is the James structure (A [B]) with A the *frame type* and B the *frame contents*.

••• ——————————— •••

The opening quote by Paul Bernays is a summary description of the goals of Hilbert's program to convert mathematics into a purely structural discipline. That indeed is the approach taken herein, with the fundamental difference that structure is illustrated by iconic images rather than expressed by typographic strings of symbols.

••• ——————————— •••

I do hope you too will enjoy this exploration of iconic form and postsymbolic thinking.

william bricken
Snohomish Washington
March 8, 2019

Iconic Arithmetic

Volume II

Chapter 16

Crossing

We have allowed only one kind of relation...
a cross is said to contain what is on its inside and
not to contain what is not on its inside.[1]
— *George Spencer Brown (1969)*

The first two chapters of Volume I retrace the earliest recorded evidence that *homo sapiens* engaged in activities to answer the question "How many?". The system in use in antiquity was *tally arithmetic*: beads and knots and marks that record a one-to-one correspondence presumably with physical objects. As tallies accumulated they were gathered into groups. Putting tallies together *defines* addition. Grouping tallies defines multiplication. Hilbert, Frege, Peano and other founders of modern formal arithmetic at the turn of the twentieth century had tally arithmetic firmly in mind as the intuitively obvious foundation of numbers. **Ensemble arithmetic** extends this belief with the iconic techniques introduced by Charles Sanders Peirce in the 1890s and by George Spencer Brown in the 1960s.[2]

The second formal system in Volume I is **James algebra**, originally developed by Jeffrey James and myself in the early 1990s at the University of Washington, and inspired by the work of Louis Kauffman at the University of Illinois at Chicago. We migrated our approach to iconic

```
|
||
|||
||||
||||
```

representation and computation to Interval Research Corporation[3] during that decade, to implement under the direction of Richard Shoup several boundary mathematics software and hardware systems. The Natural Computing Project's mission was simple: If you could redesign computation from scratch, with no concern for backward compatibility, what would you do? These volumes are a relatively small yet foundational part of the answer.

Volume I explores the nature of a unit, how pattern variables support transformation, and the iconic path that connects accumulation with counting, addition, multiplication and exponentiation, the bread-and-butter of numeric operations. Two complementary boundaries define these operations. One more reflective boundary gives us all of the inverse operations. For completeness Volume I shows how polynomials, real numbers, fractions and bases can all be understood as patterns of containment. The three James boundaries unify the diversity of numeric expressions as patterns that make *no direct reference* to numeric concepts. Volume I then shows how these patterns are postsymbolic, their iconic form can be rendered in a wide variety of spatial and experiential dialects.

round   ( )
square [ ]
angle   < >

We'll now cross into Volume II, to compare James algebra to the foundational theories of formal arithmetic developed during the early twentieth century. How can a *new* formal structure, an **iconic structure**, come into being for something we know so well? How can arithmetic not be the arithmetic that we learned in grade school? History suggests that our understanding of arithmetic is undergoing continuous evolution. Formalization was a first rather than a last step in the definition of numeric structure.

16.1 James Algebra

Figure 16-1 is a summary of the structural basis of James algebra developed in Volume I. Transformation equations have names for application in either direction. All forms

Axioms and Theorems of James Algebra

Ground Interpretations

o = ( )   ☞   1   (o)   ☞   #

< >   ☞   ∅   <o>   ☞   −1

[ ]   ☞   −∞   <[ ]>   ☞   ∞   *(volume III)*

Unit Definitions

( ) ≠ *void*   **existence**

( ) ( ) ≠ ( )   **unit accumulation**

[ ] [ ] ⇒ [ ]   **unification**

[ ]<[ ]> ⇒ *indeterminate*   **indeterminacy** *(volume III)*

Pattern Axioms

([A]) = [(A)] = A   **inversion**   *enfold/clarify*

(A [B C]) = (A [B]) (A [C])   **arrangement**   *collect/disperse*

A <A> = *void*   **reflection**   *create/cancel*

Interpretative Axiom   *(volume III)*

(<[ ]>) = <[ ]> = [<[ ]>]   **infinite interpretation**

Theorems

( ) <( )> = *void*   **unit reflection**   *create/cancel*

([ ]) = [( )] = *void*   **void inversion**   *enfold/clarify*

(A [ ]) = *void*   **dominion**   *emit/absorb*

A = ([A][o])   **indication**   *unmark/mark*

A..$_N$..A = ([A][o..$_N$..o])   **replication**   *replicate/tally*

<<A>> = A   **involution**   *wrap/unwrap*

<A><B> = <A B>   **separation**   *split/join*

<A <B>> = <A> B   **reaction**   *react/react*

(A [<B>]) = <(A [B])>
(A <[<B>]>) = <(A <[B]>)>   **promotion**   *demote/promote*

Figure 16-1: *Summary of definitions, axioms and theorems*

are represented in a minimal iconic language of typographic delimiters, with some exceptions explained more
thoroughly in Volume I. Within James algebra

— The numeric unit has both a boundary form,
( ), and a single character abbreviation, o.

— The Replication Theorem is generalized to N
replications by the composite symbol . .ₙ. . .
N is finite, although there is no implication that
N is a natural number.

As metalanguage to straddle the chasm between iconic
and symbolic languages,

— The **interpretation finger**, ☞, indicates when
we have changed formal systems.

— The **arbitrary base** made specific by interpretation
is symbolized by #.

— The **absence of a form** and the pervasive space
underneath forms is brought to awareness by
the virtual indicator *void*.

accumulation

• • ≠ •

While respecting the structural constraints of formal
systems, common arithmetic and its algebra can be fully
described within James algebra by the Accumulation
Principle and three structural axioms that are analogous
to the conventional operations of

— additive inverse   **Reflection**

— functional inverse   **Inversion**

— distribution   **Arrangement**

The Inversion and Arrangement axioms specify the interaction of round-brackets and square-brackets. They are
sufficient for addition, multiplication and exponentiation.
Reflection provides the definition of the angle-bracket,
and is necessary to establish the Dominion theorem.
Reflection provides the inverse operations, Dominion
provides the behavior of conventional 0. A Composition
Principle governs construction and deconstruction of
James forms and defines structural identity.

Numbers, and how they work, arise from ignoring differences within a vast panoply of structural uniqueness in three specific *iconic* ways.

— **No ambiguity:** Forms participate only in sameness or in difference.

— **Void-equivalence:** Two axioms identify structure that has no meaning.

— **Structural variety:** One axiom, Arrangement, generates the diversity of structures that look different but are not different.

A few structural theorems have been identified as useful, patterns that occur sufficiently often that we deem it convenient to provide them with a name. Thus far theorems have served only two purposes: to help to articulate how accumulation works, and to juggle around the structural location of angle-brackets. Two theorems, Indication and Replication, manage the generation and collection of replicated structure and help to explain the process of counting. The four theorems for angle-brackets are quite useful for transforming reflected forms, however only Promotion is essential. Arrangement and Promotion are the only patterns that rearrange containment structure. Promotion moves angle-brackets through inversion frames. Conversely, angle-brackets that cannot be promoted indicate sites of structural complexity. All other patterns create and delete structure. Form that can be arbitrarily deleted cannot impact fundamental structural variety, nor can its interpretation impact numeric value.

As indicated in the Figure 16-1, Volume III introduces one more unit definition and one more interpretative axiom. These are sufficient to organize the diversity of non-numeric forms, those forms that contain an empty square-bracket. Indeterminacy and Infinite Interpretation are postponed until infinite expressions and the exceptions they visit upon conventional arithmetic can be more thoroughly explored in Chapters 41 and 42.[4]

Concept and Design

Iconic arithmetic addresses both arithmetic and algebra. Arithmetic deals with specifics, how empty boundaries work together. Algebra deals with generalities. An algebraic pattern-variable stands in place of any form. What web of interrelations between arbitrary forms do the three James axioms induce? Of course, we have the freedom to nominate whatever structural relations we are interested in. However there are many, shall we say, **meta-constraints** that not only define what we mean by a formal system but also limit the kinds of relationships that we may choose.

a specific form

( )( ))

an arbitrary form

A

A primary design decision in James algebra is to limit forms to the physical reality of containment, augmented by an ability to produce replicas of labels. We cast our anchor out onto the shore of constructibility in the physical world. This decision is both a preference and a discipline, based on a belief that school children will be able to understand what they can touch. This decision immediately separates our exploration from what many would consider to be mathematics.

iconic existence is physical existence

The James axioms were not selected out-of-the-blue to define some forms that we would like to be equivalent. Rather the form of the axioms themselves comes with intention. A belief that guides the entire algebraic exploration is that *void* can have no relationships of any kind, contrary to symbolic concepts like zero, or the empty set, or logical FALSE. Our belief that *void has no structure* pays immediate dividends. We can simplify some structural consequences by ignoring them. **Void-equivalence** is a powerful ally in keeping it simple.

nothing has no structure

A second guiding belief is that *forms are unique* precisely because they are not other forms. Axioms create relatively small groups of forms that we can consider to be the same, and what is left outside of equality is *uniqueness*. It order to respect the uniqueness of forms we have elected to believe that *forms interact only with their container*, and with nothing else. When we put an orange into the basket with an apple, we choose to believe that the orange does not change the apple although it does change the basket by increasing its load.

To distinguish between numeric difference and conceptual uniqueness, we've incorporated the cognitive concept of **distinction** to join them both together. *A boundary is a distinction*, nothing more. It creates both inside and outside, two convenient concepts that allow us to localize differences. Axioms are choices to ignore differences, nothing more. By choosing to ignore just three kinds of difference (Involution, Arrangement and Reflection) we find ourselves able to identify within what is left that which our culture recognizes as the numbers of arithmetic.

16.2 Iconic Math

In this volume we return to the foundations of arithmetic developed over a century ago, to compare the metamathematical foundations of David Hilbert and his cohort to the perspectives and thinking induced by iconic form. We lurch into *postsymbolism* and find it necessary to abandon the comforts of set theory, logic and functions. And in the process we accomplish one of the primary goals of this work: a proof of principle, if you will, that our universally accepted way of thinking about numbers is *an option*, a temporal social decision not necessarily blessed with any absolute understanding of the nature of numeric thinking itself. Iconic arithmetic thus provides a path for numerics to follow logic into modernization from absolute Truth to relative truths.

A central idea that we are exploring is at the core of iconic notation: *a representation resembles what it means*. Boldly, we are reuniting human perception with the meaning of what we write down. The purely symbolic approach of predicate calculus cannot call upon the obvious:

Look, ( ) exists. Look, it is empty.

In symbolic notation, we must develop a non-intuitive language just to assert that we have elected to begin by drawing a distinction.

Utter Simplicity

iconic thinking

Although all results are formal, none of the three volumes on James algebra have a specifically *mathematical* style. There is little attempt to organize by definition, theorem and proof or to connect syntax to semantics. However, the philosophical commitment to remain **utterly simple** has resulted in two innovations. The first is that the use of *iconic representation* itself greatly simplifies the conceptual structure of numeric arithmetic and algebra. The second is that the consequent *iconic conceptual structure* greatly simplifies what would be considered to be algebraic computation and proof. The cost, which might not be surprising, is that iconic arithmetic throws us into unfamiliar territory. The classical styles of numeric calculation and the classical theorems of number theory are not directly motivated by the iconic foundation. Even the group theoretic foundations of modern algebra are abandoned. By looking in a pictorial direction we are able to see different facets of the mathematical enterprise. We are thus trespassing not only into Number, but also into the structure of elementary mathematics itself.

Mathematics of Mathematics

Metamathematics is about how mathematics works. What are the foundations of math? What are the essential principles? What can we believe? This entire volume is, in essence, an inquiry into the metamathematics of the arithmetic of numbers. The *computational approach* to mathematics is a variety of philosophy. The mathematical philosophies developed over one hundred years ago are being eclipsed by contemporary developments in both abstraction and computation. **Symbolic mathematics** now *means* mathematics performed by general purpose computational software such as *Mathematica*, not the kind of symbol juggling done by students in algebra class nor the symbolic metatheory envisioned by Hilbert. How should math be made accessible to humans, particularly to younger students? What is the *scope* of mathematical philosophy? Is it the historical thoughts of great minds, or perhaps very modern approaches that garner the Fields medal (the Nobel prize for mathematical accomplishment), or is it the foundational beliefs upon which mathematics rests, or possibly what practicing mathematicians actually do? Is there room in the philosophy of mathematics for what we teach to children? Is there sufficient tolerance to express formal concepts in multiple spatial-temporal dimensions?

Aesthetics

With boundary math we are attempting to maintain the aesthetic values of formal systems. A benefit of iconic containment is that spatial boundaries permit relations to be exhibited as structure rather than abstracted as symbols or imagined as concepts. Another benefit is that iconic form provides sufficient compositional structure to support formal systems of great simplicity and wide-ranging power.

Scientific success is often associated with the aesthetic value of simplicity. Mathematics too values simplicity, in fact you might say that the *goal* of mathematics is to simplify. Poincaré said "Mathematics is the art of giving the same name to different things".[5] And certainly abstraction itself is a technique to render the complex simple.

Henri Poincaré
1854–1912

The philosophical infrastructure of abstraction, however, is not simple. For example, language cleaves our unified experience of wholeness into ambiguous and fabricated partitions that lack empirical existence.

To describe is to make complex.

We can, alternatively, perceive *images* as wholes. Experience is not as chunky as the words we use to describe it. Experience has no syntax.

Naming physical containers as a ground for semantics is only a convenience used to bridge the gap from mathematical abstraction to physical experience. We could just as easily name maps and territories, or a partial ordering structure, or terminating function calls in a software program. These linguistic anchors are a convenience; in the final analysis we must recognize Wittgenstein's main point, that *mathematics is devoid of reference and meaning.*

Iconic containment does not require the objects and operations that define numeric arithmetic. Everything instead is **patterns of containment**. Over the last two hundred years the primary candidate for an intuitive foundation for mathematics has been the arithmetic of whole numbers. James algebra can be *interpreted* as numeric arithmetic. The three James axioms themselves thus provide an alternative intuitive foundation, a simple visual approach to understanding that lacks only familiarity.

It is not a necessity that a new formal approach be instantly familiar, but it should be easy to follow and easy to learn. For that reason, the proofs (called demonstrations) of each new structural idea in these volumes have been overtly recorded with the names of transformations in the margins. Making the steps in each demonstration explicit accomplishes three important goals.

1) The demonstrations show that the three pattern-transformation axioms are indeed simple and powerful. Although we have appended a dozen theorems, these theorems themselves bundle only a

few proof steps. None are abstract or difficult. All are simple structural shortcuts.

2) There is a clear grounding in physicality: semantics consists only of putting labelled things into containers. The arithmetic of numbers is relegated to interpretation of containment structures.

3) Although it has evolved to be useful, our current number system is clumsy and difficult to use, as are the conceptual structures engendered by symbolic numbers. The demonstrations illustrate a conceptual approach, a way of thinking and a new method of organizing numeric structure built on one numeric concept, that of *accumulation*, and three transformation actions: Arrangement, Inversion and Reflection.

A New Perspective

We are exploring the James form to see if it sheds light upon the complexity of the arithmetic that our global culture has embraced. The goal is not to generate new mathematical theorems, this exploration is about foundations rather than elaborations. The intention is to explore a radically different conceptualization of arithmetic. This volume examines the relationships between iconic form and foundational mathematics circa 1900, well before Mac Lane, Grothendieck, Lawvere and others essentially refocused abstract mathematics to include the structure of transformation processes.

The symbolic perspective is that *a number is what it does.*[6] The iconic perspective is that a number is what it looks like. James algebra is a new method of exposing the behavior of arithmetic, not just by showing different conceptual pathways to understanding what we already know but by showing a different conceptual model of numeric behavior itself. Our modern understanding of unified abstraction (algebraic geometry, non-commutative algebras) is constructed on top of existing foundations, elaborations that have led to the evolving conviction that apparently different maths have the same deep structure, similar to Chomsky's notion of deep linguistic structure that allows the creation of thousands of indigenous languages[7] while providing a common cognitive infrastructure for all. Iconic math does not necessarily shed more light on the deep structure of mathematical conceptualization, rather it shifts to a *different sensory modality*, not linguistic but experiential, not only written and spoken but also seen and touched.

The concept of *equality* has also greatly expanded over the twentieth century due to the influence of category theory. Functions are maps between sets of objects. Category theory considers how these maps work. When maps are equivalent, they are *isomorphic*. Alternatively, within void-based thinking equality means non-existence.

To summarize, Figure 16-2 lists several of the changes in our conception of number that are embodied in James algebra. The figure includes a name and a short description for each concept, although it is the fusion of these conceptual fragments that forms a descriptive whole. The figure also includes a rough visual comparison of iconic form to symbolic expression. In the chapters that follow each of these new perspectives is compared to current ideas about number. The particular differences in the figure are characteristic of but certainly not definitive of iconic math in general.

16.3 Declaration of Independence

According to Plato's metaphysics, mathematics is the study of eternal and unchanging abstract Forms while science is an uncertain and changeable perspective about the world of mere becoming. Plato's view on the relative standing of mathematics and science is unambiguous: mathematics is the highest form of knowledge, science

concept	description	example iconic ☞ symbolic
iconic/symbolic pictures rather than words		[] ☞ *log*
distinction difference rather than equality		≠ ☞ =
containment numeric forms are nested boundaries		([2][3]) ☞ 2 x 3
object/process objects are processes and vice versa		(2 3) ☞ n^2 x n^3
no zero eliminated in favor of pure absence		*void* ☞ 0
void-equivalent forms some forms are illusions without impact or meaning		([2][ ]) ☞ 2 x 0
transformation patterns change by rule-based substitution		⟦A B E⟧ ☞ B+C ⇒ A+C
composition construction of forms replaces induction		A ⇒ A o ☞ n ⇒ n+1
unified inverse inverse functions are one boundary type		(<[<3>]>) ☞ 1 ÷ −3
arbitrary base forms are independent of a numeric base		(2) ☞ n^2
numeric and non-numeric forms mix numeric with non-numeric concepts		([ ]) ☞ $n^{-\infty}$
no sets, no logic, no functions conventional foundations are not incorporated		A ☞ ¬(A = {A})
parallelism forms are independent and transform in parallel		2 3 4 ☞ (2+3)+4
rigorously finite all forms and processes are bounded		$o.._n..o$ ☞ $1+.._n..+1$

Figure 16-2: *Comparison of concepts*

is mere opinion.[8] Math historian Morris Kline recounts how, as a consequence of Plato's opinion, "mathematics became the substance of scientific theories."[9] By the mid-nineteenth century, however, mathematics matured beyond its applications to the Earth, to re-inhabit Plato's purely abstract realm. Mathematical theories grew with no direct (or indirect) physical interpretation. Citing the rise of negative numbers, complex numbers, n-dimensional spaces and non-commutative algebras, Kline remarks that "mathematics was progressing beyond concepts suggested by experience."[10]

Since mathematics itself is **purely virtual** and does not necessarily connect to worldly objects or to concrete experiences, we can say that math is *pure abstract distinction*. Mathematician Michal Walicki: "Number is complete ability to ignore all differences in content."[11] Mathematics has been transformed from a overt mediation between description and reality to a covert contract between cognition and further cognition. This transition laid the groundwork for Hilbert's truly outrageous proposition that mathematics should be sufficient to justify itself without reliance upon any other discipline or grounding. This is in marked contrast to the perspective of working mathematician Verena Huber-Dyson: "The positive integers are mental constructs. They are tools shaped by the use they are intended for."[12]

Symbolic Algebra

polynomial 347:

$(3 \times 10^2) +$
$(4 \times 10^1) +$
(7×10^0)

The techniques of conventional algebra grew out of the study of polynomial expressions over seven centuries ago. Its techniques are particularly well adapted for polynomials, as is the now universal representation of digital numbers. Our interpretation of James algebra does not even have special containers that represent addition or multiplication. Its fundamental disconnection from polynomials provides new perspectives on the structure of our number system.

Algebraic equations rest upon an audacious extension of notation and language: we can choose an arbitrary symbol, in many cases x, to stand in place of both "everything" and what we do not know. **Literal symbolism**, in historian John Derbyshire's words "the systematic use of letters to stand for numbers"[13], is a relatively new mathematical invention introduced by Descartes (and others) in the mid-seventeenth century. Prior, mathematical problems were largely written in words as were mathematical expressions. The *idea* of abstraction itself came slowly. Before the innovations introduced by Descartes, mathematics was about concrete relations and concrete geometrical figures. Descartes' innovation is still in use today. It "inspired Leibniz's dream of a symbolism for all human thought"[14], what today has become **digital convergence**. Derbyshire observes,

> When we compare Descartes' mathematical demonstrations with the wordy expositions of earlier algebraists, we see that a good literal symbolism really does relieve the imagination [Leibniz's words], reducing complex high-level thought processes to some easily mastered manipulation of symbols.[15]

Throughout the next two centuries, until the invention of group theory, algebra was **universal arithmetic**, manipulation of relations between numbers using symbols. It took until the mid-nineteenth century for generalization to be introduced. At the time mathematician Augustus DeMorgan explained:

Augustus DeMorgan
1806–1871

> The formation of symbolic algebra itself is a separation of the essential conditions of operation from the non-essential: the rejection of all meaning over and above the *points of meaning* on which transformations depend.[16]

Here DeMorgan identifies, in modern terms, morphisms between numbers, geometry and trigonometry, noting that "many different sets of meanings may, when attached to the symbols, make the rules necessary consequences."[17] And with James algebra, we have done likewise. The axioms suffice to define an abstract formal system that stands alone. To *avoid* abstraction, for the purposes herein, iconic forms are mapped to numeric expressions. To provide meaning James algebra itself has a concrete mapping to nested physical containers. Thus symbolic abstraction can be replaced by material representation without losing the abstract power of an algebra. In the late nineteenth century founder Richard Dedekind pursued axiomatization of algebra, converting the objects of algebra into pure abstractions based on set theory. The James axiomatization is also pure abstraction, based on the theory of distinctions, for which containers are a concrete visualization.

Arrangement provides an example of one of the recurrent organizing structures within James forms, the **inversion frame**. Frames are structural skeletons that themselves deserved names, not because they are generated often by transformations, but because they are associated with concepts that we consider frequently. Accumulation, for example, leads to frames associated with indication, with cardinality and with accumulation itself. The generic shape of an inversion frame is (A [B]), where A is the frame type and B is the frame contents. Arrangement permits frame contents to be collected or dispersed, both of which are useful for computation. Inversion and Dominion are degenerate types of inversion frames, within which respectively A or B are *void*. Indication, Replication and Promotion are also organized as inversion frames.

Algebraic Dependencies

It is clear that a boundary system requires at least one axiom for each type of boundary. The number of useful theorems that derive from those axioms, however, can be very large. For example, the entire basis of plane geometry

a generic frame
(A [B])

void inversion
([ ])

inversion
([B])

dominion
(A [ ])

indication
(A [o])

replication
(A [o...o])

promotion
(A [<B>])

arrangement
(A [B C])

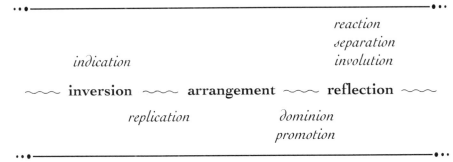

Figure 16-3: *Dependency of theorems upon axioms*

was developed from Euclid's five postulates. A theorem is an encapsulation of several transformation steps. A *useful* theorem summarizes sequences that occur often, usually across different applications of an axiom system.

The seven pattern-matching theorems included in Figure 16-3 are organized spatially by their dependency upon the axioms. The figure tracks which axioms are used in the proof of each theorem, thereby classifying each theorem by the type of boundaries that it, at its foundation, depends upon. This table is empirical. There may be other proof sequences that use different axioms or fewer axioms, the ultimate question of the most useful theorems of James algebra thus has an evolving answer. In Figure 16-3 three of the seven theorems are specialized extensions of Reflection, and one is an extension of Inversion. This limits the importance of these four theorems to that of convenience. The Replication theorem combines Indication with Arrangement of indications. It is at the heart of the process of identifying the cardinality of ensembles. But it is Dominion and Promotion that are fundamental to James transformations. Both are surprises since both facilitate and strengthen the Inversion axiom, yet neither requires Inversion for its proof. Dominion incorporates a *non-numeric form* (that is, [ ] is at the deepest level) but is derived directly from numeric axioms. It thus identifies a bridge between numeric and non-numeric mathematical concepts. The power of Dominion is to render forms void-equivalent, in essence to convert numeric forms into a different non-numeric class, that of non-existence. The power of Promotion is to move angle-brackets outside of inversion frames and thus simplify the internal structure of a form.

Arrangement

arrangement
(A [B C]) =
(A [B])(A [C])

Axioms that rearrange structure can be particularly expensive to use. There appears to be no good way to know which direction Arrangement may need to be applied (i.e. disperse or collect) to minimize a form. Heading simplification toward the canonical most dispersed form can run into intractable growth due to exponential generation of replicas. Heading toward a most deeply nested form runs into non-canonical pathways. What *deepest* means depends upon local choices about which forms to collect together. And there is a potentially exponential number of choices.

The intractable computational behavior of Arrangement is essential. Without such a rule, every transformation sequence would be *tractable*, computation would always be relatively trivial. Only systems that require a non-obvious choice of the direction of application for a transformation are powerful enough to represent useful systems such as simple arithmetic. Thus Arrangement is the primary source of computational and algorithmic complexity in James algebra.

In Entirety

The axioms and definitions listed in Figure 16-1 are used throughout this volume. The new definitions and theorems not included in Figure 16-1 are presented in Figure 18-1 of Chapter 18. These new structural theorems are all related to the Principle of Composition, permitting the equal sign to be integrated into James forms.

16.4 Remarks

Boundary forms provide new structural insights. Most interesting is the substantial structural similarity between two central mathematical systems in our culture: logic and numbers. The distinction between *Arithmetic* and *Logic* is to permit or not permit accumulation. This difference can also be expressed by the behavior of distinction boundaries. Numeric boundaries are **impermeable**, that's why they accumulate. Logic boundaries are **semipermeable**, that's how asymmetric inference works.

Since the Additive Principle is both intuitive and the historical basis of numerics, it may be palatable to accept that addition is putting together and that zero is a symbolic artifact. The same freedoms are not available for logic, a discipline that has been associated over history with how our minds work. Western rationality is built upon the grounds of TRUE and FALSE. Duality is at the heart of our world view. However boundary logic treats *void* with respect, leaving us with only one logical ground. In boundary logic, FALSE does not exist. How can we reason without duality? How can logic be *unary* rather than binary? Peirce and Spencer Brown answer these questions through their iconic foundation for logic that confounds truth with existence.[18]

We begin this volume with a new perspective on equality, abandoning induction in favor of explicit construction of forms. We then explore the elementary structure of pure boundary math. The current conventional definitions of number and arithmetic, the nature of formalism, and its relation to computation are next. The final few chapters introduce postsymbolic thinking and describe how and why set theory, logic and functions are not particularly elegant ideas. The volume ends with the network version of James algebra.

Endnotes

1. **opening quote:** G. Spencer Brown (1969) *Laws of Form* p.6-7. Online 8/18 at http://www.manuelugarte.org/modulos/biblioteca/b/G-Spencer-Brown-Laws-of-Form.pdf.

2. **and by George Spencer Brown in the 1960s:** During the 1980s and 90s I explored many representational and pedagogical varieties of iconic arithmetic, focusing especially on computational *parallelism*.

3. **our approach to iconic representation and computation to Interval Research Corporation:** Interval (IRC) was Paul Allen's research company located in Palo Alto California. IRC operated from 1993 to 2001 (thus the "interval") developing primarily new software tools and algorithms.

4. **more thoroughly explored in Chapters 41 and 42:** The center pieces of Volume III are the non-reducing composite units (<[ ]>), which is nominally called *divide-by-zero*, and [<( )>], called J. These forms provide a sufficient basis for the definition and exploration of infinite and imaginary numbers.

5. **the art of giving the same name to different things:** H. Poincaré (1908) *Science et Méthode* p.375. In G. Halstead (trans.) (1913) *The Foundations of Science*. Online 8/18 at https://www.gutenberg.org/files/39713/39713-h/39713-h.htm

6. **A number is what it does:** P. Lockhart (2017) *Arithmetic* p.182.

7. **the creation of thousands of indigenous languages:** There are estimated to be about 7000 different languages currently spoken by humans.

8. **mathematics is the highest form of knowledge; science is mere opinion:** P. Maddy (2008) How applied mathematics became pure. *The Review of Symbolic Logic*. 1(1) p.16-41.

9. **mathematics became the substance of scientific theories:** M. Kline (1972) *Mathematical Thought from Ancient to Modern Times* p.394.

10. **progressing beyond concepts suggested by experience:** Kline p.1030.

11. **Number is complete ability to ignore all differences in content:** M. Walicki (1995) The origin of mathematics. Online 8/18 at https://www.ii.uib.no/~michal/phil/om/om.pdf

12. **They are tools shaped by the use they are intended for:** V. Huber-Dyson (1998) On the nature of mathematical concepts: why and how do mathematicians jump to conclusions? Online 8/18 at https://www.edge.org/conversation/verena_huber_dyson-on-the-nature-of-mathematical-concepts-why-and-how-do-mathematicians

13. **the systematic use of letters to stand for numbers:** J. Derbyshire (2006) *Unknown Quantity* p.81.

14. **dream of a symbolism for all human thought:** Derbyshire p.94.

15. **easily mastered manipulation of symbols:** Derbyshire p.94.

16. **the points of meaning on which transformations depend:** A. DeMorgan (1849) *Trigonometry and Double Algebra* p.114. (Emphasis in original.) Online 8/18 at https://archive.org/details/trigonometrydoub00demoiala/page/n8

17. **make the rules necessary consequences:** DeMorgan p.93.

18. **iconic foundation for logic that confounds truth with existence:** On page xiv of *Laws of Form* Spencer Brown writes:

> It is possible to develop the primary algebra [his container-based rules of logic] to such an extent that it can be used as a restricted (or even as a full) algebra of numbers. There are several ways of doing this, the most convenient of which I have found is to limit condensation in the arithmetic, and thus to use a number of crosses in a given space to represent either the corresponding number or its image.

The result of limiting condensation is Accumulation. Spencer Brown's number and its image have been separately distinguished in James algebra as round-brackets and square-brackets.

Chapter 17

Equality

Things are equal which may be substituted
for one another without change of truth.[1]
— Gottfried Leibniz (c1680)

Equality is a convenient and pervasive concept at the foundation of most formal systems. Equal forms are indistinguishable, but in two different senses. *Indistinguishable* can mean **identical**; a form is identical to itself.[2] It is an unwritten rule of symbolic notation that units (and labels) do not change definition throughout the course of their manipulation. Only their context changes. The absolute stability of the unit is coupled with the *presumption of free replication*: making exact replicas of a unit imposes no cost. In 1884 founder Gottlob Frege called upon the capability of exact replication, augmented by negation, to bootstrap numbers themselves into existence. "Zero is the number of things that are not identical to themselves."[3]

The second type of equality is what Leibniz is referring to in the opening quote. Expressions are **equivalent** when they are perceptually different but are defined by rule to mean the same thing; they are equal by some specific criterion other than appearance. There can exist

identical

$$5 = 5$$
$$2 + 3 = 2 + 3$$
$$A = A$$
$$(o[A]) = (o[A])$$

equivalent

$$5 = 2 + 3$$
$$2 + 3 = 3 + 2$$
$$2 + 3 = 4 + 1$$
$$A = B$$
$$(o[A]) = (o[B])$$

$$5 = 6 - 1$$
$$= 7 - 2$$
$$= 8 - 3$$
$$= \cdots$$

an unlimited number of apparently different structures that convey the same intention. If we limit our interest to whole numbers, for example, there are still unlimited ways to record the value 5. The key to maintenance of meaning is that different structures must be declared equal by an **axiom**, that is by a belief that is accepted without question. In elementary and secondary education, teaching the meaning and use of the equal sign is notorious in its confusion.[4]

Equality is *maintained* via pattern-directed substitution of equals. The computational implementation of substitution is described in Chapter 25. In this chapter we explore the first distinction as **difference**, while Chapter 18 follows that distinction through to an calculus of equations.

17.1 Equations

An **equation** is a relation that asserts that two forms are equal based on some criteria of meaning applied equally to both. If the two forms are indeed equal, the equation is declared TRUE. We write A = B. But if they are not equal, the equation is FALSE. We write A ≠ B, so that the recorded symbolic relation remains TRUE. The truth-values, as well as the inverse operation NOT, come from propositional logic, the assumed base of our common conceptualization of equality. Logical truth is a yes or no affair. This leads us to believe that there are two collections that organize mathematical equations, those that are TRUE and those that are FALSE.

Axioms and proof and TRUE equations and logical deduction and algebraic equivalence classes and substitution of equals and void-equivalence are all essentially the same idea but seen from different methodologies. Each different methodology, however, incorporates substantively different ways of thinking.

The difference between the void-equivalence method of boundary math and all others is that *void is not symbolic*. Here we do not need to resort to logical truth. A **container equation** is an observation that two container forms can each be constructed from the other by applying valid transformation rules. There is no implication of maintenance of meaning, since the concept of *meaning* is essential only for a symbolic methodology. The analogous concept in a boundary mathematics is *structure*. Symbols, recall, have no meaning until associated with an interpretation whereas containment structures by default mean the same as their physical counterparts.

> *Structural equivalence is defined*
> *by permitted transformations.*

Necessarily transformation rules maintain structural equivalence rather than structural identity. Containment structure and numeric meaning intersect when boundary axioms are interpreted to be valid numeric transformations. Intention and meaning lie within our explicit choice of particular transformation rules.

Static/Dynamic

When stated as an equation, an **axiom** defines and enforces *invariance of intention* across perceptually different forms. From a static perspective axioms identify two equivalent patterns. From a dynamic perspective, axioms interact in several ways. The patterns of different axioms might overlap, leading to a choice. For example

axioms degrade
inequality

$$([A]) <([A])> = A <A>$$
or $$([A]) <([A])> = void$$

clarify
cancel

The direction in which a transformation might be applied makes every axiom a decision point, left-to-right or right-to-left. These decision trees map out the available choices for a sequence of transformations, whether applied to the moves in a chess game, to medical diagnosis or to determination of the chemical composition of a rock.

Alternatively, axioms are sculptor's tools for designing the shape of symbolic strings.

Axioms directly define equality by a generic pattern, and indirectly by an unlimited number of possible substitutions of that pattern. For example, Inversion directly asserts

$$([A]) \quad = \quad A$$

and when A = ([N]), it directly asserts

$$([[[N])]) = ([N])$$

But Inversion, via *two* applications, only indirectly asserts

$$([([N])]) = \quad N$$

Axioms used as transformation rules identify a specific *before-and-after* pattern and give permission to change the before-pattern into the after-pattern. The equal sign, =, does not distinguish which of the two equated forms is *before* and which is *after*. Since axioms incorporate linear steps (and time) indirectly, they are both before-after temporal structures and timeless definitions. This is an example of object/process unity.

Proof

Symbolic proof builds a sequence of permitted substitutions that change an initial form into a target form, thus *demonstrating* that two different forms can in fact be converted into one another. Frege emphasizes that equality and substitution are coupled concepts: "In fact, all the laws of equality are contained in the principle of universal substitutivity."[5]

value means intention

The maintenance of value during substitution is one of the most respected formal laws in mathematics. Here's Wittgenstein, as summarized in the Stanford Encyclopedia of Philosophy:

Ludwig Wittgenstein 1889–1951

Mathematical pseudo-propositions are equations, which indicate or show that two expressions are equivalent in meaning and therefore are inter-substitutable. Indeed, we arrive at mathematical equations by 'the method of substitution': "starting from a number of equations, we advance to new equations by substituting different expressions in accordance with the equations".[6]

Since iconic meaning is embodied in iconic structure, we have adopted herein pattern-directed substitution as the only mechanism of transformation and proof.

17.2 Forms

It is difficult to imagine the absence of a judgmental criteria within mathematics. A declaration of equality is either right or wrong, TRUE or FALSE, until eternity.[7] **Difference**, in contrast, does not rely upon absolute evaluation, just observation. In James algebra *difference between forms is fundamental*. Potential equality of different forms is mutable, depending entirely on the choice of axioms.

Existential Difference

Let's construct two James forms (using the equal sign to define a label, not to make an assertion).

$$A = (\ ) \qquad B = ((\ ))$$

We can observe that $A \neq B$. The observation is supported by two criteria. There is the **observable structural difference** that allows us to construct different labels for the two different forms. And there is an **absence of fit** between the two forms and the three James axioms. Since each of the axioms incorporates a square- or angle-bracket, there is no possible transformation path between A and B. We can easily generalize. Given that no axioms say otherwise,[8]

Structurally different round-bracket forms are mutually unequal.

arrangement

$$(A\ [B\ C]) =$$
$$(A\ [B])\ (A\ [C])$$

inversion

$$([A]) = [(A)] = A$$

reflection

$$A\ <A> =$$

*almost all
existent forms
are different*

Information is carried in forms that are **not equivalent**, while *not equivalent* is defined by the absence of transformation paths. We are now heading into potentially unfamiliar territory. The expressions of conventional algebra are presumed to *exist*, and are usually presumed to refer to something that has a *value*. James algebra includes **void-equivalent forms**, apparent but meaningless structures that can cease to exist. How should void-equivalent forms be handled? How can something that does not exist be equal to something that does? Spoiler: it can't.

*all void-equivalent
forms are identical*

void inversion

$$([\ ]) = ([\ ]) = \textit{void}$$

reflection

$$A <A> = \textit{void}$$

dominion

$$(A\ [\ ]) = \textit{void}$$

Void is non-numeric. Void-equivalent forms cannot be said to be equal to any existent forms; the concept of equivalence does not apply to illusions. Void Inversion, Reflection and Dominion each assert that some forms are phantoms that can be brought into existence by rule. Further, *void* — the absence of form — is pervasive throughout all James forms, so that void-equivalent forms can be constructed literally anywhere. Two examples:

$$([\ ]) \Rightarrow \textit{void}\ (\textit{void}[\textit{void}]) \Rightarrow ([\ ])\ (([\ ])\ [([\ ])])$$

$$\textit{void} \Rightarrow A <A> \Rightarrow A\ B <B> <A\ C <C>>$$
$$\Rightarrow A\ B <B> <A\ C <C>>\ ([D <D>](E\ [\ ]))$$

Reflection permits us to construct meaningless forms that nonetheless have a *catalytic effect* during the simplification of numeric forms. The Reflection axiom provides a bridge to convert equations into void-equivalent forms, and thus eliminate the assertion of equality within James algebra. The angle-bracket thus reflects the difference between distinction and equality. Such reflections emanate from nothing.

The empty square-bracket, [ ], is also both non-numeric and catalytic. As described in Chapter 41, equations involving [ ] cannot be said to have a numeric value or interpretation. However, we can use [ ] during a transformation sequence, given that an empty square-bracket does not occur in the final result.

Grouping

Grouping tallies is fundamental to construction of numeric forms that are easily compared. The size of a group, however, is arbitrary.

Depth-value

In the **depth-value** arithmetic of Chapter 3, nested round-brackets are interpreted as grouped accumulations. Inside and outside provide the two central functions of tally systems, accumulating multitude and putting multitudes into groups.

$$( )( ) \neq ( ) \qquad \text{☞} \qquad 2 \neq 1$$
$$( )( ) = (( )) \qquad \text{☞} \qquad 2^1 = 2 \qquad \textbf{base-2}$$
$$( )( )( )( )( ) = (( )) \qquad \text{☞} \qquad 5 \qquad \textbf{base-5}$$

The specification of the depth-value base is by rule:

$$( )..\,_b..( ) = (( )) \qquad \text{☞} \qquad b^1 \qquad \textbf{base-b}$$

The *depth-value* interpretation of brackets is as **polynomial grouping operators**, so that crossing a boundary multiplies its contents. Depth-value maps directly onto decimal notation. To express cardinal magnitude using bracket forms that can be interpreted as natural decimal numbers, groups as well as units must be additive. The axioms of depth-value assert two types of additivity that combine to support interpretation as polynomials: grouping units and merging groups.

group
$$\text{o}..\,_n..\text{o} = (\text{o})_n$$

merge
$$(A)(B) = (A \ B)$$

James Groups

Grouping of James forms also creates round-bracket forms that, within a numeric interpretation, are **different but equal**. Depth-value brackets lead to a multiplicative interpretation whereas James brackets lead to an *exponential interpretation*. Chapter 11 introduces a *unit magnitude frame* to convert from depth-value form to James form.

$$(N)_{grouped} \qquad \text{☞} \qquad ([N] \ \text{o})_{James} \qquad \textbf{unit magnitude frame}$$

In the James form the specification of a base can be constructed parametrically as an implicit characteristic of nesting *without anchoring to a specific base*. We can attach an arbitrary base to the round-bracket, $( )_{base}$. All that is needed is global substitution of a specific base when one is asserted. We thus arrive at a *definition of base* rather than a specific axiom for numeric grouping.

$$\# =\partial ef= (( ))$$

The **base** of an iconic boundary is simply the change associated with crossing that boundary. The arbitrary parametric base # within the James system can freely be assigned to *any* form, freeing us of the constraint of thinking of bases as whole number accumulation of units, and incidentally making the conventional base-e more palatable. The base-free round-bracket becomes seamlessly integrated into the exponential interpretation.[9]

$$( )_{\#} \quad ☞ \quad \#^0 = 1$$
$$(( ))_{\#} \quad ☞ \quad \#^1 = \#$$

For round-bracket forms, we have been interpreting accumulation on the inside as the magnitude of an exponent. Round-brackets are taken to be **exponential operators**. Contents designate the numeric location within an exponential space. Crossing a boundary raises that boundary's base to the power of its contents. These values grow very large very quickly, since further nesting is hyper-exponential.

$$(( )( )) \quad ☞ \quad \#^2$$
$$((( ))) \quad ☞ \quad \#^{\#}$$
$$(((( )))) \quad ☞ \quad \#^{\#^{\#}}$$

Forms with more than four or five round-bracket nesting levels represent incomprehensibly large numbers. In base-10 for example [10]

$$(( ))_{10} \quad ☞ \quad 10$$
$$(( )( ))_{10} \quad ☞ \quad 10^2 = 100$$
$$((( )))_{10} \quad ☞ \quad 10^{10} = 10 \; billion$$
$$(((( ))))_{10} \quad ☞ \quad 10^{10,000,000,000}$$

Structural Equivalence

Boundary math realigns information with change rather than with state. We observe a boundary from the outside to assess value; we cross a boundary to the inside to change value. Inversion identifies void-equivalent pairs of boundaries. It does not change a form, rather it identifies irrelevant contexts, removing particular patterns of containment. Reflection identifies void-equivalent structure. Although both Inversion and Reflection construct visual diversity, their particular diversity is void-based structure that can be freely discarded. Only the Arrangement axiom meets the criteria of supporting shape-shifting *existent* forms. The uniqueness of Arrangement is worth naming as a principle:

Principle of Structural Equivalence
Only the Arrangement axiom can construct existentially different but equivalent forms.

There are two complementary principles at work,

— Any perceived structural difference between void-equivalent forms is an illusion.

— Existent forms differ, except in rare cases when the Arrangement rule provides a path to other equivalent existent forms.

Absence of Distinction

Equations appear to be adding a new type of boundary relation, in addition to the relation of containment. Equality is a type of container, one in which the containing boundary is *transparent*. A = B is the **absence of distinction**. Equality itself is void-equivalent, and, as explored in the next chapter, equality asserts a void-equivalent structure between two forms.

$$A = B$$
$$is$$
$$A <B> = void$$

A statement of equivalence is converted into an observation of *identity* by making a sequence of permitted transformations. If we begin with an identity relation on a single form, we can then construct the equality of two apparently different forms by making a sequence of substitutions.

$$A = A \quad \Leftrightarrow \quad A \Rightarrow B \Rightarrow C \Rightarrow D \quad \Leftrightarrow \quad A = D$$

identity

| = |

• = •

( ) = ( )

Reversing the construction, we can see that all statements of equality are statements of identity coupled with permitted structural substitutions. Since identity carries essentially no information, an assertion of equivalence is devoid of constructive meaning. This is most reasonable since equality, after all, fails to make a distinction. Mathematician John Baez declares "an equation is only interesting or useful to the extent that the two sides are *different*."[11]

Equivalence does not mean coexistence within the same container. (A B) does not show that both A and B have the same meaning, it shows that they are contained within the same context. *Shared properties belong to the environment*, not to the things within an environment.

$A_{left} = A_{right}$

Frege and others at the turn of the 20th century wrestled with the distinction between context and structure. The classic philosophical example is the Morning Star and the Evening Star which are both the planet Venus. The same thing in different contexts may have different names, but both names refer to the same thing. The difference is the context. In the case of Venus, it is the Sun's relative position to the Earth that defines the different contexts.

From a structural perspective, forms are identical when they **match**, when the contents of every distinction are the same. Matching in turn is imposed by an observer, an Agent acting *as* the environment. Rather than objectify that Agent, and thus construct another distinction, the Agent *is* the Environment.

17.3 Distinction

The concept of *distinction* introduces a different way of thinking about equality. Different numbers are **unequal**, making inequality more fundamental to understanding the concept of number than is equality. This section elaborates upon Chapter 7 which introduces the equal sign, =, via **void-equality**.

"void = void"

The **Principle of Accumulation** asserts that round-bracket forms accumulate rather than simplify. Different accumulations map to different numbers. Accumulation rests upon the observation that *something is not nothing*, which itself is the **Principle of Existence**.

accumulation

$$\bullet \ \bullet \ \neq \ \bullet$$

$$(\ ) \neq \textit{void}$$

existence

The ≠ sign appears to combine two logical concepts, equality and negation, however both of these concepts are derivative of what the ≠ sign means here. Classical mathematics focuses on identifying what is the same: negation of sameness is difference. Here difference is fundamental, indicating that outside differs experientially from inside. The not-equal sign is also a distinction, a marker of difference. The existent empty boundary *is* that distinction, so more elegantly we can write

$$(\ )$$

existence

Existence asserts that a container (a boundary) and void are different, that inside and outside are different. The difference sign ≠ has both descriptive and constructive aspects. Statically the sign asserts that a container can be read as an object, as a frame. Dynamically the ≠ sign asserts that crossing a boundary changes what is visible. We can observe this change when crossing to the inside, when the former container-as-object becomes our containing environment. And we can observe change when crossing to the outside, when our surrounding environment becomes a discrete object.

Our Western European language predisposes us to think in terms of dichotomy, not in terms of existence. Within a void-based formalism, there are unlimited numbers of pseudo-objects that have form without existence. This innovation may be difficult to communicate, since such an approach is not particularly well supported by the words (and concepts) that are available in the English language, nor is it supported by the symbolic structures available within the notations of logic and algebra. The closest that logic comes to the idea of existence is **existential quantification**, the assertion that *there exists* at least one object within a predefined set that has a particular property. Existential quantification is co-defined with universal quantification through a form of double negation, and here too we part ways with logic. For example, the assertion *not-nothing* employs a different meaning of the word *not* than does the assertion *not-something*. From a void-based perspective, not-nothing is prerequisite to not-something. Not-nothing constructs the something, the **initial distinction**. Not-something however constructs something else. The negation of something does not necessarily return to *void*.[12] It can turn, for example, into the opposite of that something.

$$\exists x = \neg \forall \neg x$$

Indistinguishability

Prior to mathematical structure there is philosophy. In order to understand existence, it helps to propose a contrast. We can certainly feel the absence of contrast as total immersion in existence. Reality is indeed full. But to reflect upon all of it requires the fantasy of none of it. We fortunately do not need to delve too deeply into philosophy here. An empty boundary allows us to refer to *void* without the conundrum of destroying *void* by mentioning it.

The archetype for indistinguishability is absence. Aristotle: "The void in so far as it is void admits no difference."[13] In their simplest form, as *absence*, void-equivalent forms are obviously indistinguishable. That indistinguishability allows us to bootstrap into existence a token to acknowledge absence, producing Void Equality.[14]

$$=$$

void equality

Void Equality is an observation that the equal sign stands in place of a **transparent distinction**, with inside and outside arranged in space as the left and right side of the token. Thus, = is just a special type of boundary, one that does not distinguish inside from outside. Alternatively, we can say that = is a fully permeable boundary. The two sides can mix as operationally defined by substitution. In contrast ≠ is opaque to transmission and mixing. Logical implication is yet another type of boundary, logical boundaries are **semi-permeable** (i.e. the boundary logic axiom of Pervasion described in Chapter 15 of Volume I).

permeable =
semipermeable ⇒
opaque ≠

pervasion
A ⟨A B⟩ = A ⟨B⟩

The lone equal sign also asserts that *void* is indistinguishable, but this finesse requires a semantic oversight. Since *void* has no properties, we *cannot* differentiate the sides of the empty equation. *Void* is both indistinguishable and non-replicable.[15] How is it possible to have two replicas of *void*, one on each side of Void Equality without making a distinction, without constructing a replica? The conventional finesse is to generate equality from identity, *a form is equivalent to itself*. This finesse requires symbolic replication. By construction James replicas are also identical, indistinguishable, equal. Unit replicas provide a foundation for existent forms. Multiple units do not condense, rather they construct the natural numbers.[16] Void Equality, in contrast, requires that you and I (as Agents) make an initial distinction in order to generate and then deny a difference. The initial distinction is to carve nothing into two apparently different *things* denoted by the sides of =.[17]

As an example, within an iconic notation, equality does not necessarily invoke the concept of a truth value. The

	identity	*equality*
logic	A = A	A = B
set theory	∀x∀y x∈y ∧ y∈x	∀x x∈A ⇔ x∈B
algebra	≪A≫	≪A,B≫
computation	A	A ⇔ B
void-based	A <A> = *void*	A <B> = *void*

Figure 17-1: *Five views of equality*

two iconic forms might be said to be indistinguishable rather than equal in value. Spencer Brown suggests an interpretation of the equals sign as *"is confused with"*.[18] Iconic equality may assert that certain visual properties are to be both perceptually and cognitively ignored.

17.4 Approaches to Equality

To approach the concept of equality, to define the idea of **no-difference**, we'll need to make some design decisions. This delicate choice requires that we examine the different applications of equality into order to expose embedded logical, set theoretic, algebraic, structural, intuitive, and void-based perspectives. We'll next explore five equivalent approaches to equality:

— *logic:* the logical definition of = as a relation that has a truth-value.

— *set theory:* the predicate calculus definition of sets with equal contents.

— *algebra:* the algebraic concept of an equivalence class ≪A≫.

— *computation:* the computational process of transforming one form into another.

— *boundary:* the Reflection axiom that defines a void-equivalent formal illusion.

$A, B, C \in domain$ *labels identify members of a domain*

$A = A$ *reflexive*

$A = B \Leftrightarrow B = A$ *symmetric*

$A = B \land B = C \Rightarrow A = C$ *transitive*

Figure 17-2: *The relational structure of equality*

Figure 17-1 shows these five versions of equality for both identical and equivalent structures. Both algebra and logic confound the observation of equality with the demonstration of equality via transformation. Algebra tends to use the word *solution* to describe transformation steps, while logic uses *proof*. When several transformations are strung together, within the steps of a proof for example, both logic and algebra behave like computation. Computation differs in that steps taken together to demonstrate an equality can be both sequential and concurrent.

From the iconic viewpoint, the **space of representation** plays a defining role in the meaning of relationships. Textual, string-based notations necessarily impose notational accidents in order to squeeze spatial relations into linear channels. An **accident of notation** is an illusion that has been imposed by notation rather than by intention.

The conventional relational concept of equality is dominated by notational accidents.

Logical Equality Relation

The **equality relation** in logic, $A = B$, specifies that two structurally different forms share the same value. The relation itself represents a truth-value, it is either TRUE or FALSE. Figure 17-2 shows the conventional logical definition of the equality relation. Labels refer to expressions in a given domain, such as natural numbers or logical propositions or in our case, patterns of containment. Equality is **reflexive**, **symmetrical**, and **transitive**. In

Figure 17-2, the arrows ⇒ and ⇔ are *logical* implications, not transformations of form. The logical symbol ∧ means AND.

The notion of **identity**, A = A, makes sense only when considering symbolic form, not actual objects.[19] Here is a primary caution:

Equality is about structure rather than things.

Objects are unique, but when we take the liberty to construct *cognitive replicas* (via multiple indications of objects with a common property), we need some assurance that the replicas are indeed invariant. The **reflexive** relational property asserts that identical replicas indicate the same intention. Existence, however, is atemporal, it requires *one* observation of an object. That observation is, as well, our label for the object. Identity requires a second look, or in the case of symbols, a replication of the original label, to construct two replicas that do not make a distinction. In its desire to be timeless, logic has disconnected itself from temporal implementation details. But the reflexive property has hidden within it an implicit action, to construct a replica that is not different. Both the symmetric and the transitive relational properties also have hidden within them implicit intentions to take steps.

The **symmetric** property gives us permission to take steps in either direction. By acknowledging a direction of reading, by being able to reverse the string equality from A = B to B = A, we are constructing *temporal* access to the two forms A and B. First find A and then find B. If you succeed then you could just as well have first found B and then found A. This temporal, step-wise story is unnecessary if we have concurrent access to both A and B. If logic is timeless, then there is no first or second, we find A and B together, at the same time. But then we have no need to assert that there is a difference in the two textual equations A = B and B = A. The symmetry relation is an accident of a linear notation with two sides, which permits a left/right illusion.

The **transitive** property is even more extreme, it embodies multiple steps. The transitive relation includes an assembly (using AND) of two equalities, which then leads to the stepwise construction (using IMPLIES) of a third equality. Implication firmly embeds the transitive relation in time, there is a before and an after, an antecedent and a consequent. In transitivity, we have a collection of three statements that together assert that three different forms are equivalent. Transitivity tells us that if we have retrieved both A and B (in any order), and we have retrieved both B and C (in any order), then we have retrieved both A and C. Yes, we have. We should expect, conceptually, to access the three forms all at the same time. It may make more sense if we strengthen the stepwise temporal interpretation. If we can follow A to B and we can also follow B to C, then we can follow, by taking *two* steps, A to C.

$A \Rightarrow B \Rightarrow C$

Transitivity has a direction identified by implication $\Rightarrow$. The inference is in one direction only because if we begin with A = C, we cannot necessarily conclude that some intermediate B exists. This asymmetry hides a defect in logical transitivity, the existential requirement that B must exist going forward but not going backward, while at the same time symmetry declares that direction doesn't matter. B in other words can be virtual.

Logical equality is conceptually messy, implicitly introducing temporal steps, directionality, conjunction, counting and existence. It is the *structure* of these relations that makes logical specification clumsy. If we treat a relation as an ordered pair, R(a,b), then the properties of equality seek to contradict this pairwise structure, as illustrated in Figure 17-3. The property R(a) refers to one label only. Specifying reflexivity as a *binary* relation requires the construction of a replica, R(a,a).

	reflexive	symmetric	transitive
relations	A = A	A = B ⇔ B = A	A = B ∧ B = C ⇒ A = C
ordered pairs	R(a,a)	{R(a,b),R(b,a)}	{R(a,b),R(b,c),R(a,c)}
unordered	R(a)	R(a,b)	R(a,b,c)

Figure 17-3: *Ordered and unordered relations*

The symmetric property refers to two relations, R(a,b) and R(b,a), that do not differ. The transitive property R(a,b,c) refers to three labels with the same value. Transitivity cannot be expressed as a binary relation without the addition of the logical concept of conjunction, R(a,b) ∧ R(b,c), which then permits the construction of a third binary relation, R(a,c). It appears as though the relational properties of equality are being defined by a perceived necessity to make logical connectives *binary*. Perhaps because the equal sign evolved during the fifteenth century within equations written on a line, we have adopted an arbitrary constraint that = has only two sides.

The logical arrows of implication are largely gratuitous if we consider what an assertion of equality means within the context of enacting transformations. Timeless logic cannot escape dynamic evolution. We need only one of these conceptual strategies: logic *or* transformation. More fundamentally, logic presumes an eternal, omniscient observer, a know-it-all Agent. For such a timeless perspective even proof is unnecessary. Proof is a way to condescend to humans who must figure things out. Human logic must take steps, make transformations, demonstrate equivalence. Proof takes time. However, we do not need to take inefficient steps by, for example, restricting our vision to binary relational structures brought together by logic signs.

Set Theoretic Equality

In standard (ZFC) set theory, the Axiom of Extensionality defines the equality of two sets. In a pure set theory there are only sets, so that equality naturally applies only to set objects. Extensionality declares that two equal sets contain the same elements.

$$\forall S_1 \ \forall S_2 \ (\forall x \ (x \in S_1 \Leftrightarrow x \in S_2) \ \Leftrightarrow \ S_1 = S_2) \qquad \textbf{set equality}$$

Depending upon what appears to be taste or culture, this axiom can be expressed as a one directional implication or as a bidirectional logical equivalence. One follows from the other given that substitution is available. (Without substitution, computational steps are also unavailable.)

Another way to state Extensionality is that *a set is determined solely by its members*. This places the axiom at the core of set theory, since it defines what a set is. The relational definition of the properties of equality that define the logical perspective are also adopted within the set theoretic perspective. Sets of elements are co-defined by a shared property, while reflexivity, symmetry and transitivity relate members of sets as well as the sets themselves. However, these relations are derivative for a pure set theory in which set membership is the only property available to support description of the concept of sameness.

It is a rather strange historical artifact that there are two types of predicate calculus, *with* or *without* the inclusion of equality. If sets are axiomatized without equality, then it is taken that both equality and substitution are defined by the logical subsystem, as described earlier in this section. But if sets are defined using a predicate calculus that itself does not include equality, then it becomes necessary to define equality within the set theory. The axiom of equal sets with the same members becomes the *definition* of equality, while substitution is then facilitated by another axiom that states that two sets that are defined to have the same members are both contained within a third set.

set substitution $\forall S_1 \forall S_2 \ (\forall x \ (x \in S_1 \Leftrightarrow x \in S_2) \ \Rightarrow \ \forall y \ (S_1 \in y \Leftrightarrow S_2 \in y))$

The trouble is that this entire approach is awkward. The idea that equality itself can be defined as an add-on places transformation also outside of the theory. On the inside then we find a rigid crystalline web that lacks transformation, thus disempowering both perspective and understanding.

Algebraic Equivalence Classes

If we collect together all the forms that can be transformed into one another, that collection is an **equivalence class**. Each equivalence class identifies a disjoint subset of all possible forms. This version of indistinguishability bypasses operational and computational definitions by assuming that all possible transformations have already occurred. Equality is determined not by evaluating a relational structure, but by validating membership in the same equivalence class.

The algebraic perspective is that axioms inherently *partition* a given domain into discrete groups that each define a specific property. Equivalence classes are necessarily **independent**. Every form must fit into one and only one equivalence class. Logic would say that the algebra is *consistent*.

We will need to introduce a new type of container to identify equivalence classes. As it turns out, the conventional notation for an equivalence class is a square-bracket. To avoid confusion with the James square-bracket, we'll use a **double-struck large-angle-bracket** to indicate an equivalence class.

⟪A⟫ is the equivalence class of the form A.

The notation ≪A≫ stands in place of a potentially infinite collection of forms that can be transformed from one into another. The specific form A can be any form in the class, or there may be a special simplest form that serves as the **archetype** of that class. For example, 4 is the archetype of the equivalence class (under addition) of the set of whole number expressions that add to four. Of course, the equivalence class of forms constructed under a different operation such as multiplication would be different.

In effect, the idea of equivalence classes provides a conceptual, infinite database that contains all possible forms and all possible results of multiple transformation between forms. If there is only one equivalence class, the accompanying transformation system is *degenerate*. All forms would be equivalent, so there is no need to assert that some are equal to others. In logic, degeneracy is cursed by the label *inconsistent*.

The properties of the equality relation read quite differently from the algebraic perspective. There is an equivalence class (reflexive) in which we can access two (symmetric) or more (transitive) members.

$$≪4≫_+ = \{1+1+1+1, 1+1+2, 1+3, 2+2, 4+0\}$$

$$≪4≫_x = \{1x4, 2x2\}$$

reflexive
≪A≫
symmetric
≪A,B≫
transitive
≪A,B,C≫

17.5 Structural Transformation

The dynamic counterpoint to static logic and omniscient equivalence classes is pattern-matching coupled with substitution. Statically, we might observe two forms, A and B, and declare them to be equal. Dynamically, we first observe one form, A, and then change it into another, B, by substituting permitted subforms into A until it looks like B.

In computational pattern-matching, there is generally no privileged direction.[20] **Transformation** is literally a way of moving through the members of an equivalence class, with the important difference that only those forms that are constructively visited are relevant. Since

PROPERTY	*reflexive*	*symmetric*	*transitive*
sequential			
concurrent			

Figure 17-4: *Relational structure as graph paths*

we do not visit an infinite number of forms, there is no necessity to postulate an infinite collection of forms in each equivalence class. The computational perspective is *uber*-constructive. Sure there may be an infinity of forms in our imagination, but only those along a transformation path have been shown to exist. As an analogy, if there is a huge natural number that is so huge and so specific that humanity will never visit it, never construct it, and never think of it, then from the computational perspective, that number does not exist. In the language of transformation of forms, *there is no infinite sequence of transformations*. Systems that have this property are **algorithmic**.

> *Equivalence is a journey*
> *quantized by transformation steps.*

Whether a transformation is sequential or concurrent depends upon the machine one is using. Equality asserts that a *transformation path exists*. From this perspective, the **reflexive** relation declares the existence of a null transformation. Doing nothing is a path. When relations are expressed as graphs, a reflexive path is often added as a self-reference, as shown in Figure 17-4. The **symmetric** relation declares that two forms are connected by the same transformation path, and that this connection has no preferred direction. Symmetry converts a directed graph into an undirected graph.

The **transitive** relation declares that paths may be longer than one step. Paths are temporal structures. A step costs a tick of time, so the computational model has embedded within it an *economics*, the effort it may take to transform A into B. Effort is subtle; we could also envision that there are specialized theorems that connect any two equivalent forms. In this case, given the pre-compiled theorems, all steps are of length one. The transformation graph is completely connected. This is, of course, just another way of saying that we have pre-built the equivalence class with an impossibly efficient indexing system (or that our domain is finite and sufficiently small to accommodate human temporality).

Form Equality

In James algebra equality means **mutual transformability**. Equality is an observation of permitted structural change rather than an assertion of truth. Alternatively, equality is **mutual cancellation**. Equal forms cancel one another via Reflection to yield *void*, the ground of sameness.

Containers with equal contents are equal. This is essentially the same definition as set theory, with a focus on process rather than description. Patterns of containment are identical when outer containers match and when each container, recursively, has identical contents. Container identity can be determined by a **graph matching algorithm** that tests whether or not two graphs are the same. This task is known to be computationally intractable. It gets exponentially more difficult each time we add a new graph node. The implication is that forming equivalence classes is an abstract ideal but not a pragmatic reality. This circumstance separates mathematics from computer science.

Void-based Computation

The void-based perspective for identity is expressed by the Reflection Axiom. An application of Composition (defined in the Chapter 18) converts Reflection into Identity.

$$\langle A\rangle\ A\ =\ \textit{void}$$

compose
$$A\ \langle A\rangle\ A\ =\ A$$

cancel
$$A\ =\ A$$

Container equality has this same void-based structure.

form equality

$$A = B\ \Leftrightarrow\ A\ \langle B\rangle\ =\ \textit{void}$$

Void-based algebra supports a fundamentally different approach to both arithmetic and computation. Although boundary forms can, under our current three axioms, be interpreted as numeric expressions, the axioms and the structure of forms are completely independent from the numeric concepts of counting, adding and multiplying. Simplification of numeric expressions and reduction of James forms both require pattern-matching and substitution to trigger transformation. Substitution maintains equality. For numeric expressions it is equality of *numeric value*, for James forms it is equality of *containment structure*. The fundamental difference is that James reduction is driven primarily by deletion, by elimination of structures deemed to be void-equivalent.

The same change of perspective occurs within equations, within numeric relations that declare both equal value and validity of mutual substitution. The **equal sign** is a convenient abbreviation within James algebra, but as shown above, it equates a form with its non-existence. Void-based transformations are therefore simplification of form rather than solution of equations. The concept of equal numeric value becomes the observation that there is nothing left to reduce. Thus, whenever structure (arithmetic or algebraic) remains after reduction, that structure represents the interpretable value of the form in the case of arithmetic, or the structure of constraints imposed upon remaining under-determined variables in the case of algebra. Within a void-based regime, the equal sign is no longer necessary. A similar approach is taken in the study of numeric polynomials which are conventionally set to equal zero so that the roots of the polynomial are more easily exposed.

17.6 Remarks

In this chapter we have suggested that equality can be interpreted as both concurrent (having both sides at the same time) and sequential (having one side and then obtaining the other). The next chapter describes Composition, a primary tool used to assemble and disassemble containment structures while maintaining their equality. It leads to a void-based method of algebraic proof. Composition also takes the place of the conventional tool of mathematical induction which is described in greater detail in Chapter 19.

Endnotes

1. **opening quote:** translated from Latin by G. Frege (1884/1950) *The Foundations of Arithmetic* §65. Also in J. vanHeijenoort (ed) (1967) *From Frege to Gödel.* Online 8/18 at http://www.naturalthinker.net/trl/texts/Frege,Gottlob/Frege,%20Gottlob%20-%20The%20Foundations%20of%20Arithmetic%20(1953)%202Ed_%207.0-2.5%20LotB.pdf

2. **a form is identical to itself:** Identicality was a central philosophical issue in the Leibniz-Clarke correspondence (Clarke was a messenger for Newton) of 1715-16. The debate resulted in Leibniz' Principle, also known as the Identity of Indiscernibles, which is also Spencer Brown's Law of Calling. Things that have exactly the same properties are the same thing. Alternatively, forms are identical when they have the same structure.

3. **Zero is the number of things that are not identical to themselves:** Frege, §74. (Emphasis added.) See Chapter 21 for details.

4. **the meaning and use of the equal sign is notorious in its confusion:** The definition of the equal sign in elementary math textbooks is inconsistent and often contradictory. The classroom use of = confounds many different concepts, including:

— an identity: $7 = 7$
— a label: $x = 7$
— an instruction: $3 + 4 = ?$
— a logical question: is it TRUE that $3 + 4 = 7$?
— an arithmetic assertion: it is TRUE that $3 + 4 = 7$
— an arithmetic axiom: $3 + 4 =\partial ef= 7$
— a computational result: $3 + 4 => 7$
— a relational question: $3 + 4 = 5 + ?$
— a balance point: $3 + 4 = 5 + 2$
— an algebraic axiom: $a + b = b + a$
— a false statement: $x + 4 = x + 3$
— a puzzle to be solved: $2x + 3 = 8$
— a sequence of transformations: $1+2+3+4 = 3+3+4 = 6+4 = 10$

In our context the equal sign identifies an approved substitution of forms. If either side can be matched, then the other side is a permitted replacement.

C. Kieran (1981) Concepts associated with the equality symbol. *Educational Studies in Mathematics* 12 p.317-326. Online 8/18 at https://oak.ucc.nau.edu/smg224/401pdfs/algebrareadings/kieran1.pdf

E. Knuth et al (2006) Does understanding the equal sign matter? Evidence from solving equations. *Journal for Research in Mathematics Education* **37**(4) p.297-312.

S. Powell (2012) Equations and the equal sign in elementary mathematics textbooks. *Elementary School Journal* **112**(4) p.627-648.

5. the laws of equality are contained in the principle of universal substitutivity: Frege §65.

6. new equations by substituting different expressions in accordance with the equations: L. Wittgenstein (1921) *Tractatus Logico-Philosophicus* §6.24. In V. Rodych, Wittgenstein's Philosophy of Mathematics, *Stanford Encyclopedia of Philosophy*. Online 3/17 at https://plato.stanford.edu/entries/wittgenstein-mathematics/

7. right or wrong, TRUE or FALSE, until eternity: Can we predict with confidence that mathematical tools themselves exist to answer any mathematical question? The strategy in the past has been to ban apparently unanswerable questions as monsters. Recently many apparently valid mathematical questions have been proposed that are not clearly TRUE or FALSE. For example, the proposition "Somewhere in the decimal expansion of π there are thirty-nine 7s in a row" does not necessarily have a truth-value that can be determined without potentially examining the entire infinity of decimals in a real number. Yes, it may be the case that in the future we will develop mathematical tools to answer this sort of question. Equally as likely by then we will be able to formulate questions that elude those tools.

Another class of examples is the paradoxes, such as "This sentence is false", which can be said to oscillate in value. And another class is iterated functions that are known to become chaotic. They are deterministic but not predictable in advance. That is, chaotic functions are immune to mathematical abstraction.

8. Given that no axioms say otherwise: In an iconic tally arithmetic, the primary method of generating different but equal forms is *grouping*, which itself is a variety of exponentiation. As discussed in Chapter 3, place-value notation condenses and obscures the exponential structure of numeric variety, leaving the impression that multiplication of different numbers is more fundamental than repeated multiplication of the same number.

Grouping creates an exception to the principle of structural difference since it introduces an axiom that *overloads* structure with two different meanings. Conventionally grouping imbues position with the meaning of multiplication, the famous positional notation for numbers greater than 9. The resulting **base** of the number system then confounds the meaning of units. Technically the behavior of a number should be independent of the base. James forms do not have a base. The base is an arbitrary assignment available to the interpretation of round-brackets as exponential operators.

9. **seamlessly integrated into the exponential interpretation:** Even the convention that a negative exponent represents a reciprocal integrates nicely.

$$(< \; (\;) \; >) \quad ☞ \quad \#^{-1}$$
$$(<[\; n \;]>) \quad ☞ \quad 1/n$$
$$(<[((\;))]>) \quad ☞ \quad 1/\#$$

10. **For example, in** base-10: The acceleration is slightly slower in base-2.

$$((\;))_2 \quad ☞ \quad 2^1 = 2 \qquad ☞ \quad (\;) \qquad (\;)$$
$$(((\;)))_2 \quad ☞ \quad 2^2 = 4 \qquad ☞ \quad ((\;)) \quad ((\;)) = (\;)(\;)(\;)(\;)$$
$$((((\;))))_2 \quad ☞ \quad 2^4 = 16 \qquad ☞ \quad (((\;)))(((\;)))$$
$$(((((\;)))))_2 \quad ☞ \quad 2^{16} = 65536$$

11. **to the extent that the two sides are different:** J. Baez & J. Dolan (2001) From finite sets to Feynman diagrams. In B. Engquist & W. Schmid (eds.) *Mathematics Unlimited — 2001 and Beyond* p.30. (Emphasis in original.)

This quote has subtle overtones. Since the two sides are different but equal, all that is interesting is to find a transformation path.

12. **negation of something does not necessarily return to** *void*: To return to *void* is to return to the circumstance prior to the initial distinction. To negate the intention of communication does not mean that we negate the communicator. As an analogy, not-nothing is an observer/writer/Agent recording a mark on the blank page. The Agent and the mark come into awareness. Not-something might be the Agent erasing the mark. The mark goes away but the Agent unambiguously remains to mark again.

13. **The void in so far as it is void admits no difference:** Aristotle *Physics* Book IV Part 8.

14. **a token to acknowledge absence, producing Void Equality:** It is debatable whether Void Equality is an axiom, or a theorem, or an observation, or a necessity. One perspective is that these metamathematical concepts themselves are inappropriate.

15. *Void* **is both indistinguishable and non-replicable:** That *void* is indistinguishable does not imbue it with a property. Any philosophically imposed properties of *void* are those of the Agent that constructs a boundary capable of supporting an empty interior.

16. **rather they construct the natural numbers:** Idempotency, as in A A = A, is a property of logic, not numerics.

17. **carve nothing into two apparently different things denoted by the sides of =:** This is the same initial distinction that we call upon to differentiate ourselves from the blank page in order to generate written communication.

18. **an interpretation of the equals sign as "is confused with":** G. Spencer Brown (1969) *Laws of Form* p.69.

19. **makes sense only when considering symbolic form, not actual objects:** On p.26 of *Number and Numbers*, philosopher of mathematics Alain Badiou asks

> For what could it mean to speak of the substitutability of an object? Only the letter is entirely substitutable for itself. 'A is A' is a principle of letters, not of objects....the object must fall under the authority of the letter, which alone renders it over to calculation. If A is not identical at all moments to A, truth (or rather veridicality) *as calculation* collapses.

Here Badiou is referring to symbolic representation, however his comment applies equally as well to indices and icons.

20. **there is generally no privileged direction:** Irreversible computation is *lossy*, it loses information by moving forward. Such regimes are rather common, for example, a positive output of a silicon OR gate loses which of the inputs is positive. This is an implementation efficiency choice, however, not an intrinsic logical property.

Chapter 18

Composition

Put 'em together and what have you got?
Bibbidi-bobbidi,
bibbidi-bobbidi,
bibbidi-bobbidi-boo.[1]
— The Fairy Godmother (1950)

The **Composition Principle** is a method to construct and deconstruct container equations. *Forms* are built, or constructed, by putting containers into other containers. If the put operations are the same for two forms, then the forms are identical.[2] Essentially Composition does not change existent forms into void-equivalent forms, and does not convert *void* into existence. Composition is a self-similar procedure that identifies when two patterns have been constructed by the same combination of substitutions. Self-similarity means that Composition applies independently to all subforms within a given form.

Composition Principle (context)

Adding and removing identical outermost containers maintains equality.

Composition Principle (content)

Adding and removing identical outermost contents maintains equality.

18.1 The Composition Principle

The Composition Principle is based on identity rather than equivalence. However, it does not require that two forms be identical. Rather, if two forms are given to be equivalent, then composition provides a way to expose the subforms that require a transformation rule to convert equivalence into identity. Like substitution of equals for equals, composition does not change the truth-value or the equivalence class shared by the two forms.

Identification of constructors and deconstructors for algebraic structures is necessary for computational models and in general is associated with the mathematical approach of initial algebra. An **initial algebra** consists of construction rules for building structures and transformation laws that identify different structures that have been defined to be equivalent. Labels within the initial algebra accommodate any formal interpretation.

Structure itself can be string-based expressions, containment-based forms, or more complex representations such as lists and graphs. Spencer Brown identifies his boundary logic as an initial algebra in *Laws of Form*. Abstract data structures in software programming are also initial algebras, and are particularly well adapted for functional and parallel programming. By formulating James algebra as an initial algebra, we will in Chapters 26 through 28 be able to bypass the conventional complexities of set theory, logic and functions, relying solely upon pattern-directed substitution.

Composition of Context

To illustrate the idea of composition by adding and removing outermost boundaries, we will need a **container variable** that stands in place of any of the three boundary types. We'll use the generic *curly-brace* { }.[3] Here, ⇔ means that the equality relation is maintained.

$$A = B \quad \Leftrightarrow \quad \{A\} = \{B\}$$

compose context
decompose ⇌ compose

Some instances of context composition include

$$
\begin{array}{rcl}
A = B & \Leftrightarrow & [A] = [B] \\
[A\ C] = [B\ D] & \Leftrightarrow & ([A\ C]) = ([B\ D]) \\
A = B & \Leftrightarrow & <(<A>)> = <(<B>)>
\end{array}
$$

From the functional perspective, adding an outer boundary to equivalent forms is an application of Leibniz' law of function substitution. Applying the same function to two equal forms maintains equality. Unlike Leibniz' Law composition is bidirectional as permitted by Inversion and Involution.

$$
\begin{array}{lll}
(A) = (B) \Rightarrow [(A)] = [(B)] \Rightarrow A = B & \quad \text{clarify} \\
[A] = [B] \Rightarrow ([A]) = ([B]) \Rightarrow A = B & \quad \text{clarify} \\
<A> = <B> \Rightarrow <<A>> = <<B>> \Rightarrow A = B & \quad \text{unwrap}
\end{array}
$$

Composition of Content

Adding or deleting equal forms within equal containers also does not undermine equality. The simple case is addition or deletion of equal forms in the shallowest level of equal containers. That is,

$$\{A\} = \{B\} \quad \Leftrightarrow \quad \{A\ C\} = \{B\ C\}$$

compose content
decompose ⇌ compose

Composition of Content can be used to constructively convert Void Equality into any identity, thus embedding the concept that *all forms are identical to themselves*. Given void-equality as a visually obvious axiom, identity then becomes a trivial theorem. Forms can be added to or deleted from deeply nested locations as well, but only in the case that all other forms in both equal containers are also equal. For example,

$$([A][B]) = ([C][D]) \Leftrightarrow ([A][B\ E]) = ([C][D\ E])$$
$$\textit{only when}\ A = C\ \textit{and}\ B = D$$

Here is an applied counterexample when A ≠ C and B ≠ D

$$([2][6]) = ([3][4])\ but\ ([2][6\ 1]) \neq ([3][4\ 1])$$
$$\Leftrightarrow\ 12=12\ but\ 14 \neq 15$$

And a counterexample in the direction of decomposition:

$$([2][7\ 5]) = ([3][3\ 5])\ but\ ([2][7]) \neq ([3][3])$$
$$\Leftrightarrow\ 24=24\ but\ 14 \neq 9$$

Content and Context Together

The Composition Principle can be expressed by combining both content and context together in one rule.

composition

decompose ⇄ compose

$$A = B\ \ \Leftrightarrow\ \ \{A\ C\} = \{B\ C\}$$

Composition is comparable to founder Giuseppe Peano's axiom that defines the equality of numbers: *equal successors means equal numbers.*

$$m+1 = n+1\ \Rightarrow\ m = n$$

and to its equivalent formulation in predicate calculus.

$$\neg \exists z\ x+z = y\ \lor\ y+z = x$$

Peano's axiom is burdened by one-directional implication, while the predicate calculus definition is burdened by existential assertion. Worse, predicate calculus, in its desire to eliminate process and computation, must invoke a void-equivalent variable, stated twice no less, as central to its definition of equality.

0^0 ☞

$((\lbrack\ \rbrack\lbrack\lbrack\ \rbrack\rbrack))$

Composition of context and of content have an important restriction, they *apply only to numeric forms*. In the James notation, we also have creatures such as [ ] that are non-numeric. So, for example,

$$A\ [\ ] = B\ [\ ]\ \textit{does not mean}\ A = B$$

For now, we'll impose the restriction that forms containing an irreducible [ ] must be avoided, and revisit the empty square-bracket in Chapter 41. We'll also treat the outermost curly-braces as implicit, to enhance readability.

18.2 The Reflection Bridge

Identity, equality, void-equivalence and angle-brackets are tightly coupled. In failing to make a distinction, equality defines a void-equivalence. Using Composition then any equation can be converted into a void-equivalent form. Equality Inversion extends Composition of Context while Equality Reflection extends Composition of Content. The Reflection Bridge permits transfer between equational thinking and void-based thinking.

Equality Inversion

Composition allows the movement of outer boundaries across an equal sign, establishing the Equality Inversion theorem.

$$(A) = B \quad \Leftrightarrow \quad A = [B]$$
$$<A> = B \quad \Leftrightarrow \quad A = <B>$$

equality inversion

cover ⇄ cover

The demonstration of Equality Inversion is direct.

```
 (A)  =  B
[(A)] = [B]          compose
  A   = [B]          clarify
```

Similarly for the angle-bracket,

```
  <A>   =  B
<<A>> = <B>          compose
  A   = <B>          unwrap
```

Equality Reflection

Composition allows the movement of subforms from one side of an equation to another, establishing the Equality Reflection theorem.

$$A \, C = B \quad \Leftrightarrow \quad A = B <C>$$

equality reflection

move ⇄ move

Again the demonstration is direct.[4]

```
A C       = B
A C <C> = B <C>      compose
A         = B <C>      cancel
```

Connecting Reflection to Accumulation shows that accumulation arises from the first distinction. Unit accumulation is then rightfully a theorem.

	$\bullet \neq \mathit{void}$
create	$\bullet \neq \bullet <\bullet>$
compose	$\bullet\ \bullet \neq \bullet <\bullet> \bullet$
cancel	$\bullet\ \bullet \neq \bullet$

The Bridge

The **Reflection Bridge** theorem provides a void-based definition of the equal sign.

reflection bridge
bridge $\rightleftarrows$ *bridge*

$$A = B \quad \Leftrightarrow \quad A <B> = \mathit{void} = <A> B$$

The Reflection axiom provides a bridge between two ways of thinking that can be loosely characterized as comparison vs. transformation. Any test for equality can be converted into a test for non-existence. The demonstration calls upon the Composition Principle.

	$A \qquad = B$
compose	$A <B> = B <B>$
cancel	$A <B> = \mathit{void}$

This type of void-based perspective is common in conventional numeric approaches as well.

$$3 = 3 \quad \Leftrightarrow \quad 3 - 3 = 0$$
$$A = B \quad \Leftrightarrow \quad A - B = 0 = B - A$$

Here are some immediate corollaries:

reflection corollaries

$$A = B \quad \Leftrightarrow \quad A <B> = <A> B$$
$$A = B \quad \Leftrightarrow \quad A <B> = <A <B>>$$
$$A = B \quad \Leftrightarrow \quad A <B> = A <A>$$

In contrast, the **unequal sign** identifies forms that can coexist without Reflection rendering them void equivalent. The inequality $A \neq \mathit{void}$ means that A maintains an existent structure after it has been reduced by pattern axioms. Using the angle-bracket

form difference

$$A \neq B \quad \Leftrightarrow \quad <A> B \neq \mathit{void}$$

Equality inversion   *cover ⇄ cover*

$$[A] = B \iff A = (B)$$
$$(A) = B \iff A = [B]$$
$$<A> = B \iff A = <B>$$

Equality reflection   *move ⇄ move*

$$A\ C = B \iff A = B <C>$$

Reflection bridge   *bridge ⇄ bridge*

$$A = B \iff A <B> = void = <A>\ B$$

Equality operations do not apply to reduced forms containing [ ].

Figure 18-1: *Operations across equality*

The distinction between A and B, written either as <A> B or as A <B>, must be consequential, existent, for A to be different than B.

Figure 18-1 shows the equality theorems facilitated by Composition. The variables A, B and C stand in place of any form that does not contain the non-numeric unit [ ]. Both Equality Inversion and Reflection are included in the common algebraic rule that equality is maintained when we do the same operation to both sides. Equality Inversion maps to the multiplicative inverse, while Equality Reflection maps to the additive inverse.

The Reflection Bridge provides a basis for comparison of forms. Substitution of equals, which in Chapter 2 was written as

$$(\!(A\ C\ E)\!) = E \qquad given\ A = C$$

can now be defined using void-based techniques. Any void-equivalent form can be inserted anywhere within

	logic	*angle-bracket*	
reflexive	A = A	A <A> = *void*	*reflect*
symmetric	A = B ⇔ B = A	A <B> = *void* = B <A>	*bridge*
transitive	A = B ∧ B = C ⇒ A = C	A <B> B <C> <A> C = *void*	*repeat*

Figure 18-2: *From relation to reflection*

another form, allowing substitution itself to revert to the Reflection axiom. For example:

```
                    (        B C)
void substitute     (A <B>  B C)      given  A = B
        cancel       (A         C)
```

The three conventional relational properties of equality can each be expressed as applications of Reflection, as illustrated in Figure 18-2. The reflexive property is axiomatic Reflection; the symmetric property uses Composition and Reflection as the bridge; and the transitive property is repetition of Reflection three times. In boundary form, transitivity is no longer constrained by unidirectional implication. Here is a demonstration of the transitivity of equality using void-based forms.[5]

```
        bridge      A = B  ⇔  <A> B    = void
        bridge      B = C  ⇔     B <C> = void

void equivalent        <A> B  =  B <C>
        bridge         <A> B    <B <C>> = void
         react         <A> B    <B> C   = void
        cancel         <A>           C  = void
        bridge          A     =     C
```

In sum, substitution and equality can both be decomposed into Reflection and Composition. Composition provides an equivalent to the ladder of induction, while Reflection provides an absolute ground for any sequence of transformations.

18.3 Solving for Inverses

We can apply the equality theorems to generate the **containment inverse** for any numeric container structure. Here is a simple example, the form of multiplication.

$$A \times B = C \; \text{☞} \; ([A][B]) = C$$

We will solve for A.

$$
\begin{array}{lll}
([A][B]) = & C & \\
[A][B] \; = & [C] & \text{cover} \\
[A] \quad = & [C]<[B]> & \text{move} \\
A \quad = & ([C]<[B]>) & \text{cover} \\
\end{array}
$$

$$\text{☞} \quad A = C/B$$

The inverse of the form of multiplication is the form of division. To illustrate that the container inverse generates an identity, we'll substitute the derived structure of A for A itself in the original equation.

$$
\begin{array}{ll}
([\quad A \quad][B]) = C & \\
([([C]<[B]>)][B]) = C & \text{substitute} \\
(\quad [C]<[B]> \quad [B]) = C & \text{clarify} \\
(\quad [C] \qquad) = C & \text{cancel} \\
\qquad C \qquad = C & \text{clarify} \\
\end{array}
$$

Here is the demonstration using void-based techniques. The idea is to reduce all forms to their void-equivalence, and then introduce them freely wherever they might be needed to reach a goal. The Bridge is used only as a final step, to shift from a void-based system back to an equational system.

$$([A][B]) = C \quad \Leftrightarrow \quad ([A][B]) <C> = \textit{void} \qquad \text{given}$$

$$
\begin{array}{ll}
\qquad\qquad \textit{void} & \\
([\qquad\qquad] <[B]>) & \text{emit} \\
([([A][B]) <C>] <[B]>) & \text{void substitute} \\
([([A][B]) \quad] <[B]>) \; ([<C>] <[B]>) & \text{disperse} \\
(\quad [A][B] \qquad <[B]>) \; ([<C>] <[B]>) & \text{clarify} \\
(\quad [A] \qquad\qquad) \; ([<C>] <[B]>) & \text{cancel} \\
\qquad A \qquad\qquad\qquad ([<C>] <[B]>) & \text{clarify} \\
\qquad A \qquad\qquad\qquad <([\; C \;] <[B]>)> & \text{promote} \\
\qquad A = ([C]<[B]>) & \text{bridge} \\
\end{array}
$$

Inverse of a Power

Here the logarithmic form is generated from the exponential form.

$$B^N = A \quad ☞ \quad (([[B]][N])) = \quad A$$

cover	$[[B]][N]$	$= \quad [[A]]$
move	$[N]$	$= \quad [[A]]<[[B]]>$
cover	N	$= \quad ([[A]]<[[B]]>)$

$$☞ \quad N = \log_B A$$

Inverses are a natural consequence of solving a formula for a particular variable. Now we'll solve the same exponential form for the *base* B. This generates the power/root pseudoinverse.

$$B^N = A \quad ☞ \quad (([[B]][N])) = \quad A$$

cover	$[[B]][N]$	$= \quad [[A]]$
move	$[[B]]$	$= \quad [[A]] \quad <[N]>$
cover	B	$= \quad ((([[A]] \quad <[N]> \quad))$
enfold	B	$= \quad ((([[A]][(<[N]>)]))$

$$☞ \quad B = A^{1/N}$$

Alternatively, we would reach the same result by starting from the logarithmic form.

$$(<[[B]]>[[A]]) = \quad N$$

cover	$<[[B]]>[[A]]$	$= \quad [N]$
move	$<[[B]]>$	$= \quad [N] \quad <[[A]]>$
cover	$[[B]]$	$= \quad <[N] \quad <[[A]]>>$
react	$[[B]]$	$= \quad <[N]> \quad [[A]]$
cover	B	$= \quad ((\quad <[N]> \quad [[A]] \quad))$
enfold	B	$= \quad ((([(<[N]>)][[A]] \quad))$

$$☞ \quad B = A^{1/N}$$

It's apparent why the power function has both an inverse and a pseudoinverse. In contrast to addition and multiplication, the power function is asymmetric. With three variables in play and no canceling symmetries, there are three unique form equalities.

conventional	☞	*James*
$A = B^N$		$A = ((([[B]] \quad [N] \quad))$
$B = A^{1/N}$		$B = ((([[A]]< \quad [N] \quad >))$
$N = \log_B A$		$N = \quad ([[A]]<[[B]]>)$

Importantly, the **base** is just another variable, since the boundary operations are patterns that do not assign variables particular roles or interpretations.

Isolating Unknowns

How would we solve a containment equation for an unknown variable directly? Here's an example, a simple linear equation

5x + 1 = 2x + 7   ☞   ([5][x]) o = ([2][x]) 7

We want to solve for x. The technique is straightforward: remove the forms around x by covering and moving, simplifying the arithmetic along the way. Arrangement may be needed to "collect like terms".

```
([5][x]) o           = ([2][x]) 7
([5][x])             = ([2][x]) 7 <o>        move
([5][x])             = ([2][x]) 6            cancel
([5][x])<([ 2 ][x])> =          6            move
([5][x]) ([<2>][x])  =          6            demote
([5 <2>][x])         =          6            collect
([3    ][x])         =          6            cancel
 [3    ][x]          =         [6]           cover
       [x]           = <[3]>   [6]           move
        x            = (<[3]>  [6])  ☞ 6/3   cover
```

To simplify the fraction, we can disperse and cancel:

```
x = (<[3]>[6])
x = (<[3]>[3])(<[3]>[3])           disperse
x = (       )(       )     ☞ 2     cancel
```

As an example that avoids arithmetic, here is the solution to the generic linear equation.[6]

```
ax + b = c  ☞  ([a][x]) b =    c
               ([a][x])   =    c <b>          move
                [a][x]    =   [c <b>]         cover
                   [x]    =   [c <b>]<[a]>    move
                    x     = ([c <b>]<[a]>)    cover

        ☞  (c – b)/a
```

Quadratic Equation

Here is a void-based solution to the general quadratic equation using James algebra. The steps assume a knowledge of where the solution is heading since the purpose is demonstration rather than discovery.

$$y = ax^2 + bx + c \quad \text{☞} \quad ([a][x][x])([b][x]) \; c \; \text{<y>} = \textit{void}$$

The idea is to rearrange the form so that there are no replicas of the label x. We'll establish two convenient structural labels that will later participate in the form of the solution. v is for *vertex* and d is for *discriminant*.[7]

$$v = ([b]<[a \; a]>) \qquad \text{☞} \quad v = b/2a$$

$$d^2 = ([c]<[a]>) \qquad \text{☞} \quad d^2 = c/a$$

y/a =
x² + bx/a + c/a

The usual technique is to divide the standard equation through by a to set the coefficient multiplying x^2 to 1. The two structural labels v and d are both divided by a, but do not rely upon setting y to 0. We'll take a slightly different path and replace b and c by v and d while keeping a to be factored out later. The entire derivation calls upon the James axioms only, with no appeal to parabolic graphs, the quadratic formula or completing the square.

First b in terms of a and v:

	([b]<[a a]>) =	v
cover	[b]<[a a]> =	[v]
move	[b] =	[v][a a]
cover	b =	([v][a a])

And c in terms of a and d:

	([c]<[a]>]) =	([d][d])
cover	[c]<[a]> =	[d][d]
move	[c] =	[d][d][a]
cover	c =	([d][d][a])

Substituting v and d for b and c in the form of the quadratic:

	([a][x][x]) ([b][x])	c	<y>
substitute	([a][x][x]) ([([a a][v])][x])	([a][d][d])	<y>
clarify	([a][x][x]) ([a a][v] [x])	([a][d][d])	<y>
disperse	([a][x][x]) ([a][v][x])([a][v][x])	([a][d][d])	<y>

We'll now collect the [a] form (factor out a) and add the void-equivalent form ([v][v])<([v][v])> via Reflection so that x v can be collected into the same frame. This collection will require four smaller frames.

   ([x][x])([v][x])([v][x])([v][v]) ⇒ ([x v][x v])

The concept of "completing the square" is replaced by a Cartesian multiplication.

```
([a]    [x][x]) ([a][x][v])([a][v][x])  ([a][d][d])   <y>
([a][ ([x][x]) (   [x][v])(   [v][x]) (   [d][d])])<y>     collect
([a][ ([x][x v])                    ([v][x])([d][d])])<y>  collect
([a][ ([x][x v])<([v][v])>([v][v])([v][x])([d][d])])<y>    create
([a][ ([x][x v])<([v][v])>    ([v][x v])([d][d])])<y>      collect
([a][ ([x v][x v])  <([v][v])>       ([d][d])])<y>         collect
([a][ ((([x v]][2]))<([v][v])>       ([d][d])])<y>         collect
```

The variable x now occurs only once in the form. We'll use the Bridge to convert to equational format and solve for x directly via cover and move operations.

```
([a][((([x v]][2]))<([v][v])>([d][d])]) =   y            bridge
 [a][((([x v]][2]))<([v][v])>([d][d])]  =  [y]           cover
    [((([x v]][2]))<([v][v])>([d][d])]  =  [y]<[a]>      move
    ((([x v]][2]))<([v][v])>([d][d])   = ([y]<[a]>)      cover
((([x v]][2])) = ([v][v])<([d][d])>([y]<[a]>)            move*
  [[x v]][2] = [[([v][v])<([d][d])>([y]<[a]>)]]          cover
  [[x v]]  =   [[([v][v])<([d][d])>([y]<[a]>)]]<[2]>     move
   x v  =   ((([[([v][v])<([d][d])>([y]<[a]>)]]<[2]>))   cover
   x = ((([[([v][v])<([d][d])>([y]<[a]>)]]<[2]>))<v>     move
```

This is a **general equation** for the quadratic since y is still incorporated within the form. In standard notation,

$$\text{☞ } x = \sqrt{(v^2 - d^2 + y/a)} - v$$

We can "solve" for x when y is 0 by making y void-equivalent, i.e. delete y from the form.

```
x = ((([[([v][v])<([d][d])>([y]<[a]>)]]<[2]>))<v>
x = ((([[([v][v])<([d][d])>([ ]<[a]>)]]<[2]>))<v>     y = void
x = ((([[([v][v])<([d][d])>        ]]<[2]>))<v>       absorb
```

$$\text{☞ } x = \sqrt{(v^2 - d^2)} - v$$

Since both v and d are expressed in terms of the coefficients a, b and c, substituting the original forms named v and d into this equation retrieves the standard formula.[8]

This is an unusual format for the quadratic equation. There is no ± sign in front of the square-root. In this formulation it is unnecessary. At this point in the explanation, I'll revert to standard notation for clarity. We'll first back up to the earlier James form marked by the asterisk.

$$y = a(x^2 + 2vx + d^2)$$

$$(([[x \; v]][2])) = ([v][v])<([d][d])>([y]<[a]>)$$

☞ $(x + v)^2 = (v^2 - d^2 + y/a)$

Again setting y to 0,

$$(x + v)^2 = (v^2 - d^2)$$

This equation is in the form of a simple parabola $Y = X^2$, with $Y = (v^2 - d^2)$ and $X = (x + v)$. The axis of symmetry is offset horizontally along the x-axis by the value of v. This makes sense since $-v$ itself is the formula for the x-coordinate of the vertex. The vertex is offset vertically from the x-axis by the distance $(v^2 - d^2)$. The two solutions for x on the x-axis are also offset from the y-axis by v, as we can see by factoring Y.

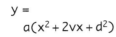

$$Y = (v^2 - d^2) = (v + d)(v - d)$$

When $Y = 0$ we thus have

$$(x + v)(x + v) = 0 = (d + v)(-d + v)$$

By pattern-matching, the solutions for the values of x when $y = 0$ and the vertex is offset by v are

$$x = \pm d.$$

The two values of x arise naturally from factoring the expression $v^2 - d^2$. The square-root operation is never performed. Instead the two values of x show up as the difference of squares. This explains the labels: v incorporates only the x-offset of the axis of symmetry while d contains the information normally associated with the discriminant of the quadratic.[9] If $v^2 - d^2$ is negative for example, then the solutions are imaginary. The compression factor a is also embedded into the v and d parameters. When $a = 1$ for example

$$v = b/2 \quad \textit{and} \quad d^2 = c.$$

Without numeric values for v and d, the equation

$$(x + v)^2 = v^2 - d^2$$

is that of a *cone* within which is embedded not only the generic parabola, but also circles and hyperbolas associated with the general Cartesian form of the conic section.[10]

18.4 Comparing Magnitude

Numeric comparison, as expressed by the **greater-than** relation, >, relies upon a principled ordering of numeric values. To compare two numbers we can examine the difference between them.

$$M > N \quad \textit{only when} \quad N - M < 0$$
$$M = N \quad \textit{only when} \quad N - M = 0$$
$$M < N \quad \textit{only when} \quad N - M > 0$$

How do we compare numeric boundary forms? Can we read the structure of a James numeric form to determine its polarity and its magnitude? Well, no, not as easily as we can decimal numbers. It is very easy to compare the magnitudes of common integers because unlike $\sqrt{2}$ they directly express their cardinality. Depth-value notation (Chapter 3) provides the same ease of comparison as positional notation while seamlessly integrating into James arithmetic as a notation for whole numbers. Rational and irrational numbers, however, are more challenging to compare.

The primary difficulty in numeric comparison is numbers that are expressed as **hybrid forms**, part operation and part numeral. Fractions for example are somewhat difficult to compare. Which is larger, 7/11 or 18/29? The issue is that neither of these fractions is expressed as a single number. Both require computation to convert them into comparable expressions.[11] Irrational numbers are more difficult still. Which is greater, e^{π} or π^{e} ?

form	☞	interpretation
o..$_N$..o		*natural number* N
o		1
<o>		−1
<N>		< −1
(N)		> 1
[N]		> 0
(<[N]>)		0 < 1/N < 1
<(<[N]>)>		0 > 1/N > −1
[<(N)>]		*imaginary*

Figure 18-3: *The range of magnitudes for numeric forms*

Boundary forms similarly combine cardinality and trans-formation. James forms do provide some broad categories for reading magnitude directly. Figure 18-3 shows the structure of forms associated with different parts of the number line.[12] In the figure N is restricted to be an arbitrary natural number. A reduced form is interpreted as being *negative* if an angle-bracket is outermost. Thus the angle-bracket serves the same role as a minus sign. For N to be positive, it cannot match the template <A>. We will need to assert that the embedded base # of (N) and [N] is positive and not equal to 1.[13] This restriction does not eliminate irrational numbers since the form [N], when interpreted as a logarithm, is almost always irrational.[14]

To determine relative magnitude, we can use the Composition Principle, the same reduction procedure that determines whether or not forms are equal. In general, there is a form A that will make any comparison void-equivalent.

M < N	N <M> *is positive*	N <M><A>	= *void*
M = N	N <M> *is zero*	N <M>	= *void*
M > N	N <M> *is negative*	N <M> A	= *void*

18.5 Remarks

We have seen that Composition and Void Equality combine to render both identity, A = A, and Accumulation, oo ≠ o, as theorems rather than as basic assumptions. The Equality theorems (Inversion and Reflection) provide a mechanism for manipulating equations. Finally the Reflection Bridge allows void-based solution techniques for equations.

We next explore **concurrency**, a computational concept that is usually not considered to be within the domain of mathematics. The distinction between *sequential* and *parallel* is incorporated deeply within computer science. In mathematics sequence is embedded as a conceptual default and parallelism is almost completely ignored. An exception is infinite series, which rely on concurrency to convert an infinite process to an infinite object. The main point is that both sequential and parallel processing are equally implementation details.

Endnotes

1. **opening quote:** The Magic Song (1948), sung by the Fairy Godmother in the Disney animated movie *Cinderella* (1950). Lyrics by Jerry Livingstone.

2. **are the same for two forms, then the forms are identical:** In Chapter 29, we will express the entire mechanism of James algebra using one type of function, put one form into another.

3. **We'll use the generic curly-brace { }:** We used the tortoise-shell bracket, ( ), in Chapter 4 to signify a generic outer bracket, standing in place of an implicit outermost container. This use is the same but broader. The generic container is any singly nested sequence of containers. Here are the transformations that convert the curly-brace to any type of outer bracket without changing the intention of a form.

$$\{A\} = ([A]) = [(A)] = <<A>>$$

The generic container applies equally well to multiple forms to convert them into the James standard of forms with a single outer boundary. The form {A B C} serves to specify an arbitrary *inert* outermost boundary just as well as our selected void-equivalent turtle-shell outermost container, (A B C).

4. **Again the demonstration is direct:** Technically, adding a reflection to both sides of an equation is not the same as adding an arbitrary form to both sides. The reflected form that is added is validated as safe because it reflects a particular form already present in the equation prior to transformation. Thus, for example, the "intermediate" form B within the specification of the transitivity property no longer requires existential quantification for transitivity to be valid in both directions since it is presumed to "pre-exist" by the structural definition of transitivity.

5. **the transitivity of equality using void-based forms:** Note that logical concepts such as AND, IMPLIES and TRUE are not used in the James demonstration. Not only do the equivalence relations not require a logical substrate language, neither does logic have the status of contributing necessary axioms to the demonstration.

6. **the solution to the generic linear equation:** Jeffrey James' thesis includes a non-optimized solution to the general quadratic equation that takes about fifty transformation steps. The additional length compared to standard

notation is balanced by the grain-size of the solution. The fifty steps do not include any hidden theorems or definitions. The atomic James transformations thus define a foundation for quadratic polynomials.

7. v is for *vertex* and d is for *discriminant*: These labels are not the conventional vertex and discriminant, rather they are convenience labels. I came across this nonstandard way to organize the solution for the quadratic while experimenting with the James forms. The iconic representation literally exposed this approach, which I then had to reinterpret via conventional algebra to come to an understanding of what was going on.

On a technical note, this method retraces a more powerful technique of **Lagrange resolvents** with a slight modification of building the factor of 1/2 into one of the resolvents and a major modification of avoiding the square-root.

8. forms named v and d into this equation retrieves the standard formula: This is a case of *reverse engineering* the quadratic formula to discover the rationale for the constants v and d. Here's what it looks like in standard notation.

$$x = \pm \sqrt{(v^2 - d^2)} - v$$

$$x = \pm \sqrt{((b/2a)^2 - c/a)} - b/2a$$
$$x = -b/2a \pm \sqrt{(b^2/4a^2 - 4ac/4a^2)}$$
$$x = -b/2a \pm \sqrt{((b^2 - 4ac)/4a^2)}$$
$$x = -b/2a \pm \sqrt{(b^2 - 4ac)/2a}$$
$$x = (-b \pm \sqrt{(b^2 - 4ac)})/2a$$

Notice that ± has been added in front of the square root to accommodate standard technique.

9. normally associated with the discriminant of the quadratic: While the first part of the standard quadratic formula, $-v = -b/2a$, identifies the x-coordinate of the axis of symmetry, the rest of the quadratic formula identifies the x-distance of the solutions from the axis of symmetry. Deleting the offset v from the quadratic formula gives

$$\pm x = \sqrt{(b^2 - 4ac)}/2a$$
$$x^2 = (b^2 - 4ac)/4a^2 = (b/2a)^2 - c/a = v^2 - d^2 = (v + d)(v - d)$$

The two values of d, i.e. ±d, resolve into the difference of squares, thus rendering the square-root operation as a structural artifact.

10. **associated with the general Cartesian form of the conic section:** The general conic equation is

$$Ax^2 + Bxy + Cy^2 + Dx + Ey + F = 0$$

If v is specified numerically (say $v = n_1$) and d remains a variable, then the equation converts to that of a *circle*, with d taking the place of y.

$$(x + n_1)^2 + d^2 = n_1^2$$

Alternatively, if d is specified numerically ($d = n_2$) and v remains a variable, then the equation converts to that of a *hyperbola*, with v taking the place of y.

$$(x + v)^2 - v^2 = n_2^2$$

And if both v and d are specified numerically, then the equation becomes that of a *parabola*.

$$(x + n_1)^2 = (n_1^2 - n_2^2)$$

11. **to convert them to comparable expressions:** School children call this particular computation "finding the lowest common denominator," a premature optimization that often removes context and sensibility from fractions.

12. **different parts of the number line:** There is a deeper exploration of the number line in Chapter 38.

13. **the embedded base # of (N) and [N] is positive and not equal to 1:** This restriction is lifted in Volume III, landing us in non-numeric territory.

14. **when interpreted as a logarithm, can be irrational:** It is a general, although not very powerful, rule of James forms that all irrational forms either include a square-bracket [A] or have the arbitrary base # assigned to an irrational number.

Chapter 19

Concurrency

Time is what keeps everything from happening at once.[1]
— *Ray Cummings (1922)*

A thesis of iconic form is that much of what we currently consider to be common mathematics can be understood as implementation details that support text-bound linear thinking.[2] This does not denigrate the magnificent edifice of mathematical technique, nor does it depreciate the deep abstractions that mathematicians contemplate, nor does it criticize spoken language and literature. It does suggest that alternatives exist that have not yet been explored. It does observe that we are often limited by our tools. And it does advocate that images, video and direct experience can also meet the constraints of formal systems.

More fundamentally, the digital revolution has deconstructed the foundations of commerce, education, politics, communication and entertainment. Contrary to its claim to eternal truth, mathematics too is fundamentally different in the electronic age. A premiere example is the introduction of **experimental mathematics**, in which a computer explores formal possibilities with human invention occurring at more abstract levels such as search algorithms and evaluation functions.[3] Computers do the digging, people filter out the gems. In the case of the Appel and Haken proof of the four-color map theorem[4], the task was almost all digging. The final result of an exhaustive analysis by computer is a proof by denial-of-all-possible-contradictions that is too long for a person to read and verify.

In today's world, it is becoming more and more difficult to determine where mathematics leaves off and computation begins. It is clear that mathematical creativity is human invention. This exploration, however, is focused on elementary mathematics and on mathematics education, a place where "maths" is seen to be purely computation.[5]

19.1 Parallel Thinking

Most people use three types of computing tools: wetware, software and hardware (Figure 19-1). The original computational techniques were customized for **wetware**, the biological tools of our fingers, our eyes and our brain. The dominant mathematical technique was the tally system, augmented by physical devices such as counting beads, parts of the body, the abacus, the knotted rope, the counting table and the tally stick. Educator Paul Lockhart: "Piles of Rocks is the world's first calculator."[6]

School arithmetic introduced **software**, the structured rules of how to do arithmetic computations. The dominant mathematical teaching is the **algorithm**, a clear sequence of steps, designed usually for pencil and paper, that would allow us to add and to multiply quantities.[7] The electronics revolution has provided ubiquitous **hardware**, silicon machines that can do all computations far better than humans. Hardware has introduced as well new types of software and new ways to use wetware. Crowd-sourcing difficult mathematical problems via the internet, for example, allows many people to contribute to a complex computational exploration concurrently.

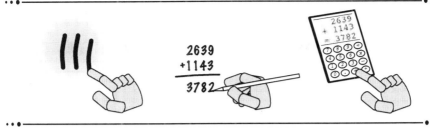

Figure 19-1: *Wetware, software and hardware*

We are also familiar with *computational parallelism* from social media. Everyone can log on and interact together, all at the same time.

James algebra is *spatial* rather than purely temporal. This change in the dimension of representation facilitates seeing, thinking and computing using spatial concepts and constructions. Boundary calculi support both **cognitive and computational parallelism**. Just like people in a room who breathe and think independently, all at the same time, the contents of every container are *mutually independent*. Mutual independence leads directly to a capability for parallel processing. Every container is conceptually capable of transforming each of its individual contents without having to wait for containers in its context or its content to complete transformation. All are active concurrently.

independent processes occur concurrently

Sequential thinking was strongly supported by book publishers of the eighteenth and nineteenth centuries who had not yet discovered inexpensive layout and illustration. If you wanted it printed, then it had to conform to the tools of the time: *linear typography*.[8] This chapter encourages us to wean ourselves from the one-step-at-a-time metaphor that dominates how we learn to count. Counting in young children and adults using perceptual concurrency is called *subitizing*. We have the innate capability to look at many and know how many without counting one, two, three.... People can do this easily up to five or six objects.

Beyond that there is a very narrow range of experience for which exact counting matters. Outside of that range, when we need non-experiential exact counting, we have sophisticated devices to do the job for us. For purposes of human communication, large numbers are approximate, not exact. The physiological reality of human counting is that once we get past what we can see directly, we enter into broader and broader estimations. It is not 17, but instead close to 20. It is not 1729, it is the early eighteenth century.[9]

Spencer Brown is explicit about parallelism in LoF, although he does not use that word. Rather he identifies parallelism as "the freedom offered by an added dimension". Continuing, he contrasts spatial form to verbal form:

> In speech we can mark only the one dimension of time. Much that is unnecessary and obstructive in mathematics today appears to be vestigial of this limitation of the spoken word.[10]

We currently take sequential steps in proof and in computation partly because parallelism was historically not a feature of mathematical communication. Mathematics supposedly has no inherent concept of time built into its notation. It should not matter *when* a computer implements mathematical operations. The difficulty is that mathematical processes have historically evolved within a one-step-at-a-time paradigm, an artifact of thinking without silicon support rather than an inherent property. As a consequence the dominant mechanism of algebra has been built around typographic concepts such as ordering, grouping and processes defined to proceed one-step-at-a-time.[11] From the perspective of a boundary that holds contents independently, these fundamental algebraic ideas are an overlay of structure needed only in cases of non-commutativity and non-associativity. Kauffman and Varela state this perspective nicely:

$$x+y=y+x$$
$$(x \ y)$$

$$x+(y+z)=(x+y)+z$$
$$(x \ y \ z)$$

Here it is not so much that commutativity and associativity are tacitly assumed, but that we are articulating a level at which they do not yet exist! [12]

The contrast between parallel correspondence and serial succession is broader than an implementation detail. As mathematician Tobias Dantzig observes:

Correspondence and succession, the two principles which permeate all mathematics — nay, all realms of exact thought — are woven into the very fabric of our number system.[13]

Historian Timothy Lenoir notes the pervasive tension between these concepts within our culture

across many types of activity: music (melody versus harmony), symbolic forms (text versus image), arithmetic (ordinal versus cardinal numbers), film editing (Eisenstein versus intercut montage), electrical circuits (series versus parallel), and especially serial versus parallel modes of computing.[14]

Both types of processing are implementation details, depending upon the capabilities of the tools (human or silicon) we happen to be using.

Both sequential and parallel processing are imposed upon numeric operations rather than being fundamental.

19.2 The Inductive Principle

Our current conceptualization of numbers rests upon work done by Frege, Peano and Dedekind over a century ago, before the invention of digital computers and before the concept of parallel processing. We'll explore Frege's definition of numbers and Peano's formal model of natural numbers in greater detail in Chapter 22.

At the foundation of stepwise linear counting is the concept of **adding one**, what Peano calls the *successor operation*. In turn the concept of successor is a necessary component of mathematical induction, an inherently sequential proof strategy. The Inductive Principle lays at the heart of numeric abstraction. **Induction** is the process of climbing the ladder of a well-ordered sequence. The concept of *one* provides a base for the ladder to stand upon. The concept of *successor* constructs a well-ordered sequence of rungs to climb. Formally it looks like this:

induction over natural numbers

$$(1 \in S \wedge (n \in S \Rightarrow n+1 \in S) \Rightarrow S = \mathbb{N}$$

The set of natural numbers can be defined by a base, $(1 \in S$, 1 is a number) and a ladder $(n+1 \in S)$. The set S so formed is *all* the natural numbers $\mathbb{N}$.

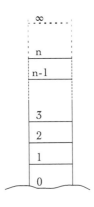

We know that 2 is greater than 1 and that 3 is greater than 2. Well-ordering assures us that the ladder does have a next rung. *Equivalent successors* allow induction to generalize any specific rung to a generic rung. And *induction* itself promises that if we begin at the first rung, and if a generic rung leads to the next, then we can climb the entire ladder of natural numbers.

Modern mathematical induction over natural numbers generally establishes zero as the base case and add1 as the operation that gets us from here to the next one. From these two concepts, the Induction Theorem takes an infinitely large step: *and so on for every number in a countable infinity of numbers.*

A more powerful statement of induction allows any function or any property P of numbers that we may wish to consider.

induction over a property

$$(P[0] \wedge (P[n] \Rightarrow P[n+1])) \Rightarrow P[x \in \mathbb{N}]$$

If 0 has the property P and further, if given (by assumption) that an arbitrary number n has the property P and we can show that its successor n + 1 has that property, then all numbers have that property. The Inductive

Principle specifies a notational shortcut: we can assert that a property applies to all natural numbers given just two conditions. A shortcut is not essential, since we can with more effort simply climb the ladder, 1, 1, 1, ... until we reach infinity.

Technically, induction can be replaced by two simpler axioms, one to assure that the inductive ladder has no loops, and the other to assure that it is well-ordered.

$$\forall k \quad k > 0 \quad \forall n \quad n{+}1 {..}_k{..}{+}1 \neq n \qquad \qquad \textit{no loops}$$

$$\forall n \quad n \neq 0 \;\Rightarrow\; \exists m \quad m{+}1 = n \qquad \qquad \textit{well-ordered}$$

However a significant problem is that the global inductive conclusion, for *all* numbers, is not a meaningful mathematical proposition and is not proved in any symbolic sense. The inductive conclusion is "understood" or "perceived" as being reasonable under certain cognitive assumptions, but it cannot be algorithmically demonstrated.[15] No algorithm can reach infinity.

Bounded Induction

What Induction permits is a free *cognitive* excursion to infinity. From a computational perspective, this is no gain. Mathematical induction goes upward to reach infinity while computational recursion goes downward to reach zero. This is a huge difference. Recursion is finite while induction is infinite. Both achieve the same result, however the mathematical approach generates an infinity of whole numbers, while the computational approach requires that we name one specific finite number to serve as the top of the ladder. The trouble with taking steps toward infinity (Figure 19-2) is that every step is the first. Progress is an illusion. The Inductive Principle inevitably requires a leap of faith. Philosopher Alain Badiou: "'passage to the limit' is an operation of thought entirely different from 'taking one more step'."[16]

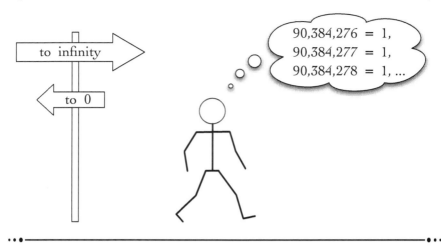

Figure 19-2: *Every step toward infinity is the first one*

An embodied finite approach to numbers can still call upon the Inductive Principle by replacing the cosmic leap of faith (and therefore infinity!) by a pragmatic, bounded, *You can go on as far as you need to, there are sufficient natural numbers for any purpose.* Induction that stops short of infinity is called **bounded induction**. Of course the pragmatic perspective limits *purpose* to any physical purpose, not any metaphysical purpose.[17]

∀x≤n F(x)

Numbers are usually coupled with counting. Counting not only identifies cardinality as its end-product, it also stops every step of the way to identify an ordinal position. Rotman's criticism of induction is not that we cannot go on adding 1 as long as we like, it is that the *we*, the Agent who is counting, cannot go on forever because both we and time do not have infinite extent.[18] The Platonist believes that numbers are preordained, they exist before the Agent and are independent of the Agent. This is tolerable, however the Agent still has to produce a desired number in order to validate that number's existence. Even if they are (virtually) real, *real numbers* do not a priori have claim to individuality since each is infinitely detailed and since there are uncountably many. That would require two leaps into mysticism, one into infinite extent and the other into infinite duration. In the parlance of computer science, countable means computable while computable means finite.[19] A related problem that we will consider in Chapter 28.2 is the recent algorithmic specification of whole numbers that are so huge that they are beyond any form of comprehension.

Hidden within the add1 function is the tally system, i.e. **ensemble arithmetic**.[20] Tallies do not require the additional structure of well-ordered steps, each of the same size. Instead, the well-ordered property of the successor function is replaced by the communality imposed by replicas rendered as ensembles. More importantly, tallies are *constructed*, we accumulate them by indication rather than by belief. This implies a small but quite significant change in what induction asserts. We can add1 indefinitely, but the numbers that are generated are those for which the process of adding 1 actually occurs. Accumulation generates new numbers only to the extent that accumulation occurs, and occurrences are finite.

Sequence

The rungs of the inductive ladder do not have to be equally spaced, but they do have to head upwards. Equal spacing of rungs is a property of natural numbers, not necessarily a required property for induction. A continually increasing (monotonic) change is sufficient. We can climb the inductive ladder using ensembles of different sizes. All we really need to know is that there is a next rung, somewhere up there. Even monotonic increase is not necessary. Three steps up and two steps down also works. All we need is an assured net gain over some finite repeatable span to jump to an infinite conclusion.

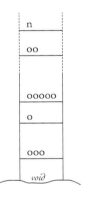

Neither distance between rungs nor step size matter for *infinite* induction to work. What is mandatory is an infinite number of steps. Consider steps that increase

$1+\frac{1}{2}+\frac{1}{3}+\frac{1}{4}+\frac{1}{5}+...$

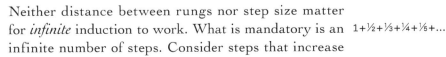

not by 1, but by $1/n$ where n is the nth step. The ladder is still infinitely tall, since this series does not converge. Step-size shrinks but we do visit every whole number, this time embodied in the denominator of unit fraction steps. Induction still works.

$1^2 + \frac{1}{2}^2 + \frac{1}{3}^2 + \frac{1}{4}^2 + ...$

Consider now steps that go up by $(1/n)^2$. This sequence does converge, so the top of the ladder is always in sight.[21] Still it takes an infinite number of steps to reach the top, and we pass every whole number (indicated by n) along the way.

$1 - \frac{1}{2} + \frac{1}{3} - \frac{1}{4} + \frac{1}{5} - ...$

Finally consider the alternating $1/n$ sequence, but we go up only every other step and down a bit less each step in between. This sequence is convergent and non-monotonic,[22] and still a ground for induction. The inductive add1 function is very broad indeed. Philosopher of mathematics Paul Benacerraf observes,

Paul Benacerraf
1920–2011

> This is the crux of the matter — that any recursive sequence whatever would do suggests that what is important is not the individuality of each element but the structure which they jointly exhibit.[23]

All the Numbers

Any particular number does not have a singular referent, such as the prior number. Instead with induction reference applies promiscuously. Each number is intimately constructed from *all* of the numbers that precede it.[24] In Nature there are also no particular groupings of referents that we can count. We perceptually construct groupings and particularizations that may correspond to a specific number, as described in Chapter 8. *Numbers do not have individual properties*, they have a universal co-dependent relation that is usually described as greater-than, >. We have been calling this relation contains.

A number is not an object,
it is part of a system of mutually interdependent relations.

Brian Rotman identifies the deep problem illustrated by Figure 19-2. If indeed induction allows us to reach the infinite, via an infinite number of steps, then we are in fact embracing a **completed infinity**. Taking a step, engaging in construction, is meaningless in the face of an existent everything. There is only one infinite step that can be taken, and once taken we have gone all the way, we have constructed something new, something that is not a number. And we have violated one of Wittgenstein's central premises: There is no such thing as "all numbers", simply because there are infinitely many.[25] We cannot *quantify* over a concept that is not a quantity.

In passing to the limit, in introducing infinity, a question remains. Can infinity be subdivided to expose any finite number? Induction suggests that we can move from a sequence of finite numbers to a totality of all the numbers. Infinity identifies the interdependence that unifies all the numbers. But does it allow us to decouple the totality in order to identify an individual member within that totality?

In the current context, shifting from a stepwise approach to a global approach is simply shifting from a sequential to a parallel implementation. **Potential infinity** is the illusion of always; **actual infinity**, the illusion of everywhere. Both are equally flawed, and as Wittgenstein warns, *dangerous*. Is it at all reasonable to embrace a fundamental tool (mathematics) that ignores all we know about what is real and what is potentially real, and then claim that the tool is in fact the true reality? Does an intelligible act committed once remain intelligible if committed an unimaginable (indeed unintelligible) number of times? Rotman asks: should the mathematician be

> a being able to "act" and to "count" (assuming meaning can be given to these verbs) outside of the regularities of space, time, energy, materiality, and entropy theorized by physical science as governing "acting" or "counting"?[26]

Parallel Recursion

Recursion is not so much a principle as a mechanism. With recursion we do not try to reach infinity, rather we begin at some specific step on the ladder and climb down until we reach to ground. Parallel recursion maintains the essential self-similar structure of recursion but abandons the stepwise sequential implementation.[27] Here are five similar examples of a simple story to compare:

> We have a large bag of coffee beans. We want to demonstrate that by taking out beans, the bag will eventually become empty.
>
> Method 1: *step-wise linear recursion*
>> Take out one bean at a time until empty.
>
> Method 2: *step-wise monotonic recursion*
>> Take out a handful of beans at a time until empty.
>
> Method 3: *parallel monotonic recursion*
>> Get several friends to take out handfuls of beans all at the same time.
>
> Method 4: *parallel non-monotonic recursion*
>> Get several friends to take out two handfuls of beans all at the same time, and then put back one handful.
>
> Method 5: *concurrent*
>> Turn the bag upside down and shake until empty.

Parallel recursion within a containment structure means that each content subform within a given form can act independently of other content subforms, regardless of level of nesting. By construction, the nesting of containers incorporates a base case, a finite limit defined by an empty container at the deepest level. Nesting thus provides a **partial ordering principle** for container recursion.

In conventional definitions, *nested forms* are shown to be equal by an induction over depth of nesting. Nesting is determined by a process of descent into a form. The ground for induction by depth is the deepest nested form,

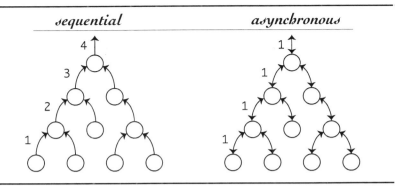

sequential   *asynchronous*

Figure 19-3: *Sequential and parallel recursion over nested containers*

which in the case of James forms, is a unit. Unlike linear accumulation, *nesting is inherently ordered.* Ensembles serve to model **cardinal numbers**, while nesting models **ordinal numbers**. Cardinal numbers can be processed in parallel, each unit independent of the others. The cardinal numeral 4, for example, represents four independent replicas, ••••. But to count 1, 2, 3, 4, we must pass through, in order, each of the groupings that compose it.

cardinal

one, two, three

( )( )( )

ordinal

first, second, third

((( )))

Parallel Computation

Figure 19-3 shows recursive communication between nodes in a network that might implement numeric evaluation. A typographic form can be converted into a spatial tree graph by extruding brackets downward, and then closing the sides of the brackets to form nodes. For example, the network in Figure 19-3 maps to this bracket structure:

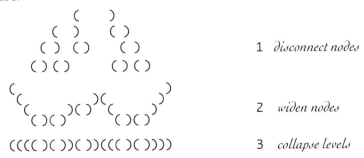

1 *disconnect nodes*

2 *widen nodes*

3 *collapse levels*

Figure 19-3 illustrates the difference between sequential and parallel container recursion. There are two types of parallelism available within the network, locally between connected containers and globally across paths from bottom to top of the network. The **sequential network** on the left sends messages up the node hierarchy. The time it takes to communicate a result is proportional to the depth of the network. In the example, it takes four cycles to generate an output. Each node can still operate independently, but must wait for lower nodes before acting. In the **asynchronous network** on the right, communication is local and no nodes are waiting. Output might still take a maximum of four steps, but depending on local results each node does not necessarily need to wait for the results from prior nodes.[28]

Imagine a room full of people. Sequential linear communication allows only one person to speak to one person at one time. Sequential parallel communication would allow multiple one-to-one conversations with each group waiting for the prior group to finish. With concurrent communication, everyone can speak and listen to everyone else all at the same time. In terms of the Inductive Principle, Peano's successor function can take one step at a time, while Arrangement can `collect` or `disperse` many frames at the same time. In terms of how we think, Kahneman has demonstrated that people rarely think sequentially using slow conscious deliberation.[29] Most of the time we think (subconsciously) in parallel, considering many things all at once.

19.3 Self-similarity

A geometrical form is **self-similar** when the same pattern repeats at different scales. Nesting of containers is self-similar in that each container, regardless of depth of nesting within other containers, has the same behavior, the same local structural rules. The mutual independence of content forms means that there are no tangles of relationships that may propagate up and down through levels

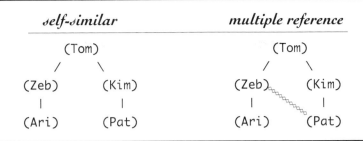

Figure 19-4: *Simple and interacting inheritance relations*

of nesting. The great advantage of a system with only one relation (containment) is that all containers can be addressed at the same time with the same messages and the same responsive behavior, without having to untangle interdependencies. *Self-similarity permits concurrency.*[30]

No Cousins

Imagine that a container represents a parent within a family. Figure 19-4 shows this example. The contents of the parentOf container are the children. Now each child may also be a parent; the container that stands in place of that child might also have contents, the grand-children of the original parent. This is not the case with the structure of kinship. Let's embed the relation parentOf into the round-bracket, and uncleOf into the square-bracket. Each bracket is subscripted with a name to make the example clearer.

> parentOf(A) ☞ (A)
>
>> *Tom is the parent of* A ☞ (A)$_{Tom}$
>
> uncleOf[A] ☞ [A]
>
>> *Zeb is the uncle of* A ☞ [A]$_{Zeb}$

As illustrated in Figure 19-4, Tom has two kids, Zeb and Kim. Kim has a kid Pat, and Zeb has a kid Ari. Zeb is Pat's uncle. In text, the parentOf structure looks like this:

> ((Ari)$_{Zeb}$ (Pat)$_{Kim}$)$_{Tom}$

But how does the uncleOf relation fit into this pattern? We can say that Zeb is Pat's uncle, but to embed that information within the parentOf structure, we need to make an awkward substitution.

$$(\ (Ari)_{Zeb} \ (\ [Pat]_{Zeb} \ )_{Kim} \ )_{Tom}$$

One difficulty here is that Zeb gets referenced twice, and multiple symbolic reference is the source of symbolic complexity. Worse, the form now reads that Pat is no longer directly Kim's child. Kim's child is instead the person who Zeb is the uncleOf. Kim's child is represented as Zeb's niece. Not only do we loose the direct parentOf relation, we also have to introduce a new concept, nieceOf, which is one of the varieties of uncleOf.

In contrast, the parentOf structure maintains self-similarity. No matter what container we may visit, the contents are children and the contents two-levels deeper are grand-children. But self-similarity is lost when we introduce the idea of a sibling or an uncle.

The consequence of introducing relations between contents is complexity.

It is indeed remarkable that elementary arithmetic does not require this type of complexity. Arithmetic avoids direct relations between numbers by keeping them separated by operators such as plus and times.

In order to represent the full range of numbers as James container configurations, we need three different types of containers. These too add complexity, but with an essential difference. The three types of containers provide structural diversity in that the structure ([A]) acts differently than the structure (<A>). However these differences are limited to *simple nesting*. Inversion for example matches the pattern ([A B]) but it does not match the pattern (A [B]).

sequential operations	☞	*concurrent operations*	
count $\quad$ $1 +..._N..+ 1$	☞	$o..._N..o$	*parallel counting*
add $\quad$ $A +..._N..+ Z$	☞	$A..._N..Z$	*parallel addition*
multiply $\quad$ $A \times..._N.. \times Z$	☞	$([A]..._N..[Z])$	*parallel multiplication*

Figure 19-5: *The parallel numeric operations*

19.4 Parallel Arithmetic

Figure 19-5 shows the conventional numeric operations of early grade school in their serial and parallel forms. Each parallel form shares the common feature of placing forms together within the same container. The finesse for multiplication is that square-brackets model logarithms, so we are *adding* logarithms rather than multiplying quantities. Of course, the logarithmic transformation can be applied to all forms at the same time, while the antilogarithm to obtain the result of multiplication via addition needs to be applied only once. Thus the form of multiplication consists of a single round-bracket that contains multiple square-brackets.

Counting

Counting requires us first to *place indicators together*. Putting indicators into the same container to create ensembles can, of course, occur all at once.

$$1 +..._N..+ 1 \quad ☞ \quad o..._N..o$$

parallel counting

The Indication theorem establishes a one-to-one correspondence between objects and unitary tally marks. **Parallel counting** is assembling unit tallies via the Arrangement axiom.

$$(A\ [o])..._N..(A\ [o]) = (A\ [o..._N..o]) \qquad \textit{aggregation of tallies}$$
$$(A\ [B])\ ...\ (A\ [Z]) = (A\ [B\ ...\ Z]) \qquad \textit{general arrangement}$$

We count 1, 2, 3,… because formal arithmetic was built in the late nineteenth century upon the idea of adding one and then doing that again and again and again. Aggregation, however, can occur in one step, all that is needed is N actors (processors) each to contribute o at the same time to a communal container. Frege notes "Time is only a psychological necessity for numbering, it has nothing to do with the concept of number."[31] Were aggregation a sequential operation, it would look like this.

sequential
construction
of an ensemble

$$(A [o]) \quad ..\,_N.. \quad (A [o])$$
$$(A [oo]) \quad ..\,_{N-1}.. \quad (A [o])$$
$$(A [ooo]) \quad ..\,_{N-2}.. \quad (A [o])$$
$$...$$
$$(A [o..\,_{N-1}..o]) \quad (A [o])$$
$$(A [o ..\,_N.. o])$$

The task of giving the aggregate of unit tallies a name (that name is usually the last number in a count) does not imply stepping through a sequence of different names in order to arrive at the final name. We do not need to count 1, 2, 3,…, we do not need to keep a running tabulation of partial results. It is important to be able to count sequentially, just in case observations require an explicit ordering. It is just as important to look at an ensemble and name the cardinality without going through the ritual chant, without confounding ordinal with cardinal numbers. Rarely does the ordinal position of objects being counted matter. Looking at items *all-at-the-same-time* encourages a global, unified perspective. Conventional counting (1, 2, 3,…) pretends that each item is different enough to support a different name (i.e. the assigned counting numeral) while at the same time being identical enough to be counted as the same type of thing.

One-to-one correspondence, the concept underlying counting and cardinality, can occur in parallel or in sequence. The following spatial layout illustrates a parallel counting machine that takes groups of six (slots for example that can be filled in parallel) and returns one half-dozen. It can, of course, be applied recursively to take six groups of half-dozen each to return a grouping of thirty-six.

				6					*parallel counting*

$$
\begin{array}{ccccccc}
 & 1 & 1 & 1 & 1 & 1 & 1 & \\
\{ & o & o & o & o & o & o & \} \\
 & 1 & & & & & & \\
 & & 2 & & & & & \\
 & & & 3 & & & & \\
 & & & & 4 & & & \\
 & & & & & 5 & & \\
 & & & & & & 6 &
\end{array}
\qquad \Rightarrow 6
$$

indicators

sequential counting

Here's another example of parallel counting. A single shepherd can count his sheep as they pass through a gate by sequentially picking up one pebble for each sheep. Alternatively, if there were one shepherd for each sheep, then each shepherd could pick up one pebble at the same time. The sheep do not have to leave one-by-one, but rather, as they prefer, in a pack. The number of picked up pebbles, which corresponds to the number of sheep, remains the same in both cases. Determining *how many* sheep does not depend upon the time sequence of pebble gathering, nor does it depend upon who ends up holding the pebbles.

The central question of *How many?* is often irrelevant, for example when the counting operation ends in a comparison of two quantities, all that matters is the difference. Visual alignment is sufficient for comparison. Often an approximate result is appropriate, sometimes counting may require only *one, two, many,* or even *enough, not enough.* Counting, as taught today to young children, contributes to loss of number sense which in turn encourages the subservience of humanity to digitization.

Addition

The general operation of addition is defined by the Additive Principle: *a sum looks like the collection of its parts.* To add is to *place ensembles together.* We can place together as many ensembles as we want at the same time.

Here we put N ensembles into the same container.

**parallel
addition**

$$A + . ._N . . + Z \quad ☞ \quad A . ._N . . Z$$

Sequential processing supports the viewpoint that the operators of arithmetic must act only on pairs of numbers, restricting the addition operation to exactly two ensembles at one time while nominating one of the ensembles as first (being put into) and the other as second (being put). Here is a comparison of sequential and parallel addition in conventional symbolic notation.

sequential addition

$$((((1 + 2) + 3) + 4) + 5) + 6 \ = 21$$

parallel addition

$$1 + 2 \ + 3 \ + 4 \ + 5 \ + 6 = 21$$

We no longer need to embed a **computational model** (for example, an iterated loop or a reentrant recursion or counting up to n or taking steps of various sizes) into our description of the fusion of ensembles into a sum. If addition occurs in parallel, for example, the descriptive language we are using changes from the sequential idea of *repeated steps* to the parallel idea of *collected ensembles*. In both, things are being put together.

20 *intersections*

5

4

Multiplication

The general operation of multiplication is defined by the Multiplicative Principle: *every unit of one ensemble interacts with every unit of another ensemble*. The James form of multiplication is to put each ensemble into a square container and then to place them all together into a round container.

**parallel
multiplication**

$$A \, x . ._N . . x \, Z \quad ☞ \quad ([A] . ._N . . [Z])$$

As a visual example, consider modeling the multiplication A x B as a two dimensional plane and the multiplication A x B x C as a three-dimensional cube. As illustrated in Figure 19-6, the unit squares (or cubes respectively) cover the entire plane (volume) and represent the result

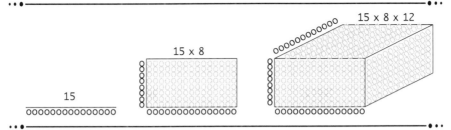

Figure 19-6: *Cartesian space as multiplication*

of parallel multiplication. Should we wish to provide unlimited extent over unlimited dimensions, then the resultant space itself represents all possible multiplications. The particular multiplication A x B x C would be only a selected subset of these unit (hyper)cubes.

Above we have separated the determination of *How many?* from the algorithm to compute the multiplication itself. After multiplication, we have an ensemble of units. Like addition, determination of cardinality can proceed independently via one-to-one correspondence of the unit cubes with the whole numbers, individually or in groups.

Here is a definition of multiplication as symbolic recursion.

$$m \times 1 = m \qquad\qquad\qquad\text{\textit{base case}}$$
$$m \times n = (m \times (n-1)) + m \qquad \text{\textit{general case}}$$

Computation proceeds by matching and substitution. Here's what the process looks like for multiplying 5 by 4 using sequential steps.

```
        5 x    4
      (   5 x (4–1)          ) + 5            substitute definition
      (   5 x    3           ) + 5
      (( 5 x (3–1)     ) + 5) + 5            substitute definition
      (( 5 x    2      ) + 5) + 5
      (((5 x (2–1)) + 5) + 5) + 5            substitute definition
      (((5 x    1  ) + 5) + 5) + 5
      (( 5              + 5) + 5) + 5         substitute base case
      ( 10                  + 5) + 5
        15                      + 5
        20
```

boundary definition

m x n ☞ ([m][n])

---

parallel implementation

([5][4])	
([5][oooo])	unlabel
([5][o])([5][o])([5][o])([5][o])	disperse
5 5 5 5	unmark
ooooo ooooo ooooo ooooo	unlabel

☞ 20

Figure 19-7: *Parallel implementation of multiplication*

The sequential steps are almost painful. But this is the *operational definition* of multiplication. Climb down the recursive ladder one step at a time, while accumulating the additions that have been generated one at a time. Also note that this machine counts groups of five, it does not count single units. To carry out the accumulated additions, technically, requires further application of the recursive definition of addition.

base case   m + 0 = m

general case   m + n = (m + (n–1)) + 1

In contrast, Figure 19-7 shows the James implementation of multiplication, using the same example of 5 x 4. The implementation is now in parallel. Dispersal constructs four unit multiplication forms. Indication unmarks them to yield four replicas of 5 added together by virtue of each sharing the same (implicit) container. The difference in technique is deeper than symbols since the James multiplication in the figure closely matches how young students are taught to understand multiplication while the stepwise recursive technique is how symbolic multiplication might be computed by a sequential silicon processor, a technique that you would rarely see in a classroom.[32]

Accumulated Multiplication

A good example of accumulated multiplication is the whole number factorial function, n!, which multiplies together all the natural numbers from 1 to n.

$$n! = 1 \times 2 \times ... \times n \quad \text{☞} \quad ([o][2]...[n])$$

factorial

The above boundary form of factorial illegitimately mixes boundary structure with an ellipsis that signifies an implicit iteration from 1 to n. Factorial is commonly defined by a pair of recursive equations, a base case and a general case for iteration. Specifically

$$fac[1] = 1$$
$$fac[n] = n \times fac[n-1]$$

base case
general case

These two equations not only provide a definition, they also provide instructions for calculating the value of fac[n]. The definition does not stand alone as sufficient, we also need to understand how such a definition is implemented.[33] Implicit within this conventional inductive definition is a substrate of logic that steers both the implementation and the process of thought. Logical IF...THEN...ELSE... statements guide the sequence of steps that generate the result.

$$fac[n] = IF \; n=1 \; THEN \; 1 \; ELSE \; n \times fac[n-1]$$

For 5!, the logical instructions embed like this:

```
IF 5=1, THEN 1 ELSE
    5 x (IF 4=1 THEN 1 ELSE
        4 x (IF 3=1 THEN 1 ELSE
            3 x (IF 2=1 THEN 1 ELSE
                2 x (IF 1=1 THEN 1))))
```

implementation
of factorial

The inherent sequentiality of *logic* was incorporated into mathematical thought two millennia ago, and it remains as a artifact, in the form of logical implication. Mechanism and meaning are entwined. Recursive/inductive definitions that traverse a well-ordered sequence tell us how to think as well as what to think.

The implementation of factorial is confounded with the generation of the numbers to be multiplied. How we determine the value of 5!, for example, should be independent of how we get the number 5. The recursive definition tells us to take downward steps of one unit from where we start until we reach the ground of 1. On each step we need to check if we are done. Along the way we generate the specific whole numbers that will eventually be multiplied together. Before reaching the bottom of the recursion at n=1, we first accumulate 5x4x3x2. The result of this recursion is only the numbers that need to be multiplied. No multiplication has taken place. The definition then is more about how to accumulate a sequence (i.e. how to count up to 5) than it is about how to multiply. For that we would need to appeal to the recursive definition of multiplication presented earlier as successive addition.

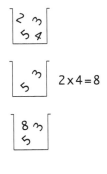

2 x 4 = 8

Here's a sequential implementation of multiplication that does not depend upon an ordered sequence. Toss the numbers from 2 to n into a container. Draw out two at a time randomly. Multiply them and toss the result back into the mix. Continue until there is only one number remaining. This draw-and-toss algorithm still multiplies only two numbers at a time. A silicon multiplier reduces numbers to binary streams, and multiplication to a series of logic gates. It is certainly possible (but not necessarily economical) to weave together the logic network to make a three-multiplier or a four-multiplier.[34] A silicon implementation of factorial could literally multiply all of the numbers (up to a limit determined by available hardware) at the same time. Alternatively, we could have $n/2$ binary multipliers that in parallel withdraw numbers and return multiplications, reducing the timesteps in an accumulated multiplication from order n to order $\log_2 n$.

8!

$\log_2$ *time steps*

Figure 19-8 shows the parallel multiplication of 4! using James ensembles. The major difference is that the parallel multiplication disperses an entire ensemble in one step. Any ensemble can be dispersed at any time. In the

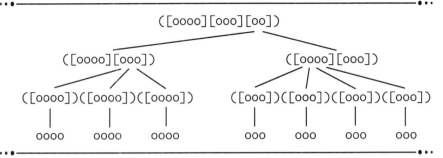

Figure 19-8: *Parallel multiplication of ensembles for 4!*

figure, the ensemble of 2 is first dispersed and unmarked, resulting in two replicas of ([oooo][ooo]). Each of these replicas then disperses independently. To illustrate the variety available to local decision-making, the left-hand path disperses [ooo] by replicating [oooo] three times while the right-hand path replicates [ooo] four times. When the resulting forms are clarified, the cardinality of the resulting ensemble of units identifies 24 as the value of the multiplication.

The generation of replicas to disperse is in parallel, as are the separate dispersions, nonetheless there remains a sequential component to the process. Figure 19-8 also shows the sequential steps of constructing replicas and then dispersing them. This cycle requires $\log_2 n$ sequential steps to multiply n numbers together (again given sufficient resources). A second potentially sequential process is the generation of the original form itself. Given the common need to generate the whole numbers, one might imagine a parallel device designed to output them all at one time.

A definition of factorial that is free of presumed implementation mechanisms might look like this:

```
fac[n] = multiply[upto[n]]
```

Upto provides the natural numbers from 1 to n, by whatever means is appropriate including retrieving an unordered set of integers all at the same time. Multiply specifies an operation to be applied to all of the retrieved integers, again by whatever means that is appropriate. This specification of factorial cleanly separates multiplication from counting. It does not require an ordered, incremental sequence of integers. It also does not require that the integers be multiplied two at a time.

The main point here is that how we currently conceptualize mathematical definitions and operations, at least at the schooling level, is locked into ancient (to a computer scientist) patterns of incremental iteration, sequential steps and counting by 1s. Our inductive definitions of the primary operations of counting, adding and multiplying are not informed by the digital revolution or by the growth of our understanding of the process of computation. Chapter 26 takes steps even further into the present to explore postsymbolic arithmetic.

19.5 Computational Architecture

Computational parallelism, of course, offers significant advantages, at the cost of a greater infrastructure. What is being processed does matter. Our pixelated computer screens refresh rapidly because groups of pixels can be updated concurrently. The older style scan-line television screens are refreshed line-by-line, from top to bottom, in a sequence. At the silicon level, addition is essentially sequential; for a place-value numeric system we need to know the carry-over from one column in order to know the results of the next column. To address this delay, there are **carry-look-ahead adders** that compute the sum in the next column both with and without a carry, and then choose the right result when the prior carry is determined. But fundamentally, the central processing unit (CPU) of desktop computers is managed by software that employs sequential instructions to organize linear streams of data that perform one-at-a-time processing steps.[35] This is not the way the supporting levels of a hardware architecture work, where all gates and all wires are active all the time. The CPU exchanges parallel for serial processing so that it can accommodate a diversity of reprogrammable software instructions.

The iconic language of containers abandons the distinction between representation and meaning. The syntax/semantics barrier has found a new home as the *implementation/concept distinction*. In software languages, a **procedural language** tells the computer every step to take, making the programmer responsible for the strategy that achieves the desired computation. A **declarative language** tells the computer what the goal is and provides essential information. The programmer is responsible only for the accurate specification of the desired result. The same procedural/declarative distinction can be applied to algebraic proof. Procedural proof must distinguish between sequential and parallel processing, whereas declarative proof need not. The procedural style of programming models step-wise inductive reasoning, while the declarative style models parallel reasoning.

19.6 Remarks

Cognitive complexity and computational complexity travel hand-in-hand. If the relationships between numbers could not be decomposed into simple operations, then arithmetic would become incomprehensibly complex. It is indeed the goal of mathematics to identify ways in which we can avoid these interactive complexities. Elementary arithmetic builds numeric understanding upon addition only and the Additive Principle is inherently parallel.

To reiterate a theme: in this digital age, determining *exactly how many* is best left up to electronic devices. Humans are best suited for determining *approximately how many* since approximation is highly context dependent. Our brains are far better suited for perceptual approximation than for symbolic exactness. Numeric results are more sensible when context determines the effort needed to achieve the results.

Although mathematical structure is unique, implementation algorithms are diverse. The Inductive Principle and its underlying Well-ordering Principle are facets of an implementation architecture and a way of thinking. Inductive proof is an important tool, however we have introduced two other perspectives, that of computer science and that of mathematics education. If mathematical education is evolving with the times, then we have added three modifications to the field:

— Computation in arithmetic (i.e. determining cardinality) is best left to digital devices.
— Math education should focus on understanding the input and output of computational devices, but not on the mechanism that transforms input to output.
— The mathematics that we teach needs to incorporate parallel thinking since digital communication and computation are parallel processes spread across the one internet.

The reason these distinctions are of vital importance is that humanity needs to learn how to see the Earth as a unified whole, all at the same time. Sequential counting fractures aggregations by isolating and naming each member separately. It teaches us to see every replicated item differently, even as we are unifying them under a common property that we use to create their ensemble. Counting elicits an object/subject dichotomy, while the world is an integrated whole. Objects are defined only by their mutual relationships, not by pointing, separating and indexing. Parallel counting is not necessarily more difficult. It does require a different concept of number, specifically that of seeing numbers both globally and concurrently.

Endnotes

1. **opening quote:** This quote is commonly misattributed to John Wheeler, who did use it in *Complexity, Entropy, and the Physics of Information* (1990) p.10. (Online 8/18 at https://archive.org/details/ComplexityEntropyAndThePhysicsOfInformation). Its first appearance, according to Wikipedia, is in a 1922 science fiction novel, *The Girl in the Golden Atom* by Ray Cummings.

2. **details that support text-bound linear thinking:** Our focus here is on exploring the potential parallelism in elementary arithmetic, so the emphasis is on *common* mathematics. The bulk of processing in the brain is subconscious and in parallel. Our subconscious manages breathing, walking, generating words, sorting out perceptions, filtering and distilling sensations, regulating our metabolism and a multitude of other physiological and cognitive tasks concurrently. Our conscious brain is strictly limited to one thing at a time. Two good references are S. Dehaene (2014) *Consciousness and the Brain* and D. Kahneman (2013) *Thinking, Fast and Slow*. Linear thinking is conscious thinking. Of course, professional mathematicians do a lot of focused conscious processing. They also report much creativity coming from the unfocused unconscious.

In Bateson's essay, Redundancy and coding, in *Steps to an Ecology of Mind* (1972) p.411ff, online 8/18 at http://shifter-magazine.com/wp-content/uploads/2015/11/gregory-bateson-steps-to-an-ecology-of-mind-1.pdf, he asserts that

> our iconic communication serves functions totally different from those of language and, indeed, performs functions which verbal language is unsuited to perform.

Iconic communication includes music, dance, poetry, dreaming, and mathematics. Bateson continues

> Still more astonishing is that world of religious fantasy which we call mathematics, a world forever isolated by its axioms and definitions from the possibility of making an indicative statement about the "real" world.

3. **search algorithms and evaluation functions:** Wolfram's *A New Kind of Science* is a superb example of using computation to redefine not only mathematics itself, but also the use of mathematics in science.

4. **proof of the four-color map theorem:** K. Appel & W. Haken (1977) Solution of the four color map problem, *Scientific American* **237**(4) p.108-121.

Appel and Haken and Computer reduced the number of different types of planar maps to just under 2000. One of them searched every one of these maps for all possible counterexamples and found none. Then Appel and Haken published Computer's work.

5. **a place where "maths" is seen to be purely computation:** Math classes do teach styles of thinking. My college, for example, has tasked the Math Department to teach the collegiate global objective of *critical thinking*. Here we are beginning to think critically about formal thinking itself.

6. **Piles of Rocks is the world's first calculator:** P. Lockhart (2017) *Arithmetic* p.19.

7. **allow us to add and to multiply quantities:** Unfortunately too many math classrooms continue to treat students as tools to implement algorithms.

8. **the tools of the time:** *linear typography***:** Typesetting has played a significant role in the growth of mathematics. It reduced transcription errors in Gutenberg's time (circa 1450), however the mathematical illiteracy of typesetters placed severe proofing burdens on authors well into the twentieth century.

9. **it is the early eighteenth century:** How we count depends upon what we are counting and how much we care. Unfortunately many of my students, by the time they reach college, are so indoctrinated by exact counting that they have abandoned their native ability to think about what they are counting for.

10. **appears to be vestigial of this limitation of the spoken word:** G. Spencer Brown (1969) *Laws of Form* p.92.

11. **processes defined to proceed one-step-at-a-time:** Reading a linear sequence of mathematical tokens has lead to exotics such as Reverse Polish Notation, stack-based processing and PEMDAS. The binary varieties of notation such as *prefix* +xy, *infix* x+y, and *postfix* yx+ that connect operators to labels are typographic accidents, of course.

12. **at a level at which they do not yet exist!:** L. Kauffman & F. Varela (1980) Form dynamics. *Journal of Social and Biological Structures* 3 p.182. Online 8/18 at http://homepages.math.uic.edu/~kauffman/FormDynamics.pdf

13. **woven into the very fabric of our number system:** T. Danzig (1930) *Number: The language of science.* J. Mazur (ed.) (2005) p.9. Online 8/18 at http://www.engineering108.com/Data/Engineering/Maths/Number_the_language_of_science_by_Joseph-Mazur_and_Barry-Mazur.pdf

14. **serial versus parallel modes of computing:** B. Rotman (2008) *Becoming Beside Ourselves: the alphabet, ghosts, and distributed human being.* From the foreword by T. Lenoir p.xxvi.

15. **but it has not been algorithmically demonstrated:** L. Wittgenstein (1929-30) *Philosophical Remarks* §148, 155 and 157. Online 8/18 at https://www.gutenberg.org/files/5740/5740-pdf.pdf

Wittgenstein's perspective is that the inductive step introduces a new and different methodology. It may well be a supportable step, but the finite logic prior to the step and the infinite logic after the step are essentially incommensurate.

16. **an operation of thought entirely different from 'taking one more step':** A. Badiou (1990) *Number and Numbers* p.85.

17. **limits purpose to any physical purpose, not any metaphysical purpose:** Using bounded quantification, a formal arithmetic can set an upper bound on the magnitude that a natural number can have, in effect demanding that natural numbers possess some semblance of being natural. The mathematical question with this approach is what to do about rapidly increasing recursive functions like the Ackerman functions. Without going to infinite lengths, these functions can succinctly define hyperexponential growth in cardinality, analogous to millions of nested James round-brackets. Another difficulty is Gödel numbering itself, which also generates unimaginably huge but still finite whole numbers.

18. **both we and time do not have infinite extent:** B. Rotman (2000) *Mathematics as Sign: writing imagining counting* p.92.

19. **countable means computable while computable means finite:** Who, politically, gave mathematics the right to ignore reality? Who placed a discipline above the existence and the knowledge of its practitioners? Why should we not, rationally, insist that knowledge be embodied in at least *something*? Rotman (p.123.) observes that the alternative is to

conjure into being a totally disembodied agent, an imagined surrogate of ourselves that operates outside the regimes of time, space, and any kind of material presence — a being unsituated and free of any context we can name, godlike in its ghostly and untouchable otherness.

20. **within the add1 function is the tally system, i.e. ensemble arithmetic:** Chapters 2 and 3 introduce *ensemble arithmetic* with the parallel processes of fusion and merging of depth value numerals.

21. **the top of the ladder is always in sight:** This infinite series converges to the value $\pi^2/6$, approximately 1.645.

22. **This sequence is convergent and non-monotonic:** This infinite series converges to $\ln 2$.

23. **the structure which they jointly exhibit:** P. Benacerraf (1965) What numbers could not be. In P. Benacerraf & H. Putnam (eds.) (1983) *Philosophy of Mathematics 2nd ed.* p.290.

24. **constructed from *all* the numbers that precede it:** For a modern construction of the diversity of numbers based on Conway's surreal numbers, see J. Conway (1976) *On Numbers and Games*, and A. Badiou (1990) *Number and Numbers*.

25. **simply because there are infinitely many:** Wittgenstein §126 and §129.

26. **physical science as governing "acting" or "counting":** Rotman p.94.

27. **but abandons the stepwise sequential implementation:** Computational parallelism has become a well-studied area. In 2020 decreasing wire size of circuitry will reach a minimum of around 3 nanometers, which is about ten atoms in width and close to the minimum width to conduct a flow of electricity. The miniaturization that has driven the exponential growth of computer hardware capabilities for 60 years will run into the limits of physical reality. Multicore processors, some up to 1000 parallel CPU elements, have been built to continue computational speed-up, but parallelism requires new algorithms to be designed that separate parallel and sequential computational components. One early example of this research is J. Misra (1994) Powerlist: A structure for parallel recursion. *ACM Transactions on Programming Languages and Systems* 16(6) p.1737-1767.

28. **does not necessarily need to wait for the results from prior nodes:**
In both sequential and asynchronous computing, it takes several steps to
reach a result. In the example, each sequential step takes four cycles; each
asynchronous step takes a maximum of four cycles as well, but interior processes do not need to wait. Four cycles is the *worst case* scenario rather than
the *every case* scenario. For example, consider four separate processes each
feeding into the same OR gate. An OR gate passes along its information when
any input is hot. So a parallel OR can dynamically obsolete slower processes.
At IJCAI'87 my colleagues and I demonstrated a fully local, asynchronous,
fine-grained parallel model of propositional deduction based on *Laws of
Form* and implemented on a 16-node Intel Hypercube. W. Bricken (1995)
Distinction networks in I. Wachsmuth, C. Rollinger & W. Brauer (eds.)
KI-95: Advances in Artificial Intelligence p.35-48. Online 8/18 at http://wbricken.
com/pdfs/01bm/05arch/01dnets/04distinction-networks.pdf

29. **rarely think sequentially using slow conscious deliberation**: Kahneman,
Thinking, Fast and Slow.

30. *Self-similarity permits concurrency*: First-class programming languages
such as LISP and Mathematica are self-similar in that a program in the
language is a legitimate data structure. These languages can process their
own processing instructions. Computational parallelism itself rests mainly
upon available hardware resources.

31. **nothing to do with the concept of number:** G. Frege (1884/1950) *The
Foundations of Arithmetic* §40.

32. **that you would rarely see it in a classroom:** The first time I studied
recursive definitions was in grad school in Computer Science.

33. **also need to understand how such a definition is implemented**:
This point is something that computer scientists understand well and that
mathematicians generally avoid. That's what makes the two fields of study
different, doing it vs. imagining it. I believe that imagining it is far more
important than doing it, since it's imagination that suggests that there is
something to do at all. I also believe that imagination can lead to deeply
flawed thinking if it is not coupled with doing. But do not be mislead, both
mathematics and computer science dwell in virtual reality.

34. make a three-multiplier or a four-multiplier: One way to do this efficiently is with look-up-table (LUT) technology. The LUT multiplier stores all possible results of multiplying four binary numbers together within its internal wiring. When digits are input, the multiplied output is pretty much instant.

35. to organize linear streams of data that perform one-at-a-time processing steps: Single core processors were standard across the computing industry for sixty years. During that time there were many hardware implementations of parallel computing but none were commercially successful. A primary stumbling block is that parallel computers are difficult to program. When clock-rates peaked due to fundamental physics at around 4 GHz, computing cores began to multiply.

How we think about mathematics, in sequence or in parallel, has manifested in silicon technology as the *vonNeumann bottleneck*, the chasm between hardware and software. The kind of parallelism described in this chapter is **very-fine-grain parallelism**, where every boundary has the capabilities of an operating system, as described in W. Bricken & G. Coco (1995) VEOS: The virtual environment operating shell. In W. Barfield & T. Furness (eds.) *Virtual Environments and Advanced Interface Design* p.102-142. Online 8/18 at
http://wbricken.com/pdfs/03words/02vr/02veos/01describe/04veos-proj-book.pdf

Compilers are software systems that prepare data for processing. Compilers can handle course-grain parallelism, dividing a task between two or three processors, but fundamentally, if the parallelism hasn't been written into the software, it does little good in the hardware. Some advances in the rapidly advancing field of parallel software design are reported in U. Vishkin (2011) Using simple abstraction to reinvent computing for parallelism *Communications of the ACM* **54**(1) p.75-85.

Modern compilers can figure out what may happen in parallel and what has temporal dependencies. Parallel computing does require exacting choreography, and there are some tasks, like hardware multiplication, that have inherently sequential components. The linearity of software languages has contributed to the current dominance of sequential computers. The hardware design community thinks about parallel processes, because at the level of electrons traveling down wires, the entire computer chip is active all at the same time.

Chapter 20

Boundary

(an unmatched left parenthesis creates an unresolved
tension that will stay with you all day.[1]
— Randall Munroe (2016)

In the *Elements* Euclid defines a boundary as "that which is an extremity of anything".[2] This inward looking definition ignores context; Euclid defines only a one-sided boundary. Aristotle expanded this definition to include the concept of outside. He defined Euclid's *extremity* as "the first thing outside of which no part is to be found, and the first thing inside of which everything is to be found".[3] To what then does a boundary belong, the inside or the outside, or perhaps both, or is it neither?

When Spencer Brown calls the boundary a **cross**, he is emphasizing the active perspective of a distinction, seeing it as a mathematical instruction to act by crossing the boundary. It is also accurate to say that the boundary is brought into existence by the act of crossing. The distinction-based reading is that the outside and the inside are identical, it is the boundary itself that creates both. Thus the question is ill-formed, outside and inside both belong to the boundary that defines them. The inside is the content that the boundary operates upon, thus the

change
inside
outside

boundary itself imposes a change upon its contents. There is no concept of contact between forms. In the case of James algebra, the outside of the outermost boundary is of a different logical type.[4] This perspective perhaps is closest to that of Frege:

> A definition of a concept (of a possible predicate) must...unambiguously determine, as regards any object, whether or not it falls under the concept (whether or not the predicate is truly assertible of it). We may express this metaphorically as follows: the concept must have a sharp boundary.[5]

Having invested the effort to become accustomed to the rather exotic James calculus, we can now play with its fundamental structures, exploring how our conventional concepts of number and numeric operation interact with the boundary concepts of James forms.

20.1 Arithmetic

An *arithmetic* addresses the structures of a calculus without variables. Arithmetic includes both the stable forms and the transformations that construct the equivalence classes of stable forms. With variables such as A standing in place of an arbitrary form, we have an *algebra*.

> There are in fact many other arithmetics in mathematics....Each arithmetic is designed to represent some class of phenomena of the physical world.

Historian Morris Kline goes on to say:

> Only experience can tell us where ordinary arithmetic applies to any given physical phenomena. Thus one cannot speak of arithmetic as a body of truths that necessarily apply to physical phenomena.[6]

In this chapter, we'll look at the arithmetic and algebra of James forms and the implications of viewing the arithmetic of numbers as a *derivative subset* of iconic form. The idea is to apply the James axioms to reduce the variety of possible containment structures. After ignoring the void-equivalent forms, there remain stable structures, the structural invariants that define the **ground forms** of the James arithmetic. Applying the three axioms will reduce any James arithmetic form to a stable ground structure. *The minimal stable structures are the archetypes for each equivalence class.* Analogously, the whole numbers are the invariants of the arithmetic of natural numbers. All of the expressions combining whole numbers with the operations of addition or multiplication reduce to the equivalence class of one of the whole numbers. The irreducible James forms are also the elementary *operations* within the calculus, since forms can be read both as objects and as operators. A ground form is converted into an operator by placing any other form, with or without variables, within its boundary, usually at the deepest level.

$$3 + 5 \Rightarrow 8$$
$$2 + 2 + 2 + 2 \Rightarrow 8$$
$$4 \times (1 + 1) \Rightarrow 8$$

James Units

There are two elementary James ground forms, the units ( ) and [ ], and one vacuous unit, < >, that is void-equivalent. When these three units are interpreted, they provide a working basis for the essential mathematical concepts $\{1, -\infty, 0\}$. The grounds are also archetypes of the three possible types of form: numeric, non-numeric and void-equivalent. Round and square units are **form archetypes**. After reduction by the axioms, the type of unit (round or square) that *exists at the deepest level* of a form identifies that form as a member of the equivalence set of that archetype. You can tell the type of a form by reducing it and then looking in the deepest space. A round unit in the deepest space identifies a numeric form, while a square unit in the deepest space identifies a non-numeric form. If the reduced form is void-equivalent it cannot belong to any equivalence class since it no longer exists.

form archetypes

numeric ( )
non-numeric [ ]

	AXIOMS	
Accumulation	( ) ( )	*does not reduce*
Unification	[ ] [ ] ⇒	[ ]
Indeterminacy	[ ] <[ ]> ⇒	*indeterminate*
	THEOREMS	
Unit reflection	( ) <( )> =	*void*
Dominion	( ) [ ] =	[ ]

Figure 20-1: *Unit transformations*

It is a semantic error to consider void-equivalent forms an equivalence class, there is no existent form archetype and there are no possible members.

20.2 Forms with Multiple Contents

All forms are contained by either an explicit or an implicit outermost boundary. Mathematically forms are **rooted trees**. The containment relation is the only type of relation within James arithmetic, making nesting a fundamental structural feature. Containers can, as well, contain more than one content form. Forms thus have both depth and breadth.

The transformations shown in Figure 20-1 define the behavior of the various types of *units* within any container. In the figure, the outermost container itself is implicit. The **unit transformations of the arithmetic** are

- **Accumulation:** Round units accumulate.
- **Unification:** Square units do not replicate.
- **Indeterminacy**: A square unit contained with its reflection is not interpretable.

The Dominion Theorem shows the result of mixing square-brackets with round-brackets in the same container. Square units are dominant. That is, a non-numeric

unit accumulation		interpretation
$(( ).._N..( ))$	N	positive whole number
$<( ).._N..( )>$	−N	negative whole number
$(( ).._N..( ))$	#N	whole number exponent
$[( ).._N..( )]$	$\log_\# N$	whole number logarithm
$(<[( ).._N..( )]>)$	1/N	unit fraction

Figure 20-2: *Accumulation within bounds*

unit **absorbs** numeric units.[7] The angle-bracket interacts with other units only as a modifier, as a container
of forms. The Unit Reflection theorem is a special case
of Reflection, in which a round unit and its reflection
is void-equivalent. When a square unit and a reflected
square-unit are in the same container, the entire form
becomes indeterminate.[8]

Accumulation

Accumulations of James ground forms identify a broader
class of objects than the whole numbers, as presented in
Figure 20-2. The natural numbers are represented by
accumulations of round-bracket units. When the outermost boundary is an angle-bracket, accumulations of
round units represent the negative integers.

Numeric forms with complex nesting structures will accumulate round units at their deepest level. Each of the
forms below shows a different container with an accumulation of three units. The shorthand symbol 3 represents
the cardinality of accumulated round units.

$$(( )( )( )) \quad = \quad (3) \quad ☞ \quad 3$$
$$<( )( )( )> \quad = \quad <3> \quad ☞ \quad -3$$
$$(( )( )( )) \quad = \quad (3) \quad ☞ \quad \#3$$
$$[( )( )( )] \quad = \quad [3] \quad ☞ \quad \log_\# 3$$
$$(<[( )( )( )]>) \quad = \quad (<[3]>) \quad ☞ \quad 1/3$$

unit configuration ☞	interpretation	value
	NUMERIC	
(< >) = ( )	$\#^{0}$	1
<( )>	$-\#^{0}$	-1
(( ))	$\#^{1}$	#
	VOID-EQUIVALENT	
<< >> = < > = *void*	$--0$	0
([ ]) = *void*	$\#^{\log_{\#} 0}$	0
[( )] = *void*	$\log_{\#} 1$	0
	NON-NUMERIC	
[< >] = [ ]	$\log_{\#} 0$	$-\infty$
<[ ]>	$-\log_{\#} 0$	∞
[[ ]]	$\log\log_{\#} 0$	*undefined*

Figure 20-3: *The nine double-boundary simple forms with interpretation*

20.3 Double-boundary Forms

A **simply nested** form is one in which no container has more than one content form. There are nine possible *double-boundary simply nested forms* as shown in Figure 20-3. These double-boundary forms are the simplest non-units. Four of the double-boundary forms are stable while five reduce under the three James axioms.

Reducible

Figure 20-4 shows the five double-boundary forms that reduce, together with their interpretations. Two reduce to the two fundamental James units and one is void-equivalent. These reductions each delete the void-equivalent pseudo-unit < >. The two remaining forms, the Inversion pairs, are defined to be void-equivalent by rule.

When these double-boundary forms have inner content, as indicated by the variable A in Figure 20-4, three of the

form ☞	interpretation	application

Delete inner < >: *three forms revert to ground units*

$(< >) = (\ )$	$\#^0 = 1$	$(<A>)$ ☞ $\#^{-A}$
$[< >] = [\ ]$	$\log_\# 0 = -\infty$	$[<A>]$ ☞ $\log_\# -A$
$<< >> = < > = void$	$--0 = 0$	$<<A>>$ ☞ $--A = A$

Inversion: *two forms are reduced by the Inversion axiom*

$([\ ]) = void$	$\#^{\log_\# 0} = 0$	$([A])$ ☞ $\#^{\log_\# A} = A$
$[(\ )] = void$	$\log_\# \#^0 = 0$	$[(A)]$ ☞ $\log_\# \#^A = A$

Figure 20-4: *The five reducible double-boundary forms*

five reduce to A by deleting nested pairs of boundaries. Two *special forms* remain. If A is the non-numeric ground [ ], then (<[ ]>) can be interpreted as *divide-by-zero*, providing a natural explanation why it is forbidden: the form of divide-by-zero has the non-numeric archetype in the deepest nested space. When A is numeric, (<A>) is the archetype for a geometric fraction, $(1/\#)^A$. When A is a logarithm in the form of [B], (<[B]>) is the archetype for a unit fraction, $1/B$.

Similarly, the form [<A>] is the archetype for a negative logarithm, a conventionally forbidden class of numbers. When A is the numeric unit ground ( ), [<( )>] can be interpreted as the *logarithm-of-negative-one*. Since a round-bracket is in the deepest space, this form is **numeric**. It leads to an entire class of new numbers, the J forms. [<( )>], not i, is the *archetype for imaginary numbers*!

Stable

Figure 20-5 shows the four stable simply nested double-boundary forms. *Stable forms reoccur*, they are the

form	☞	*interpretation*	*application*		

Add outer < >: *two forms identify reflected units*

<( )>		-1	<(A)>	☞	$-\#^A$
<[ ]>		$-\log_\# 0 = \infty$	<[A]>	☞	$-\log_\# A$

Stable: *two forms do not reduce*

(( ))		$\#^{\#^0} = \#$	((A))	☞	$\#^{\#^A}$
[[ ]]		$\log\log_\# 0 \Rightarrow$ *undefined*	[[A]]	☞	$\log\log_\# A$

Figure 20-5: *The four stable double-boundary forms*

skeletal framework of James patterns. (( )) is numeric; [[ ]] is non-numeric (and for now uninterpreted); and <( )> and <[ ]> are numeric and non-numeric reflected forms respectively. Three can be interpreted conventionally while one, [[ ]], creates a conundrum.

The angle-bracket increases the conceptual realm of numeric forms to include reflected forms that can be interpreted as negative numbers. Via <[A]> the realm of numeric forms increases to include the real numbers between 0 and 1 that can be expressed as negative logarithms.

Two of the stable forms are somewhat surprising. The form (( )) represents the arbitrary base of James numbers. Remarkably (( )) is a mechanism to bootstrap into any arbitrary number #, just the thing we need to be able to treat the base of a power and a logarithm as irrelevant within a form and as arbitrary within an interpretation.

[ ] can be interpreted as a type of infinity. However, we may have to draw the line at [[ ]], since the interpretation as $\log_\# -\infty$ also challenges our concept of logarithms. Volume III explores these and other forms of infinity.

reduce			stable	
unwrap	*void reflect*	*clarify*		
<<< >>>	((< >))	([( )])	((( )))	[[[ ]]]
<<[ ]>>	([< >])	[[( )]]	(<( )>)	[<[ ]>]
<<( )>>	[[< >]]	[(( ))]	[<( )>]	(<[ ]>)
[<< >>]	[(< >)]	<[( )]>	<(( ))>	<[[ ]]>
(<< >>)	<(< >)>	([[ ]])		
	<[< >]>	(([ ]))		
		[([ ])]		
		<([ ])>		

Figure 20-6: *The twenty-seven simple triple-boundary forms*

20.4 Triple-boundary Forms

We can gain a better understanding of stable boundary configurations by looking at *simply nested* triple-boundary forms, of which there are twenty-seven possibilities in all. Nineteen of these reduce, leaving eight stable triple-boundary forms, as illustrated in Figure 20-6.

Figure 20-7 shows the alignment of the simply nested stable forms with common numeric concepts. The eight stable forms exhibit a symmetry. Four are numeric, with ( ) innermost. Three of the numeric forms identify an arbitrary positive number, an arbitrary negative number, and an arbitrary unit fraction. The fourth, which is named J, is the archetype unit for imaginary numbers.

The second grouping of four forms have [ ] innermost. If we take <[ ]> to be infinity, then both (<[ ]>) and [<[ ]>] reduce to infinity, given our interpretation were to follow the conventional laws of infinity. The two remaining forms incorporate [[ ]], which we are leaving undefined for now. The two forms that include all three types of boundary

some simply nested forms

<(<[ ]>)>
[[[[ ]]]]
<[[<(<( )>)>]]>

stable forms ☞ *interpretation*		*number type*
NUMERIC		
$(((\;)))$	$\#^{\#}$	*positive real*
$<((\;))>$	$-\#$	*negative real*
$(<(\;)>)$	$\#^{-1}$	*unit fraction*
$[<(\;)>]$	$\log_{\#} -1$	*imaginary*]
NON-NUMERIC (Volume III)		
$(<[\;]>)$	$1/0$	*divide-by-zero*
$[<[\;]>]$	$\log_{\#} (-\log_{\#} 0)$	
$<[[\;]]>$	$-\log\log_{\#} 0$	
$[[[\;]]]$	$\log\log\log_{\#} 0$	

Figure 20-7: *The eight stable triple-boundary forms*

are of particular interest, and they have names. $[<(\;)>]$ is] and $(<[\;]>)$ is divide-by-zero.

Growth of Simply Nested Forms

Figure 20-8 summarizes the hierarchical structure of irreducible forms, with an emphasis on the binary growth of stable forms relative to the number of boundaries. Each form is provided with an interpretation. Of the 16 simply nested forms in the figure, all but one numeric form (indicated by ◄) is in common use. Three of the seven non-numeric forms can be found in common arithmetic, although they are conceptual outliers. The four others marked by ? are exotics. Each form in the hierarchy (going left to right) supports two types of outer boundary that do not reduce. The angle-bracket adds limited variety.

(A) *supports* $((A))$ *and* $<(A)>$
[A] *supports* $[[A]]$ *and* $<[A]>$
<A> *supports* $(<A>)$ *and* $[<A>]$

number of containers				interpretation	
none	**one**	**two**	**three**		
			((( )))	*power tower*	
		(( ))		*base*	
			<(( ))>	*negative base*	
	( )			*numeric unit*	
			(<( )>)	*1/base*	
		<( )>		*negative unit*	
			[<( )>]	*logarithm of –1*	←
void	< >			*zero*	
			(<[ ]>)	*divide-by-zero*	
		<[ ]>		*infinity*	
			[<[ ]>]	*log ∞*	?
	[ ]			*negative infinity*	
			<[[ ]]>	*–log –∞*	?
		[[ ]]		*log –∞*	?
			[[[ ]]]	*loglog –∞*	?

Figure 20-8: *The simply nested stable forms up to three containers*

Why stop at three nested boundaries? We have stopped for convenience. Interpretation becomes increasingly more unusual as the depth of stable nested containers increases. The diversity of these forms is significantly constrained by the James axioms. Without the angle-bracket, it is easy to see that inversion pairs can be deleted. This leaves only pure nested forms of one type of boundary such as (((( )))) and [[[[ ]]]]. The former is a tower of exponential powers. The latter is nested logarithms. Deeply nested round-brackets suggest that boundary techniques might contribute to *iterated exponentials*, also known as **power towers**.[9] Neither form however finds much use in conventional mathematics.

(((( )))) ☞ $\#^{\#^{\#}}$

20.5 Algebra with Two Boundaries

The angle-bracket in James algebra, the container that we have interpreted as standing in place of all common inverse operations, can itself be entirely eliminated without conceptual loss! We might have expected this since the angle pseudo-unit is void-equivalent. Jeff James and Dave Keenan explored the condensation of James algebra from a three-boundary system to a **two-boundary system**.[10] The essential idea is to combine the angle-bracket with one of the inversion boundaries. Each of the four possible combinations creates a different two-boundary notation for the James algebra. These notations share in common that the reflection attributed to the angle bracket is converted into alternating depths of nesting of round- and square-brackets.[11]

<(...)>
<[...]>
(<...>)
[<...>]

Double-struck Square-brackets

We'll modify the structure of the square bracket to incorporate the angle-bracket. The composite boundary is represented by a *double-struck square-bracket*. The new two-boundary dialect rests upon this mapping:

$$[\![A]\!] \quad \text{☞} \quad [<A>] \quad \text{☞} \quad \log -A$$

Figure 20-9 shows the complete transcription map between the James three boundary system and the new two boundary system. To arrive at this mapping James forms are converted into structures for which all square-brackets form a double boundary with an angle-bracket, [<...>]. One way to do this is to call upon Involution, which introduces two angle-brackets. The outer angle-bracket facilitates the double-struck conversion, while the inner angle-bracket can be coupled with an Inversion pair. Here's the generic conversion of a square-bracket into double-struck square-brackets.

```
              [    A    ]
wrap          [<   <A>  >]
enfold        [<([<A>])>]   ☞   [([A])]
```

units			boundaries		
			A	☞	A
( )	☞	( )	(A)	☞	(A)
[ ]	☞	⟦ ⟧	[A]	☞	⟦(⟦A⟧)⟧
< >	☞	(⟦ ⟧) = *void*	<A>	☞	(⟦A⟧)

Figure 20-9: *Map from three-boundary to two-boundary systems*

And here, for example, are the two named triple-boundary forms.

$$[<( )>] \quad ☞ \quad ⟦( )⟧ \qquad\qquad \text{J}$$
$$(<[ ]>) \quad ☞ \quad ((⟦⟦ ⟧⟧)) \qquad\qquad \textit{divide-by-zero}$$

We have entered into exotic interpretive territory. I'll call a logarithm of a negative number, ⟦A⟧, *logminus*. Logminus follows all the rules of a conventional logarithm. For example,

$$⟦(⟦A⟧)⟧ \quad ☞ \quad \log_{\#}- (\#^{\log_{\#}- A})$$
$$\log_{\#}- (-A)$$
$$\log_{\#} \quad A \quad ☞ \quad [A]$$

Round-brackets are not implicated in this redefinition, all we will need then is the angle-bracket conversion.

$$<A> = ([<A>]) \quad ☞ \quad (⟦A⟧) \quad ☞ \quad \#^{\log_{\#}- A} = -A$$

And now an arbitrary form. This conversion generates the double-struck version of the Inversion axiom.

$$\begin{matrix} A \\ < \ <A> \ > \\ ([<([<A>])>]) \quad ☞ \quad (⟦(⟦A⟧)⟧) \end{matrix} \qquad \begin{matrix} \text{wrap} \\ \text{enfold} \end{matrix}$$

Here's the interpretation. Don't say I didn't warn you.

$$(⟦(⟦A⟧)⟧) \quad ☞ \quad \#^{\log_{\#}- \#^{\log_{\#}- A}}$$
$$\#^{\log_{\#}- -A}$$
$$\#^{\log_{\#} A}$$
$$A$$

two-boundary inversion

As might be expected, fewer boundary types leads to forms with more occurrences of boundaries. The key idea, though, is that we have changed the notation of the system but not the mechanisms or the axioms and theorems. At any time we can change the double-struck square boundary back into an angle-bracket contained by a single-struck square-bracket by a simple substitution.

$[\![A]\!] \; \text{☞} \; [\langle A\rangle]$

Figure 20-10 shows the axioms and theorems of a two boundary algebra for which the square-bracket is interpreted as the logarithm of a negative number rather than as the logarithm of a positive number. The James axioms have not changed, neither has the Dominion theorem. *J-transparency* is a new and important theorem since it establishes that J is independent of the forms it might contain. The remaining theorems in the figure are those James theorems that incorporate an angle-bracket.

Phase Shift

After looking at Figure 20-10 you might agree with Jeffrey James' preliminary assessment.

> None of these combinations had the elegance of the original three, and all failed to provide insight beyond their possibility.[12]

The motivation here though is to learn new ways to think about arithmetic, and now we have a new way to think about James algebra. In particular, notice that <<A>> takes on the same form as ([A]). Involution coalesces into either of the varieties of the Inversion pairs.[13]

involution

<<A>> = A

$$\langle\langle A\rangle\rangle \quad \text{☞} \quad (\![\,(\,[A]\,)\,]\!) \quad \text{☞} \quad ([A]) = A$$
$$\langle\langle A\rangle\rangle \quad \text{☞} \quad [\![\,(\,[\![(A)]\!]\,)\,]\!] \quad \text{☞} \quad [\![(A)]\!] = A$$

The two versions of Inversion show a *phase shift* within alternating round- and double-struck square-brackets. Two boundary Inversion requires four nested boundaries, showing that the original James Inversion boundaries are

DEFINITIONS

[A]	☞	[<A>]	*double-struck square*
([A])	☞	<A>	*angle*
[ ]	☞	[ ]	*double-struck unit*
([ ])	☞	*void*	*inversion unit*
[( )]	☞	J	*J*

AXIOMS

([([A])]) = [([(A)])] = A   *inversion*

(A [B C]) = (A [B])(A [C])   *arrangement*

A ([A]) = *void*   *reflection*

THEOREMS

(A [ ]) = *void*   *dominion*

[(A)] = J A   *J-transparency*

(J [A]) = A   *involution*

([A ([B])]) = ([A]) B   *reaction*

([A])([B]) = ([A B])   *separation*

(A ([[B]])) = (J A ([J [B]]))   *promotion*

Figure 20-10: *Two-boundary James algebra*

no longer insensitive to their ordering. The *nesting order* of the new Inversion boundaries encapsulates the concept of angle-bracket Reflection.

The alternation of round- and double-struck square-brackets can be seen as an oscillation between real and imaginary spaces. The conventional inverse transformations are absorbed into the interior space of double-struck square-brackets. *All inverses are equally imaginary.* The "real" transformations (+, x, ^) rest within the interior space of round-brackets. The angle-bracket is the James embodiment of the negative sign, –. However now that we no longer have angle-brackets, negative numbers in the archetypical form of –1 become structurally integrated within imaginary numbers in the archetypical form of $\sqrt{-1}$.

The conceptual evolution of James algebra presented in Chapters 6 through 9 treats the Inversion boundaries as fundamental while adding the angle-bracket to address functional inverses. That evolution matches the historical development of functional thinking. However we now have an alternative history available in which functional inverses are less relevant than what appears to be an "alternating" Inversion associated with the form of J. By incorporating the J notation, the Inversion axiom takes on a simpler form. Substituting for the form of J,

J-transparency $\qquad$ ([([A])]) = (J [A]) = A

J-transparency $\qquad$ [([(A)])] = [(J A)] = J J A = A

Comparing notations, we see that the angle-bracket container has been converted into the *unit-like* form J. In the three boundary notation:

$\qquad$ <<A>> = [(A)] = A $\qquad$ ☞ $\qquad$ J J A = A

When A is *void*, this becomes

$\qquad$ << >> = [( )] = *void* $\qquad$ ☞ $\qquad$ J J = *void*

In the two-boundary notation, J exchanges the order of nesting of the two Inversion boundaries, indicating a binary phase shift that suggests a rotation of 180°, i.e. a reflection

J-transparency $\qquad$ ([([ ])]) = (J [ ]) = *void*

J-transparency $\qquad$ [([( )])] = [(J)] = J J = *void*

Chapter 12 demonstrates a technique for replacing angle-brackets by a form that incorporates J as an independent unit. The substitution is <A> = (J [A]). Transcribing into the two boundary calculus,

$\qquad$ <A> $\qquad$ ☞ $\qquad$ (J [([A])])

J-transparency $\qquad$ (J J [A])

J void $\qquad$ ([A]) $\qquad$ ☞ $\qquad$ (J [A])

Dominion

(A [ ])

(A [ ]) (A [ ]) ([(A [ ])])   reflect

      (A [ ]) ([(A [ ])])   collect

              void   reflect

Promote

                    ([(A [([B])])])

(A [   ]) ([(A [([B])])])   dominion

(A [B   ([B])]) ([(A [([B])])])   reflect

(A [B]) (A [([B])]) ([(A [([B])])])   collect

(A [B])   reflect

J-Transparency

[(A   )]

[([([(A)])])]   enfold

[([([([([( )])] A)])])]   void enfold

[([([( )] A)   ])]   promote

            [( )]   A   clarify

              J   A   label

Figure 20-11: *Demonstration of J-transparency*

The central theorem for each of these applications of J is J-transparency.

$$[(A)] = J\ A$$ **J-transparency**

Figure 20-11 shows the demonstration of J-transparency from the axioms in Figure 20-10. The demonstration first needs two lemmas, Dominion and Promote.

The form of J is so intimately incorporated into this two boundary calculus that it may be appropriate to abandon the model of alternating real and imaginary spaces altogether. The behavior of the log −1 is entirely adequate to provide a basis for the arithmetic operations expressed in terms of exponential and logarithmic functions as well as for the concept of an inverse function.

What we see here is that repeated or double enfolding is fundamental. The concept of functional inverses within arithmetic has been embedded into the nesting sequence of exponential and logarithmic spaces. From this perspective, the angle-bracket in the three boundary calculus is simply a marker of the polarity of a container. However, it is J itself that provides the most fundamental change in perspective. As a simply nested compound boundary, J is transparent to its contents.

$$\llbracket (A) \rrbracket \ = \ J \ A \quad \text{☞} \quad \log -A \ = \ A + \log -1$$

The greatest surprise occurs when we explore what happens when J is transparent to itself. The form J J is void-equivalent, yet J is not zero. J self-transparency leads to this appealing form:

J self-transparency $$\llbracket (\llbracket (\ ) \rrbracket) \rrbracket \ = \ \llbracket (\ ) \rrbracket \ \llbracket (\ ) \rrbracket \ = \quad \textit{void}$$

We could also explore alternative angle-bracket integration strategies, constructing a new single boundary for nested pairs such as <( )>, <[ ]>, and (< >). The patterns change

<[A]> *as the new*
integrated boundary
symmetrically, so there are no new structural types. The unexpected properties of the form of J have been hidden within our current conceptual history of arithmetic. The logarithm of −1 has been considered illegitimate since the eighteenth century. The broad exploration of the behavior of J is in Chapters 33 through 36 of Volume III.

[A] ☞ J [A]

[A] ☞ J ⟦A⟧

<[A]> ☞ ⟨A⟩
<A> ☞ ⟨(A)⟩
[A] ☞ ⟨(⟨A⟩)⟩

Kauffman One Boundary Arithmetic

Louis Kauffman
1945–
Chapter 14 describes Kauffman's *Arithmetic in the Form*, a refinement of the Spencer Brown numbers that inspired the current work with James numbers.[14] Kauffman numbers use a *single boundary* the express whole number addition and multiplication. For convenience, Figure 20-12 shows the axioms of Kauffman numbers that were

NUMBERS	*INTERPRETATION*
0 ☞ ( )	
1 ☞ (( ))	((A)(B)) ☞ A + B
2 ☞ (( )( ))	A B ☞ A x B
3 ☞ (( )( )( ))	
N ☞ (( )..$_N$..( ))	

AXIOMS

((A)) = A	*all contexts*
( )( ) = ( )	*multiplicative context*
A ((B)(C)) = ((A B)(A C))	A *in multiplicative context*

Figure 20-12: *Kauffman numbers in the form (Figure 14-3)*

first presented as Figure 14-3. Alternating nesting of forms defines additive and multiplicative contexts. Even nesting depths define multiplication while odd nesting depths define addition. This boundary system works quite elegantly. Like James numbers, Kauffman units accumulate to form cardinals as bounded collections of tally marks. Multiplication unfolds via the Arrangement axiom, a structure that is also common to the James three-boundary and two-boundary systems.

The cost of a single boundary notation is that Arrangement must be restricted to application at *alternating depths of nesting*. Here the neutral delimiter identifies nested spaces in Kauffman arithmetic.

Even Arrangement

$$(odd\ (even1\ even2)) = (odd\ (even1))\ \ (odd\ (even2))$$

Odd Arrangement

$$(even\ (odd1\ odd2)) \neq (even\ (odd1))\ \ (even\ (odd2))$$

Similarly for Dominion,

$$(odd\ (\ )) = void \qquad\qquad but \qquad\qquad (even\ (\ )) \neq void$$

depth parity	*even* (*odd* (*even* (*odd*)))
Kauffman	*multiply* (*add* (*multiply* (*add*)))
James	*add* (*power* [*logarithm* (*power* [*logarithm*])])
two-boundary	*add* (*power*⟦*logminus* (*power*⟦*logminus*⟧)⟧)

Figure 20-13: *Oscillating functional boundaries*

Oscillating Spaces

Each of the systems in Figure 20-13 embeds different conventional operations into odd and even nested spaces. From a boundary perspective, the particular type of boundary operates upon the space that it contains. In our interpretation of James algebra, the inversion pair of round- and square-brackets alternates exponent and logarithm. The outermost space, protected by an implicit neutral outermost boundary, provides addition without implicating a boundary operation. The angle-bracket is necessary to introduce reflected forms, i.e. functional inverses. In the two-boundary system, logminus captures both logarithm and inverse. It takes an accumulation of two nested logminus functions to convert the function of a space from positive to reflected and back to positive. It is interesting that the structural behavior of logminus supports this type of embedding. J itself serves to mark the parity of the positive and reflected spaces, with two Js accumulating to cancel the oscillation of inversion. The dance between reflection and J-transparency illustrates the impact of logminus nesting. As examples,

$$A \; (\llbracket A \rrbracket) \; = \; \textit{void}$$
$$J \; \llbracket (A) \rrbracket \; = \; A$$
$$(J \quad \llbracket A \rrbracket) \; = \; A$$
$$(\llbracket A \rrbracket) \llbracket (A) \rrbracket \; = \; J$$

In general, different *types of boundary* can be converted into different *levels of nesting* of one type of boundary.

20.6 Remarks

This chapter includes several surprises, most of which have not yet been fully articulated.

— Stable forms have limited structural diversity.
— The form of the arbitrary base is (( )).
— Boundary types are equivalent to levels of nesting.
— J rather than i is the prototype imaginary number.
— Dominion bridges numeric and non-numeric concepts.
— The angle-boundary is unnecessary.

The reason to use axioms rather than something like logic or intuition is that an axiomatic formal system can be implemented in software. Structural axioms are compatible with digital convergence, the forms we are exploring can be communicated in a distributed computing environment and efficiently implemented. But we also have a commitment to learnability. Mathematics historian Ivor Grattan-Guinness observes:

> The teaching of theories from axioms, or some close imitation of them such as the basic laws of algebra, is usually an educational disaster; for whatever the gains in rigour, they are achieved at the expense of a heavy loss of heuristic understanding and intuitive reasoning — the very things that lie at the heart of real educational theory.[15]

The exploration of triple-boundary simply nested forms has left us with five interpretable forms, and three that remain undefined for now. The problematic forms, particularly <[ ]> and [[ ]], are postponed until Chapter 41, after we have finished exploring conventional non-imaginary numbers. Volume III also explores the two named triple-boundary stable structures, the James forms for the concepts of infinite and imaginary numbers.

$$divide\text{-}by\ 0 \qquad ☞ \qquad (<[\ ]>)$$
$$logarithm\ -1 \qquad ☞ \qquad [<(\ )>]$$

Endnotes

1. **opening quote:** *Randall Munroe's* xkcd *cartoon* "(". Online 8/18 at https://xkcd.com/859/

2. **a boundary as "that which is an extremity of anything":** Euclid (c300 BC) *Elements*, Book I, Definition 13. Online 12/18 at https://mathcs.clarku.edu/~djoyce/java/elements/toc.html

3. **first thing inside of which everything is to be found:** Aristotle, *Metaphysics* 1022ª. Online 8/18 at http://classics.mit.edu/Aristotle/metaphysics.html

4. **the outside of the outermost boundary is of a different logical type:** There is always an iconic "outermost" container, and that icon too has an outermost container, the page upon which it is drawn. The edge of the containing page indicates a shift from reality to representation. The page itself is-contained-by the sentience that has designated the page (and its contents) as relevant, the shift from sentient intention to communication. Because the page and the containers represented upon it are self-similar, we can transfer the conventional location of semantics to any boundary. That is, boundaries are semipermeable to sentient reading.

5. **the concept must have a sharp boundary:** G. Frege (1903) *The Fundamental Laws of Arithmetic* Vol. II §56 p.159.

6. **a body of truths that necessarily apply to physical phenomena:** M. Kline (1980) *Mathematics: The loss of certainty* p.95.

7. **a non-numeric unit absorbs numeric units:** Strictly speaking, this phraseology is a colloquialism. Units within a container, both round and square do not interact. The container of a square unit renders all numeric contents void-equivalent. In the case of Dominion the equal sign associated with non-numeric forms has a fundamentally different meaning than numeric equal, since it is not possible to compare the magnitude of non-numeric forms.

8. **in the same container, the entire form becomes indeterminate:** Indeterminate forms and their behavior are discussed in Chapter 42.

9. **iterated exponentials, also known as power towers:** D. Knuth (1976) Mathematics and computer science: Coping with finiteness. *Science* 194

(4271) p.1235-1242. Online 8/18 at http://www.sciacchitano.it/Spazio/Coping%20
with%20Finiteness.pdf

Knuth introduces a notation for power towers, called the *up-arrow*. In the abstract of his paper, Knuth identifies one of his goals:

> Finite numbers can be really enormous, and the known universe is very small. Therefore the distinction between finite and infinite is not as relevant as the distinction between realistic and unrealistic.

And thus the dividing line between mathematicians and computer scientists is clearly defined.

The up-arrow notation was developed to continue the sequence of accumulations in arithmetic.

— Addition is iterated counting.
— Multiplication is iterated addition.
— Exponentiation is iterated multiplication.
— The up-arrow is iterated exponentiation.

B^N is a standard typographic notation for B^N. Knuth let B^^N mean B raised to the power of B raised to the power of B, with B occurring N times. For example:

$$B\wedge\wedge N = B\wedge(B\wedge.._N..(B\wedge B)) = B^{B^{\cdot^{\cdot^{N^{\cdot^{\cdot^{B}}}}}}}$$

In both ellipsis forms $.._N..$, N is the total number of occurrences of the base B, including the first.

Since we have available an embedded James base we can substitute the generic form of the base, B = (( )), to arrive at the close relationship between nested round-brackets and up-arrows. For example,

$$3\wedge3 = 3^3 \quad ☞ \quad (3) = ((( ))) \quad \text{base-3}$$
$$3\wedge\wedge3 = 3^{3^3} \quad ☞ \quad ((3)) = (((( )))) \quad \text{base-3}$$
$$B\wedge\wedge3 = B^{B^B} \quad ☞ \quad ((B)) = (((( )))) \quad \text{base-B}$$

Round-bracket nesting is ideal for expressing up-arrows, particularly as they extend to higher levels of embedding. A final example.

$$3\wedge\wedge\wedge3 = 3\wedge\wedge(3\wedge\wedge3) = 3\wedge\wedge3^{3^3} = 3\wedge(3\wedge(3\wedge...(3\wedge3)))$$

with 3^{3^3} repetitions of 3 in the power tower. We end up with a power tower of threes that is 19683 powers high. Yes, that would be 19683 nested round-brackets. Knuth's point is that we don't need infinity to reach incomprehensible magnitudes.

10. **from a three-boundary system to a two-boundary system:** Arthur Collings has studied the structure of four-valued logic using boundary axioms for forms nested four levels deep. A. Collings (2017) The Brown-4 indicational calculus. *Cybernetics and Human Knowing* 24(3-4) p.75-101.

11. **alternating depths of nesting of round- and square-brackets:** Of course, the non-symbolic dialects described in Chapter 13 are also available for the two-boundary notations. Although we end up with more boundaries (or boxes or blocks or rooms), construction is simpler in the two boundary systems. The path dialect particularly benefits, since a single composite inversion boundary suffices.

12. **all failed to provide insight beyond their possibility:** J. James email correspondence March 1994.

13. **Involution coalesces into either of the varieties of the Inversion pairs:** Chapter 16 associates Reflection with the *additive inverse* while Inversion was associated with the *functional inverse*. Now we can see that there is only one type of inverse, and the distinction between additive and functional is another textual acciden t.

14. **a refinement of the Spencer Brown numbers that inspired the current work with James numbers:** L. Kauffman (1995) Arithmetic in the Form *Cybernetics and Systems: An International Journal* 26(1) p.1-57. Online 8/18 at http://homepages.math.uic.edu/~kauffman/ArithForm.pdf

L. Kauffman (2017 in process) *Laws of Form — An Exploration in Mathematics and Foundations* (rough draft) Online 2/17 at http://homepages.math.uic.edu/~kauffman/Laws.pdf

Spencer Brown's approach to boundary numbers is published as an appendix to the 2009 reprint of *Laws of Form*.

G. Spencer Brown (1969) *Laws of Form*, Bohmeier Verlag Edition 2009 Appendix 4: *An algebra for the natural numbers* (1961).

15. **things that lie at the heart of real educational theory:** I. Grattan-Guinness (1997) *The Rainbow of Mathematics* p.739.

Chapter 21

Foundation

Everything can be derived from nothing;
all that is needed is 1.[1]
— Gottfried Leibniz (c1700)

The foundation of mathematics asks the question: What are the basic objects from which math is constructed? This question finds no consensus, rather it has generated diverse and antagonistic factions. Although set theory is taken to be the default foundation, there are various types of set theory, and various types of logic, and structuralists who believe that mathematics stands alone and needs no imposed meaning, and intuitionists who take natural numbers as the obvious ground upon which mathematics rests. James algebra as foundation contributes distinction and iconic form, concepts that can be shown to structurally subsume logic, numerics, and finite sets. Accumulation generates a numeric tally system, containment provides structure, while the James axioms, coupled with pattern-matching, substitution and composition, provide mechanism.

Another foundational question is: What is mathematical Truth? For thousands of years Western culture believed in Absolute Truth. There was always a definite TRUE and a definite NOT TRUE, called FALSE. In this era of relative truth, things are true depending upon their context. The structuralist position, which we have taken here, is that truth is determined by permissions to change structure. *Truth is applied form dynamics.* Permissions are called axioms. A James form maintains its intention only when the results of structural changes are permitted by axioms.

21.1 Structure in Arithmetic

Just how complicated should arithmetic be? What should the axioms of arithmetic look like? How much mechanism is needed to design and implement the objects and operations? Pure mathematicians focus on deep symmetries across multiple axiom systems as well as finding sequences of transformations that expose unexpected structure. Here we'll compare James arithmetic to those systems that currently define how numbers work. In the twentieth century, many different formal systems were developed to describe what we now consider to be grade school arithmetic, first by Peano and Dedekind in the 1890s, later by Skolem and Presburger in the 1920s, and later still by Goodstein and Robinson in the 1940s. Choosing only these names is quite unfair since the question of *what is arithmetic?* evolved hand-in-hand with the development of metamathematics in general. We'll explore the work of Frege, Peano and Dedekind in Chapter 22 and the others in Chapter 23.

Metamathematics as first defined by Hilbert seeks to justify the structure of mathematics using only the tools of mathematics itself, making math then a discipline that is entirely independent of other disciplines. Just which axioms (or belief systems) are necessary to conduct mathematical investigations? As axioms are added or eliminated, what limits do we reach? Are the theories of induction, or predicate quantification, or sets, or even propositional logic necessary for a formal understanding of arithmetic? All of these mathematical tools were themselves being invented in the early twentieth century; arithmetic was a testing ground, itself amorphous until tools took shape.

Our formal understanding of arithmetic evolved from an informal intuition that whole numbers are obvious, into Peano's axiomatic structure for an infinity of whole numbers one following the other, then into more limited fragments of formal structure that still are sufficient to define whole numbers, and then into weaker systems still that eliminate the necessity of an infinity of numbers, and then into a contemporary perspective of deep unity across all branches of mathematics. Here's Fields Medalist Alain Connes,

> The mathematical world is "connected". In other words there is just "one" mathematical world, whose exploration is the task of all mathematicians and they are all in the same boat somehow.[2]

The axioms of arithmetic have also evolved, from the methodology of logical inference to that of algebra with equality, to that of primitive recursive functions and recently to a healthy skepticism of the axiomatic method itself as a way to pursue knowledge.

Metamathematical questions arose about provability, completeness, consistency, decidability and other criteria that would help to assess the quality of a proposed set of axioms. We'll consider the definition of formal systems in Chapter 24, the intent for now is to make some structural comparisons between James arithmetic and the historical development of formal arithmetic.[3] For reference, Figure 21-1 provides the James axioms for the arithmetic of numbers. Capital letters stand in place of any containment form. The curly brace stands in place of any configuration of simply nested brackets. Figure 21-1 includes the perceptually obvious concepts of distinction

( ) ≠ *void*	*Distinction is not nothing*
( ) ( ) ≠ ( )	*Units accumulate*
A = B ⟺ {A C} = {B C}	*Composition principle*
([A]) = [(A)] = A	*Inversion axiom*
(A [B C]) = (A [B]) (A [C])	*Arrangement axiom*
A <A> = *void*	*Reflection axiom*

Figure 21-1: *James axioms and principles for natural number arithmetic*

and accumulation, as well as structural axioms that do not become intuitive until we apply them to the nesting of physical containers. Overall, the three James axioms are intended to provide a simple grounding for all of the structural transformations needed for an arithmetic of numbers.

Formalism by Hilbert

David Hilbert
1862–1943

Hilbert's original program, now familiar as the way that computation must work, was revolutionary in 1920. He suggested that the consistency of arithmetic could be based on a foundation of our primitive *concrete* intuition of whole numbers. Axioms with existential extent, such as *there exists a successor of every number*, should be converted into **constructive generating principles**, algorithms for bringing what is claimed to exist into actual existence. The idea is to abandon both the conceptual requirements of semantics (i.e. what a number might mean) and the existential presumptions that might reach into infinity (i.e. that *every* number can share the same property). To establish this inherently computational foundation, Hilbert grounds mathematics in

Paul Bernays
1888–1977

symbols. According to Hilbert's coauthor Paul Bernays, "Whenever concepts are missing, a sign will be readily available."[4] Rather than replacing an existential axiom by a procedure that constructs numbers, Hilbert replaces the *concept* of a number by a *symbol* Z together with a structural transformation axiom that includes a variable, A, that stands in place of any numeric expression.

$$Z(A) \Rightarrow Z(A+1)$$

Logical inference, set theoretic existence and conceptual semantics are all replaced by symbolic pattern-matching. Here is Bernays again:

> The methodological idea of construction is here conceived so broadly, that also all higher mathematical modes of inference can be incorporated in the constructive development.[5]

From this, Hilbert defines **proof** as a sequence of transformations, and **consistency** as an assertion that contradiction cannot be achieved via a transformation sequence. Hilbert provides a basic symbolic formula that defines consistency:

$$A = B \Rightarrow (A \neq B \Rightarrow \Omega)$$

formal
consistency

The symbol Ω stands in place of the idea of **formal contradiction**. Contradiction occurs when an equality between two expressions implies (can be transformed into) an inequality between the same two expressions. Importantly the inequality symbol $\neq$ is *not* the negation of equality,

> The relation of inequality is taken by Hilbert as a genuine arithmetical relation, just as equality is, but not as the logical negation of equality. Hilbert does not introduce a sign for negation at all.[6]

We take the same path in James arithmetic.

Difference by James

James arithmetic is grounded in difference. *The inequality symbol is primitive*, not a type of negation.

accumulation

$$void \neq (\ ) \neq (\ )(\ )$$

The arithmetic consists of finite nestings of three types of boundaries. Figure 21-1 shows these containers and the axioms that define them. Reflection identifies deletable forms. Inversion identifies deletable containment. Arrangement permits structural rearrangement. And the Composition Principle defines the maintenance of equality. These axioms are shown in Volume I to be sufficient for the representation of correspondence, cardinality and counting. Determining the cardinality of a tally requires indicating each object separately, fusing indicators, and labeling the result. Counting 1, 2, 3,... is the linearization of this process. The axioms also provide sufficient mechanism to implement addition, multiplication and exponentiation, as well as the accompanying inverse operations.

James addition is both spatial and visceral, based on the Additive Principle that a sum looks like its parts. Addition is putting indicators into the same container. Multiplication is putting ensembles of indicators into an inversion frame. Raising to a power is putting multiplications into an inversion frame. Alternatively, using the James concept of an implicit base, power is putting a form into a round-bracket while logarithm is putting a form into a square-bracket. All inverses are represented by putting forms into an angle-bracket. The primitive operation of *putting a form into a container* can be abstract or physical, sequential or parallel. Conceptually, *crossing a boundary makes a distinction*.

<A>   *inverse* A
(A)   #^{A}
[A] $\log_\# A$

So in the spirit of exploration, what can we learn about arithmetic that may make its complicated and often confusing features more palatable? What do we *not* need in order to understand how numbers work? Which common concepts get in the way of comprehension? This exploration would be less motivated were it a study of something less fundamental, such as rational polynomials. But here we are examining the good old 1, 2, 3,... and how these objects act under addition, multiplication and other common operations. The simple basis of James algebra laid thus far will continue to yield dividends as we move forward to expose superfluous concepts embedded within our current models of numbers, and as we discover surprising new concepts that have been obscured by our current numeric concepts.

21.2 Comparative Axiomatics

As we head into the work of Frege, Peano, Dedekind and the others who at the turn of the twentieth century gave us our current conceptualization of numbers, we should be aware that this is a study of *comparative belief systems*. Is it intuitively obvious that every natural number has a successor, or might very large numbers begin to fracture in meaning, to the point of no longer supporting the concept of an equidistant next number? The operation add1 might be formally meaningless for huge numbers. To make the example more concrete, the national debt of the United States in fiscal year 2020 is about 28 trillion dollars, increasing at more than $100,000 per second. Does adding exactly one more dollar to that debt generate a number that makes any sense as the next 10 microseconds of debt?

The goals of a metamathematical exploration of arithmetic are two fold: to put mathematical proof on a solid foundation and to characterize which aspects of that foundation support which aspects of mathematical rigor. According to philosopher Mary Leng,

> Genuine axioms should be immediately graspable *truths* about their objects. This was certainly Gottlob Frege's view: according to Frege, genuine axioms express 'fundamental facts of intuition'.[7]

This idealistic definition does not support what mathematicians actually do. **Self-evident axioms** justify our common beliefs about numbers, but that is insufficient to bestow upon them the status of defining what numbers are. A broader perspective includes **structural axioms**, those common patterns that organize our understanding of particular mathematical systems, but are not necessarily intuitive or obvious since they are deeply technical constructions. Pure mathematics dwells within **foundational axioms**, the technical constructions such as set theory that attempt to define mathematics as a unified whole.

Compared to axiomatic arithmetic based on strings, these are some fundamental differences of the James arithmetic:

— iconic rather than symbolic
— the absence of zero
— definition based on difference rather than equality
— void-equivalent forms
— +, x and ∧ operators as container forms
— the absence of functions, sets and logic
— Composition rather than Induction
— integrated numeric and non-numeric forms
— the incorporation of parallelism.

The Rocky Road

The road to a formal understanding of natural numbers has not been easy. There is reason to believe that the basic tools of arithmetic that have been in use since around 3500 BCE can still be improved. After all, math historian Morris Kline observes

By about 1890, only six thousand years after the Egyptians and the Babylonians began to work with whole numbers, fractions, and irrational numbers, the mathematicians could finally prove that 2+2=4.[8]

A major change in the formal approach to numbers took hold in the latter half of the nineteenth century. Mathematicians began to believe that Number should stand separately from its use as measurement within space. Euclidean space had proven unreliable as an absolute standard, so there was a resurgence of Number as an independent Platonic concept.

As a preliminary distinction, we should recognize that number is *not* quantity. Here's Gregory Bateson's perspective:

> *Numbers* are the product of counting. *Quantities* are the product of measurement. This means that numbers can conceivably be accurate because there is a discontinuity between each integer and the next.[9]

This discontinuity is the void that the Pythagoreans recognized as a necessary quality of reality. Pythagoras' paradise was not only destroyed by the advent of irrational numbers, it was forever clouded by the illusion that the irrationals can support exact measurement. The diagonal of a unit square is reputed to be $\sqrt{2}$, however that is true only of an imaginary unit square, not a measurable unit square. Mathematician John Horton Conway:

> The so-called real numbers are not as real as you might think and do not have much relevance to physical reality.... The square root of two, like other infinite precision real numbers such as e and π, is not really real in the physical sense! They are all figments of the mathematician's mind: concepts of abstract mathematics that only approximately correspond to things in the real world.[10]

Conway's inversion of perspective is as profound as it is obvious: *abstraction is an approximation of experience.*

The issue of abstract numbers having some direct connection to the physical world has been a battleground for over a century. The removal of Number from direct physical experience was an active goal of the developer's of what we today call numbers. Dedekind asserts

> In speaking of arithmetic (algebra, analysis) as a part of logic I mean to imply that I consider the number-concept entirely independent of the notions of space and time, that I consider it an immediate result from the laws of thought.[11]

Politically, geometry began losing favor to algebra during the last half of the 19th century. Number itself was the nexus of debate between the well-known mathematical political parties. The **intuitionists** believed in Number as the obvious intuitive foundation. The **logicians** developed logic extensively while attempting to define Number. The **formalists** wanted to find stable transformation rules for symbols that did not implicate meaning but that nonetheless yielded familiar numeric properties. Most found that set theory provided a path. As we know, the entire charade collapsed in the beginning to the twentieth century, with the discovery of unavoidable paradox within the structure of infinite sets. But in the decades preceding, Cantor and Dedekind and Russell (and many others) bequeathed to us our current set theoretic definitions. *A natural number is an equivalence set of all sets with that number of members.* This definition supports what mathematical physicist Roger Penrose characterizes as a *belief*

$2 =$

> that things like the natural numbers can be conjured literally out of nothing, merely by employing the abstract notion of 'set'. We get an infinite sequence of abstract (Platonic) mathematical entities — sets containing, respectively, zero, one, two, three, etc. elements, one set for each of the natural numbers, quite independently of the actual physical nature of the universe.[12]

Number Is Pattern

The distinction between exact number and approximate measurement is unfortunately lost completely in modern mathematics education. But there is something more valuable that is also lost, the ability to see that number is pattern. The loss is so severe that Bateson opines

> There is, I think, no English word, so we have to be content with remembering that there is a subset of *patterns* whose members are commonly called "numbers". Not all numbers are the product of counting.[13]

Foundational difficulties in mathematics brought into question the *existence*, using any definition of reality, of mathematical objects such as numbers. It's relatively easy to assemble a collection of axioms that guide transformation, but why should we care? It is alright to build fantasy worlds for conceptual objects generated by assumed axioms, but for the claim of existence, the axioms themselves need to come under scrutiny. This concern is deep.

We may count five people sitting at a table, but that does not connect fiveness to reality. That kind of fiveness is constructed in our minds. Fiveness is a projection created by the observer, a subjective deconstruction that requires all other features and facets of the folks around the table to be ignored. This might be valid in the case that the people and the context mean nothing but philosophically we might want more. In particular the five indicated people comprise a **system**. It is the *interactions* of the system (consider the conversation between our five people for example) that identifies the nexus. Fiveness is not even descriptive. If two people are busy eating, and two are participating in a personal conversation and one is on a cell phone call, why should we think there are five people sharing a table, other than the context provided by the table itself as a frame for their physical bodies? It is our personal subjective choice to focus on the table as the relevant property that defines the collection of people. Five then is a current property of the *table*, the current container of the people. The most we should be able to say is that from our limited viewpoint of fusing indications of our perceptual filters, there are five. *Counting can both verify and undermine truth.* Meaning is intimately intertwined[14] with context, and context is selected by perspective.

What does arithmetic tell us about the reality of the human condition? Metaphysical philosopher Javier Leach asks directly whether

> mathematics can give us a true image of the universe, or is mathematics a kind of peephole or warped mirror that gives us a limited, or even distorted, view of reality?[15]

If we have learned anything in the twenty-first century, it is that concepts are both cultural and contextual. There are no laws of thought. Further, the physiological basis of thought, as studied by today's neuropsychologists, provides a much different perspective on numbers than anything that a formalist from a century ago could imagine.

21.3 Remarks

The next chapter presents the work of the foundational architects of numerics between 1880 and 1920. We'll closely examine their beliefs and constructions with two objectives:

— to compare the epistemology of numbers developed 120 years ago to that of the James system

— to attempt to remove antiquated philosophical assumptions that do not contribute to a modern postsymbolic understanding of arithmetic.

Endnotes

1. **opening quote:** Gottfried Leibniz (circa 1700). After exploring the Leibniz archives in Hanover Germany, Stephen Wolfram reports on a medallion designed by Leibniz to commemorate, apparently, his invention of binary numbers. The quote is from the medallion's inscriptions.

S. Wolfram (2016) *Idea Makers*. p.99-124. Quote on p.120.

Leibniz' inscription is metaphysical, not numeric. By discovering binary numbers Leibniz believed he had resolved a long standing religious controversy: did God create the universe out of primary matter, or did he create from nothing? "Everything does not come from God and matter but from God and nothing." Since numbers follow nature, binary zero is the nothing, *void*, that provides everything, given that the unary one, *God*, creates.

Leibniz quote from B. Lewin (2018) *Enthusiastic Mathematics* p.269.

2. **and they are all in the same boat somehow:** A. Connes (2010) A view of mathematics. Online 11/18 at http://www.alainconnes.org/en/downloads.php

3. **historical formal development of conventional arithmetic:** The development of metamathematics includes the work of many of the greatest mathematical minds of the twentieth century. It is not the intent of this volume, nor is it within my capabilities, to summarize and synthesize the technical details of the field of metamathematics. There is a central question, however, throughout the discussion of James arithmetic: to what extent is our knowledge of arithmetic limited by the textual representations we use to specify foundational axioms and transformational methods?

4. **Whenever concepts are missing, a sign will be readily available:** P. Bernays (1922) On Hilbert's ideas for the foundation of arithmetic. P. Mancosu (trans) p.6. Online 12/18 at http://www.phil.cmu.edu/projects/bernays/Pdf/bernays02_2003-05-18.pdf

5. **mathematical modes of inference can be incorporated in the constructive development:** Bernays p.7.

6. **Hilbert does not introduce a sign for negation at all:** Bernays p.18.

7.genuine axioms express 'fundamental facts of intuition': M. Leng (2010) *Mathematics and Reality* p.87.

8. the mathematicians could finally prove that 2+2=4: M. Kline (1980) *Mathematics: The loss of certainty* p.179.

9. there is a discontinuity between each integer and the next: G. Bateson (1979) *Mind and Nature: A necessary unity* p.49.

10. abstract mathematics that only approximately correspond to things in the real world: J. Conway & R. Guy (1996) *The Book of Numbers* p.213.

11. an immediate result from the laws of thought: R. Dedekind (1901) Preface to the First Edition, *The Nature and Meaning of Numbers*. In R. Dedekind (1963) *Essays on the Theory of Numbers* p.31. Online 8/18 at https://www.gutenberg.org/files/21016/21016-pdf.pdf

12. quite independently of the actual physical nature of the universe: R. Penrose (2004) *The Road to Reality* p.64-65.

Discrete quantification by small integers, both positive, zero and negative, (called quantum numbers) has been observed in the behavior of electric charge. Penrose adds, however that there does not appear to be physical relevance for *rational numbers*. Ratio and proportion are cognitive constructions.

13. Not all numbers are the product of counting. Bateson p.49. (Emphasis in original).

14. Meaning is intimately intertwined: Latin *complexus*: entwined, woven together. Ted Nelson in *Computer Lib/Dream Machines* (1974) introduces a more entertaining portmanteau term, *intertwingled*, to identify deeply, intimately interrelated complexes of connectivity. p.DM45.

15. warped mirror that gives us a limited, or even distorted, view of reality: J. Leach (2010) *Mathematics and Religion* p.87.

Chapter 22

Architects

*The contents and the container
are both parts of the same whole.*[1]
— Aristotle (c350 BCE)

I n this chapter we'll explore the work of the founding fathers of formal arithmetic. In the early 1880s Frege proposed that numbers are concepts. To be able to do so, he had to invent much of modern logic. A few years later Peano proposed that numbers can be understood from a purely symbolic perspective, thus taking one of the earliest excursions into computational mathematics.

22.1 Numbers by Frege

Gottlob Frege's seminal work *The Foundations of Arithmetic* argued (persuasively from the perspective of a century and a half ago) that numbers describe *concepts* rather than objects. To Frege, mathematician John Bell asserts, "a number corresponds to a collection of concepts."[2] Frege's **cardinal number** associated with a concept F is defined by the number of true statements about F. The concept itself is purely cognitive, while the concept's **extension** consists of the set of propositions that makes the concept TRUE.

*Gottlob Frege
1848–1925*

*numbers are
collections of
concepts*

The *number* of the concept F is represented by #F, which stands in place of the count of the true statements supported by the concept's extension. If we have two concepts, F and G, then these concepts are numerically equal, or **equinumerate**, when

equinumerate

$$\#F = \#G$$

Number then is a property shared across extensions of different concepts that identifies that instances of TRUE statements can be put into one-to-one correspondence. *Number is a quantity of Truth*, not a quantity of things. Summarizing Frege's conclusion:

> The expression "the concept F is equal to the concept G" is to mean the same as the expression "there exists a relation which correlates one to one the objects falling under the concept F with the objects falling under the concept G".[3]

This twisted, non-intuitive definition is the price we pay to express natural numbers within the constructs of formal logic. To specify the number 3 using only the concepts of symbolic logic is even more ugly. Threeness needs to be associated with some property, say P. Then we have

exactly three ☞

3

$$\exists x \exists y \exists z \forall w\ (Px \wedge Py \wedge Pz \wedge x{\neq}y \wedge x{\neq}z \wedge y{\neq}z)$$
$$\wedge\ (Pw \Rightarrow (w{=}x \vee w{=}y \vee w{=}z))$$

Notice, strangely, that to identify that w is equal to 3, it takes writing five different symbols (xyz, $\exists$, P, $\neq$, =,) three times each and then a fourth symbol w to identify the threeness.[4]

Numbers as Logical Concepts

Frege was the champion of the school of folks who believed that all of mathematics can be reduced to logic, while logic itself was the purveyor of ultimate Truth. Since Aristotle, Western philosophy has associated logic with *thinking*. Drawing from an 18th century encyclopedia: "The precise business of logic, therefore, is to explain the nature of the human mind."[5] Logic is the way that a rational mind works. In our age of relative truth(s), it helps to recall that at the beginning of the twentieth century mathematics sought to identify Absolute Truth, thus contributing to Knowledge that was eternal and not subject to contextual interpretation.

To make progress, Frege (along with Peirce, Russell and many others) invented most of the tools of modern symbolic logic. Frege's goal however was not to identify the mechanisms of number, but rather to define a deeper meaning. As a logician, Frege believed that number arises from the logical truth of cognitive concepts. Truth rather than Accumulation is at the foundation.

Philosopher Alain Badiou: "Frege maintains that pure thought engenders number."[6] But to focus on the creation of symbols, pure thought generates structures that are themselves not concepts. Communicated thought relies upon symbolic representations embedded in a textual language. To be logical, these representations must be formal strings constrained by axioms and other rules of formation, strings that validly capture the concept to be communicated. Elementary logic permits these objects to be Propositions only: linguistic statements that are clearly TRUE or FALSE.

Alain Badiou
1937–

Frege begins by examining the history of the concept *one*.[7] It's tricker than one might imagine. He argues against number as an idea:

> If a number were an idea, then arithmetic would be psychology.... An idea in the subjective sense is what is governed by the psychological laws of association; it is of a sensible, pictorial character.[8]

Immediately the James approach is at odds since it attempts to integrate arithmetic and psychology.

Numbers are sensible as well as *pictorial* when we view them as tallies or as containers. Frege did not accept the idea that numbers represent magnitude, since this approach does not define what 0 and 1 mean. By defining 1 as *framed nothing*, James arithmetic captures both concepts within one distinction, as well as providing 1 with a visceral manifestation. Frege comes very close to the container-based boundary perspective, stripping 1 of internal content and then placing it as an object within a viewing environment.[9]

> The more the internal contrasts within a thing fade into insignificance by comparison with the contrasts between it and its environment...the more natural it becomes for us to regard it as a distinct object. For a thing to be "united" means that it has a property which causes us, when we think of it, to sever it from its environment and consider it on its own.[10]

Not Itself

Frege rather torturously identifies 0 as "the number which belongs to the concept 'not identical to itself'".[11] The symbol 0 is defined as the cardinality of the set of TRUE propositions that assert that a concept is not itself.

$$0 =_{def} = \#C \; \textit{such that} \; C \neq C$$

This puts *difference* at the foundation of number. The symbol 1 is then defined as "the number which belongs to the concept 'identical with 0'."[12] Although there are no concepts that are not identical to themselves, there is only one concept that has 0 truth instances. That concept is called 1. This puts *identity* at the foundation of natural numbers.

existence

$\neq$ ( )

After finding justification that both 1 and 0 are numeric concepts rather than symbolic ideas, Frege essentially asserts that $0 \neq 1$, what James arithmetic calls Existence. His proof of the inequality is that we cannot put 0 things in one-to-one correspondence with 1 thing. In contrast, the James approach takes the difference between some-thing and nothing as perceptually obvious. If anything might qualify as an axiom, as a secure belief, it is this: *something is different than nothing.*

But if you are using symbols, the task is more challenging. Frege is sympathetic. "Affirmation of existence is in fact nothing but denial of the number nought."[13] Unfortunately Frege's phraseology implicates logic (denial as NOT), put-ting propositional calculus at the foundation of number.

Frege's construction of zero fails on several criteria. It constructs from negation of identity without having a positive assertion of identity for any concept; it compares symbolic replicas rather than concepts or their extensions; it confuses inequality with the miraculous event of con-struction from *void*; and it tells the creation story from the wrong direction.

There are, of course, many "things" that are not identical to themselves, such as the concept *now*, which is identical to *then* once it is indicated. Anything that changes struc-ture faster than the structure can be identified (examples include wind, the internet, and any biological system) is never identical to itself. At least in my mind, a thought is never identical to itself. Mathematics handles these exceptions by declaring them to be outside of the domain of logic. Only static objects with clear boundaries are countable, but *static* and *stable* are perceptual distinc-tions, not properties of objects.

Frege, it appears, suffers from the same affliction as most logicians, confusing transient thoughts which do not themselves have Properties or Truth with textual representations and indications that do. From a modern systems (ecological) perspective, objects are epiphe-nomena, it is the network of interactions that identifies a system. From the perspective of non-existence, *void* cannot be identical to itself because it does not reach the thresh-old of existence necessary to support self-comparison.

Existence Comes First

Frege's definition of 0 presupposes a set of truth instances associated a concept C. He constructs a replica of C and then compares that replica to the original, $C =?= C$, asking if the extension of C is in one-to-one correspondence with the extension of the replica of C. The equality relation is between two *replicas of one set of truth instances*. There are zero concepts C such that $C \neq C$. The replicas are indistinguishable and thus equinumerous, so $\#C = \#C$. Therein is a problem: there are no extensions of the self-unequal concept, but Frege suggests that we can still determine the cardinality of these non-existent extensions

$C = C$ *is not* $\widehat{C}$

Without replication, the concepts of self-equality and self-inequality cannot be tested. The proposed equality relation is not over a concept, it is over a symbolic structure and its replica, after we have forgotten which is the original. The process of replicating a set of identifiers is held to be invariant. For a replica to be not-equal to itself, we must violate a rule of *representation* not conceptualization. Frege's 0 defines the logical tolerance for changing the binding of a label. The number of violations of **the canon of invariant replication** must be zero. In mathematics, there is zero tolerance for violation of a rule, of course, for all rules. Frege did not need to push the definition of zero into the realm of concepts alone.

equality applies to symbolic structure only

Affirming the existence of a rule without exceptions does deny that there is a *number* of violations. The problem is that the rule must precede the assessment of permitted violations. We cannot build a definition of *nothing* on something being *not*, without the preexisting *something* itself. Prior to consideration of self-identity there must be self. Said another way, difference directly implies contrast, not failure of sameness. One gives rise to Zero.

Consider a semi-empty universe consisting of only one concept with no extensions. We cannot characterize that universe since we do not have any properties that we can label in support of the lone concept. We can say that C=C, but we cannot say that #C=#C since the concept itself is vacuous. And we know that logic is extremely sensitive to vacuous truths. A universe might have *catness* as its only concept, but with no cats to serve as extensions, every statement about catness is TRUE. Within a universe of no cats, all cats are white *and* all cats are black. This is the fallacy of vacuous truth, every assertion is TRUE.

This idea can be expressed, albeit promiscuously, using conventional symbols. We will need to call upon the structural relationship between negation and existence.

$$\forall x \ x=x \ \textit{stands in place of} \ \neg\exists x \ \neg(x=x)$$

The relationship of self-identity that exists between all concepts is also an assertion about the non-existence of non-self-identical concepts. We might say that 0 is *co-defined with identity*. The other side of this creation story is more problematic.

$$\forall x \ \neg(x=x) \ \textit{stands in place of} \ \neg\exists x \ x=x$$

The left-side assertion constructs an empty (vacuous) universe. Quantification fails rather than defining a count of 0. The right-side asserts that there are no concepts that are self-identical, a TRUE assertion since there are no concepts at all. Frege has begged his own question by defining 0 from the not-equal relation, in the process making numbers dependent upon the contradiction of their non-existence. However, *non-existence is non-numeric*.

The not-equal of James Accumulation, in contrast, is neither logic nor algebra. It is instead the idea of *perceptual discrimination*. We can tell the difference. The initial distinction to observe that nothing is not something provides the (non-numeric) unit of difference, the ground upon which perception rests. The ground itself, the boundary unit ( ), contains non-existence at its core. By distinguishing primitive difference, we create unity. In that sense, ≠ and 1 are the same concept.

$\neq \quad is ( )$
$\neq ( ) \ is ( )( )$

Badiou is also critical of Frege's origin story.

> Number, as number of nothing, or zero, sutures every text to its latent being. The void is not a production of thought, because it is from its existence that thought proceeds, in as much as 'it is the same thing to think and to be'. [Here Badiou is referencing a poem by Parmenides.] In this sense, it is concept that comes from number, and not the other way around.[14]

The Trouble with One

Frege associates numbers with conceptual entities, since at the time logic was taken to be about concepts (propositions). So it was quite natural to introduce not-equal-to-itself as 0. We can get to 1, however, without denying it into existence by instead making it the **primitive distinction**, the unity of all perception. Frege:

> The word "one", as the proper name of an object of mathematical study, does not admit of a plural. Consequently, it is nonsense to make numbers result from putting together of ones. The plus symbol in 1+1=2 cannot mean such a putting together. [15]

Frege separates number from object by grounding number within cognition while banning the enumeration of physical objects. Yes, both experience and object are unique, only representation supports replication and counting.[16] This support is available whether or not a label has an interpretation.

indication

A = ([A][o])

The James approach begins with experience, distinguishing object from unit by marking object perception via the Indication theorem. This critical step reifies the shift from concept to symbol, and without it we are claiming that concepts are concrete enough to be counted. Number is then constructed from indications rather than from concepts. To mark is to observe difference. An indicator of that difference identifies a relationship between object and observation. Numbers are ensembles of marks. It is marks not numbers that come from cognition, via the process of associating a replica mark with a perceived object. The "object" itself can be a conceptual proposition as Frege believes, or a physical perception. We can enumerate either only after objectifying and marking our object of interest.

The **initial distinction** is created by severing the void from itself. This, however, is a miraculous event since it is not possible to identify or to sever *void*. Indication, the creation of the unit replica ( ), does not arise from imagination. The unit replica is brought into existence when we sever an object from the network of relations that define it. It arises from perceptual action rather than from conceptual reflection. Abstraction comes later.

Distinguishability

Frege wrestles with the essential ambiguity of being able to distinguish replica marks that are constructed to be indistinguishable. Unique objects can be indicated and in the process they lose their uniqueness. The accumulation of indistinguishable unit marks must then be sufficiently differentiated to be counted. "We can now easily solve the problem of reconciling the identity of units with their distinguishability."[17] Frege's finesse is to distinguish two meanings of the word *unit*, as an isolating concept and as a number of things. The James definition of unit, in contrast, is a frame around nothing. The frame serves both to isolate and to indicate. The detour into conceptualization is unnecessary because we are not constructing number from the truth of logical propositions.

distinction
  ⇒ *unit*

accumulation
  ⇒ *number*

Once 0 and 1 are in place, Frege bootstraps. The symbol 2 is the number of things that are either 0 or 1, etc. Frege argues strongly against James tallies. Indistinguishable units are untenable because:

If we use 1 to stand for each of the [unique] objects to be numbered, we make the mistake of assigning the same symbol to different things. But if we provide the 1 with differentiating strokes, it becomes unusable for arithmetic.[18]

The James perspective is that assigning "1" to every unique object is not a mistake, but a cognitive necessity in order construct an ensemble of indicators that supports the concept of cardinality. 1 is an indication, not a count.

However, we owe to Frege the ideas that units are both the same and different. He concludes that we must "ascribe to units two contradictory qualities, namely identity and distinguishability."[19] As mentioned in Chapter 2, ensembles are equal to the extent they can be put into one-to-one correspondence (Hume's Principle). Frege however was working at a time prior to the concise development of the concept of relation. He had to invent relational calculus and logical quantification as well as numbers. So his wording is rather clumsy. James arithmetic does not have this particular problem, we can just say contains.

Summarizing the James perspective: Yes, Number must be associated with Relation if we are to reduce Number to Logic. AND is not plus. But we do not need the conceptual abstraction of logic if we begin with experience. We do not need the uniqueness of set membership if we begin with containment, because the act of putting into a container works whether or not the PUT things are unique. Thus we can return to the naturalistic experience of Number that is supported by over 10,000 years of evolution.

The route of mathematical abstraction that we are tracing probably arose from language, as concrete objects (most probably fingers) were counted out loud. Sounds gave way to symbols, words became concepts, ensembles became sequences. However, historically, tallies and marks preceded written words.[20] Historically, Tobias Dantzig reports

Peano axioms	symbolic expression
1. one is a number	$1 \in N$
2. every number has a successor	$n \in N \Rightarrow n+1 \in N$
3. one is not the successor of any number	$n+1 \neq 1$
4. equal successors means equal numbers	$m+1 = n+1 \Rightarrow m = n$
5. induction over the set of numbers	$(1 \in S \wedge n+1 \in S) \Rightarrow S = N$
addition-base	$m + 0 = m$
addition-step	$m + (n+1) = (m + n)+1$
multiplication-base	$m \times 1 = m$
multiplication-step	$m \times (n+1) = (m \times n) + n$

Figure 22-1: *Peano axioms for natural number arithmetic*

Wherever a counting technique, worthy of the name, exists at all, finger counting has been found to either precede it or accompany it.[21]

22.2 Structure by Peano

Giuseppe Peano, in the late nineteenth century, developed a decidedly modern approach to the definition of Number. He embodied definition and mechanism within symbolic notation, avoiding the philosophical debates over meaning, existence and cognition.

I have denoted by signs all ideas that occur in the principles of arithmetic, so that every proposition is stated only by means of these signs.[22]

Giuseppe Peano
1858–1932

Peano introduced *signs* via the definitions in Figure 22-1. He built the numbers by extending the signs of set theory, predicate logic and equality with three new primitive

Peano number

LOGIC

and

SETS

and

CONCEPTS
number
unity
successor

and

PROPOSITIONS
unit is number
successor is number
zero
equality
induction

symbolic ideas: *number, unity* and *successor*, respectively using the signs N, 1, and +1. A primitive symbolic idea is simply accepted, without contest, as *given*. Numbers are a network of interrelations of signs, without a deeper meaning. Peano then identified a collection of nine axioms that put a firm structural foundation under what is meant by number.[23] Today, Peano's axioms for numbers are generally accepted as the definition of natural numbers and how they work. Bertrand Russell declared:

> Having reduced all traditional pure mathematics to the theory of natural numbers, the next step in logical analysis was to reduce this theory itself to the smallest set of premises and undefined terms from which it could be derived. This work was accomplished by Peano. He showed that the entire theory of the natural numbers could be derived from three primitive ideas and five primitive propositions in addition to those of pure logic.[24]

James number

CONCEPTS
distinction
accumulation

and

STRUCTURES
unit/existence
composition
pattern substitution

Let's look at these primitive axioms in the light of James arithmetic. We will accept the idea of equality =, discard the ideas of sets S and N as well as set membership ∈, remove both successor and infinity from the idea of induction, and absorb the mechanisms of pure logic into the mechanisms of equality. This will allow us also to reduce Peano's five primitive propositions to three, and his three primitive concepts to two.[25] Operations on whole numbers (addition and multiplication) will require more axioms.

Peano Axioms

$a=a$

$a=b \Rightarrow b=a$

$a=b \ \& \ b=c \Rightarrow a=c$

$a \in N \ \& \ a=b \Rightarrow b \in N$

Peano begins with four axioms that define the equality relation. We'll accept them without further analysis, so that we may have free and non-controversial use of the structural definition of equal, =. Chapter 17 however argues that these relational axioms are accidents of a sequential notation.

For Peano, the domain under consideration is the natural (whole) numbers. Figure 22-1 shows Peano's five primitive propositions that define numbers. In Peano arithmetic, the properties of natural numbers are defined using one constant (1), one operation (+1), and one methodology (induction). 1 is the ground from which induction builds the numbers. Inductive steps are taken by applying the function +1. The successor of an arbitrary number n is n+1. Very elegant!

As is the convention for the use of variables in algebra, universal quantification is assumed. So we do not necessarily need to declare that all bindings to the label n belong to the set of natural numbers $\mathbb{N}$, as in

$$\forall n \quad n \in \mathbb{N} \Rightarrow n+1 \in \mathbb{N}$$

successors are numbers

By default, when the variable n occurs, it is presumed to refer to some n that is a number. This is facilitated by the absence of assertions of existence (i.e. existential quantification) in the Peano axioms. James algebra includes Composition so that no non-forms can be brought into existence, but there is no implication that *every* form can be composed, primarily since the restriction of finitude may exclude some possible forms.

Peano states the Induction Axiom in its simple form, since the only goal here is to define numbers, rather than to make a more powerful statement about any property that a number might possess. We start with any set of numbers S. If 1 is in that set, and the successor of an arbitrary number n is in the set, then the set contains all of the whole numbers. We know by the first axiom that 1 is in the set. The second axiom assures that every number has a successor, so that for any number n we can find in the set, we can also find n+1. The third axiom provides a base for induction by asserting that 1 is the smallest number.

induction

$(1 \in S \wedge n+1 \in S)$
$\Rightarrow S = N$

universal
quantification
$\forall n \quad n \in \mathbb{N}$

bounded
quantification
$\forall (n \leq x) \quad n \in \mathbb{N}$

Induction (Axiom 5 in Figure 22-1) is the mechanism by which Peano imagines starting at 1, identifying its successor (which is 2), and then continuing to identify successors forever. Induction reaches all numbers through its well-ordering principle, while the successor function generates all the numbers. Induction also permits transcendence into the non-numeric by permitting an activity to go on forever. Well, at least that's the idea. I personally see nothing in the statement of induction that generates infinity. Induction does, certainly, permit us to generate any desired finite number. Finite induction is called *bounded induction*, quantification is limited up to an arbitrary but specific number and refrains from leaping into infinity. Peano too, by stating induction as an axiom, avoids any mention of infinity or of an infinite process. However, hidden in universal quantification, $\forall n$, is an existent infinite set. To put a finite bound on that infinity, one should write $\forall (n \leq x)$. Peano also avoids quantification of the domain $\mathbb{N}$ although it enters unavoidably through induction. This approach is in marked contrast to say Dedekind who believed that the concept of infinity is fundamental to the definition of numbers.

Not Zero

In *The Principles of Arithmetic*, Peano clearly states as Axiom 1,

$$1 \in \mathbb{N} \quad \text{☞} \quad \textit{1 is a Number}$$

Since the successor operation adds 1, it is quite natural to begin with an object that is also required by the successor function. Yet almost immediately, Peano's system was recast to begin with 0. Russell, for example, states in 1919: "The three primitive ideas in Peano's arithmetic are: 0, number, successor."[26] It was Frege who took care to begin at 0, since he identified the zero concept with the empty set, { }. Today, almost every source but Peano's original manuscript begins Peano's axioms with zero. From the perspective of a void-based algebra, concern over this modification is not nit-picking because iconic arithmetic does not have a zero. This is an example of how a prevalent mathematical/political idea, that of the empty set of set theory in this case, invades the content of other ideas, in the process giving the impression that the invader is native. Yes, this may seem like a minor diversion, but it is a primary contributor to a prevalent failure to understand the innovations of James algebra. In mathematics, innovation must generally be based on existing systems in order to be *recognized*.

The Peano formalization of natural numbers calls upon set theory, logic, universal quantification, injective functions, induction and transcendence. Not an auspicious collection from which to define a *simple* idea. The apparent elegance rests upon a very complicated foundation.[27]

A formal understanding of natural numbers does not necessarily require the components of the Peano foundation. Figure 22-2 shows how the Peano axioms are modified by a void-based boundary system. Iconic arithmetic dispenses with the constant zero, casting it into *void* and accessing it indirectly as the contents of a unit. It dispenses with the functional concept of successor, in favor of the structural concept of difference implemented by Accumulation.[28] And it dispenses with the method of induction in favor of generic composition and decomposition. Composition merges the idea of successor with the idea of induction. Although induction is very powerful and quite fundamental for defining mathematical objects and processes, it is not essential for the definition of the natural numbers. We will explore an induction free definition of numbers, Robinson arithmetic, in the next chapter.

In Figure 22-2, the Accumulation axiom occurs twice, once as Existence which distinguishes the initial form from *void*, and once again as Unit Accumulation which

Peano	James
IDEAS	
number	*distinction*
unity	*initial distinction*
successor	*accumulation*
AXIOMS	
1. one is a number	( ) is a distinction
2. every number has a successor	( ) ( ) ≠ ( )
3. one is not the successor of any number	( ) ≠ void
4. equal successors means equal numbers	composition
5. induction over the set of numbers	composition
NUMBERS		
addition-base	m + 0 = m	identity
addition-step	m + (n+1) = (m + n)+1	identity
multiplication-base	m x 1 = m	inversion
multiplication-step	m x (n+1) = (m x n) + n	arrangement

Figure 22-2: *Comparing Peano and James natural numbers*

establishes different forms.[29] We do not need an assertion such as

An empty container ( ) is a unit.

since this simply supplies the name *"unit"* to the object "empty container". All that remains as necessary is Composition which is analogous to Peano's definition of successor equality (Axiom 4 in Figure 22-1).

successor equality
$m+1 = n+1 \Rightarrow m = n$

Like the assumed use of equality, there are hidden axioms that define how containers work, these coming from the substrate language of graphs and networks described in Chapter 29. An analogy is Peano's use of predicate calculus; both predicate calculus and set theory are substrate languages prior to Peano's conceptualization of numbers. Indeed a *number* can be viewed as an interpretation of

logical connectives or it can be viewed as an interpretation of containment relations.

Peano Arithmetic

Peano arithmetic provides *inductive definitions* of the
operations of addition and multiplication; no operations,
specifically addition and multiplication, have yet been
introduced. The function add1, +1, is the successor function that identifies the next number. It does not necessarily
identify the next *unit* since, technically, the successor can
be any step size. Peano, himself, however, was definitely
describing the addition of the unit $1.$[30]

The most fundamental difference between Peano and
James is that addition and multiplication are not James
algebra operations, but are rather interpretations of the
structure of forms. Addition emerges from containment;
multiplication from inversion frames.

$$A + B \quad (A \quad B)$$
$$A \times B \quad ([A][B])$$
$$A^B \quad (([[A]][B]))$$

The base case for Peano addition identifies 0 as the identity element. The inductive case defines the successor of
the sum of m and n as the act of adding the successor of
n, written as n+1, to an arbitrary number m.

$$m + 0 = m$$
$$m + (n+1) = (m + n)+1$$

Peano addition

The Additive Principle, and its implementation as the
Accumulation Axiom, together with the absence of binary
associativity, converts the definition of Peano addition
into identity statements for James containers.

$$m = m$$
$$m \ n \ o = m \ n \ o$$

identity
identity

Composition allows us to add arbitrary forms to each
side of an equality, here n o is added to the identity m. The
concept of a successor is not needed, any numeric form
is a successor. Addition maintains its historical meaning
of putting things together.

The base case for Peano multiplication defines 1 as the multiplicative identity element. The inductive case defines multiplication of m by the successor n+1 as the product of m times n plus an additional number m. Note that the +1 successor concept is converted into the addition of an arbitrary number m.

Peano
multiplication

$$m \times 1 = m$$
$$m \times (n+1) = (m \times n) + m$$

This definition reduces to the application of two James axioms, Inversion and Arrangement. The base case is an application of the Indication theorem, which itself consists of one application of Indication.

$$([m][o]) = m$$

$$([m][o])$$

unmark   m

The inductive case of multiplication is simply Arrangement followed by Indication.

$$([m][n\ o]) = ([m][n])\ m$$

$$([m][n\ o])$$

disperse $([m][n\quad])\,([m][\quad o])$

unmark $([m][n\quad])\qquad m$

From the James perspective, Peano's definition is not a definition of multiplication *per se*, but rather a definition of the conventional rule of Distribution.

distribution

$$m \times (n + 1) = (m \times n) + (m \times 1)$$

Addition and multiplication are consequences of the James axioms rather than new concepts added on after a separate development of the idea of number. Natural numbers are co-defined with the operations upon them. This is another example of merging the conventional concepts of object and operator into the singular boundary concept of containment.

In the case of Peano addition, 1 is the common form that is replicated whenever the +1 successor function is invoked. This creates a sequential dependence of one number upon the next. We can elect to put units into a container one-at-a-time, but "one-at-a-time" is *external* to the James arithmetic. Rather than a successor *number*, what is created when we put a unit into a container is a contains **relation** between the container and the unit.

Contains relations do not depend upon one another, so they are not limited to occur in a sequence, and they are not built into the concept of number. Said another way, *cardinality is independent of counting*. Addition no longer depends upon a sequence of successors for its definition. Instead, successor and addition and multiplication (and exponentiation) have the same operational basis, that of putting replicas into a container. The difference between succession and addition is one of degree, putting in one or putting in many. The difference between addition and multiplication however is fundamental, since multiplication calls upon the two James axioms while addition requires none.

22.3 Dedekind and Cantor

The number of whole numbers is obviously infinite. With the reservation, of course, that infinity is not a number. And with the reservation that we accept an unbounded Axiom of Induction. The James calculus includes a unit that can be interpreted as a type of infinity; the exploration of the concept of infinite numbers is postponed until Volume III when we consider the square-boundary [ ] as a unit. Here, for historical inclusion Dedekind's and Cantor's concepts of number are briefly mentioned.

Both Dedekind and Cantor conceptualized numbers within the framework of set theory. The individual numbers are identified by different types of sets. Both considered numbers to be **ordinal** rather than cardinal. This contrasts with Frege and Peano, who defined numbers to be cardinal. However, the fundamental difference is that Dedekind and Cantor considered numbers to emanate from the infinite. For them the infinite was the *source* of natural numbers. In contrast, Frege and Peano did their best to avoid the concept of infinity.

Cantor's central discovery was considered by Dedekind to be a definition. *A set is infinite if it can be put into one-to-one correspondence with a subset of itself.* Dedekind believed that the infinite is *simpler* than the cardinal collection of whole numbers. The system, the whole, singularly unifies the parts. According to Badiou,

cardinal

> Dedekind abhors the void and its mark, and says so quite explicitly: "[W]e intend here for certain reasons wholly to exclude the empty system which contains no elements at all."[31]

Dedekind is barring both the empty set and boundary units. The ordinal infinity does not include the concept One, although it does include the relation **greater-than**, > , which permits the potential definition of a smallest number. The ordinal infinity *is* the concept One.

Ordinals

Cardinal numbers identify a count, while **ordinal numbers** identify a sequence. In English we distinguish cardinal numbers by the name of their numeral, for example: one, two, three. We distinguish ordinal numbers by their position, for example: first, second, third. Ordinal numbers are each connected to their neighbor, they form an entire system, a singular structure that is the entirety of the chain beginning with the first and ending with the last. Cardinals, in contrast, stand alone.

ordinal

To construct the chain of ordinals, Dedekind calls upon the theory of functions. Dedekind's motivation is to establish that *numbers are not measurements* and cannot be associated with physical parameters such as space and time. "I wholly reject the introduction of measurable quantities."[32] Numbers are purely objects of thought, a perspective that Dedekind shares with Frege. This disconnection from the embodiment of thought allowed both to venture into the pure fantasies of infinity.

Dedekind provides one ground object that is not generated by function application. We have designated it here as ( ). The round-bracket acts as a function upon its contents, however a function cannot act upon *void*, since *void* is a pure non-participant. The first appearance of an ordinal is the unit ( ). The second ordinal is defined by the first application of the round-bracket as a function, (( )), that is, as a container that holds contents. Here we are not employing the interpretation of the round-bracket as an exponential operator. We're viewing it instead simply as a generating function that creates the next form by nesting. From the cardinal perspective, the numeral two , ( )( ), is defined by accumulation rather than by nesting.

cardinal

( )

( )( )

( )( )( )

ordinal

( )

(( ))

((( )))

The structure of James forms accommodates both cardinal and ordinal concepts by differentiating the *location* of the replica. The **cardinal location** is one of sharing a common outer boundary, thus implying no relation or connection to the accumulated forms within that outer boundary. The **ordinal location** is the nesting depth of a form. Ordinal, in contrast to cardinal, inherently refers to the *relational structure* between multiple forms. Dedekind:

> If we scrutinize closely what is done in counting an aggregate or number of things, we are led to consider the ability of the mind to relate things to things, to let a thing correspond to a thing, an ability without which no thinking is possible.[33]

Figure 9-3 of Volume I displays a similar theory of counting. Counting is initiated by the cognitive steps of identification and categorization, essentially establishing an abstract collection of things to be counted. Dedekind defines this set as a *system* with interrelated parts. James categorization is the cognitive act corresponding to Dedekind's necessary ability to relate things to things.

Dedekind's next step is to consider the entirety of the chain of ordinals as a single object. He *defines* infinity into existence, constructing first the singular infinite chain of ordinals, and later deriving the behavior of the finite numbers. This definition became the Axiom of Infinity within set theory. Dedekind:

infinite ordinal

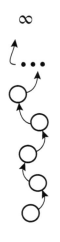

> A system S is said to be *infinite* when it is similar to a proper part of itself; in the contrary case S is said to be a *finite* system.[34]

Self-similarity here means that any number can be the base, that the chain of ordinals looks the same no matter where we start. 1 is not a privileged number but "1" is the label of the smallest ground object. Badiou is impressed:

> The most striking aspect of Dedekind's definition is that it determines infinity *positively*, and subordinates the finite negatively. *...for Dedekind, the infinite, upon which the existence of number depends, occupies the place which for Frege is occupied by zero.*[35]

Cantor also adopted the idea of the ordinal chain, conceiving it as a well-ordered infinite set. Like Dedekind, he postulated a number that was beyond the limit of finite iteration, the *infinite ordinal number* ω. This number is the first complete chain, the first well-ordered set in its entirety. And yes ω is a *number*, extending the domain of numbers well beyond both the natural numbers and the concept of accumulation. The initial breach of cardinality leads to a *second* infinite ordinal, and so on. It also leads to the discovery that ω cannot be a set. Cantor's innovation abandons the comfort of set theory as envisioned by Dedekind however his fundamental innovation today *defines* the theory of infinite sets. Cantor was not perturbed, rather he embraced the newly opened territories of mathematics. According to Cantor, "The essence of mathematics lies in its freedom."[36] Cantor echoed Hilbert's metamathematical program that mathematics must answer only to itself, but preferred the name *free mathematics* over the established *pure* mathematics.

What then is sacred? Cantor's conditions were *non-con-tradiction* and *axiomatic foundation*. But there was another concept that was endorsed by the architects of modern mathematical foundations, that mathematics is conducted by the rearrangement of strings of tokens. The linguistic perspective was natural for the time, since

— linearity is natural for the whole numbers
— logical implication is asymmetric
— parallelism had not yet been introduced
— non-textual forms were seen to be continuous
— structure was believed to be independent of representation.

The embrace of these presumptions effectively precluded recognition of the visual and interactive forms of logic developed by Frege and Peirce.

22.4 Remarks

James algebra includes a form, <[ ]>, that serves the same role as ω. The square-bracket too is an operator, leaving the possibility that <[[ ]]> might be interpreted as the second infinite ordinal. That route is not considered in these volumes. In Chapter 41 we instead explore the integration of [[ ]] within a cardinal approach to numbers.

Peano's formalization of whole numbers is the default standard today. However within a couple of decades after Peano's contribution, foundational mathematicians began asking whether or not Peano's axioms were minimal. Are Peano's axioms *elegant*? We'll next compare James algebra to three weaker arithmetic systems, weaker that is if we evaluate their expressibility from the perspective of string notation

Endnotes

1. **opening quote:** Aristotle (350 BCE) *Physics* Book IV Part 3. R. Hardie & R. Gaye (trans.) Online 11/18 at http://classics.mit.edu/Aristotle/physics.html

2. **a number corresponds to a collection of concepts:** J. Bell (1999) *The Art of the Intelligible: An elementary survey of mathematics in its conceptual development* p.49.

3. **with the objects falling under the concept G:** G. Frege (1884) *The Foundations of Arithmetic* §72.

Since numbers are concepts, Frege's objects are conceptual objects, that is, *propositions* that possess a truth-value.

4. **three times each and then a fourth symbol W to identify the threeness:** Due to exponential growth of pairwise comparisons, the complexity of the predicate calculus symbolic description of numbers also grows exponentially.

5. **to explain the nature of the human mind:** *Encyclopedia Britannica, 1771 edition*. Volume 2 p.984.

6. **Frege maintains that pure thought engenders number:** A. Badiou (1990) *Number and Numbers* §2.1.

7. **Frege begins by examining the history of the concept *one*:** Frege (1884) *The Foundations of Arithmetic*.

8. **psychological laws of association; it is of a sensible, pictorial character:** Frege §27.

9. **placing it as an object within a viewing environment:** As mentioned in Chapter 4, this metaphoric cognitive severance is not only how objects are created, but also a story of how the universe itself came into being as the first distinction.

10. **sever it from its environment and consider it on its own:** Frege §32.

11. **number which belongs to the concept 'not identical to itself':** Frege §74.

12. **a number which belongs to the concept 'identical with 0':** Frege §77.

13. **nothing but denial of the number nought:** Frege §53.

14. **it is concept that comes from number, and not the other way around:** Badiou §2.18.

15. **plus symbol in 1+1=2 cannot mean such a putting together:** Frege §45. Frege's idea has ancient roots, Plato attributes it to Socrates in *Phaedo*.

16. **only representation supports replication and counting:** Quantum mechanics includes a No Cloning Theorem which states that it is impossible to construct an identical replica of a quantum state.

17. **the problem of reconciling the identity of units with their distinguishability:** Frege §54.

18. **with differentiating strokes, it becomes unusable for arithmetic:** Frege §39.

19. **two contradictory qualities, namely identity and distinguishability:** Frege §45.

20. **tallies and marks preceded words:** D. Schmandt-Besserat (1999) *The Evolution of Writing*. Online 4/18 at https://sites.utexas.edu/dsb/tokens/the-evolution-of-writing/

21. **counting has been found to either precede it or accompany it:** T. Dantzig (1954) *Number* p.9. Online 8/18 at http://www.engineering108.com/Data/Engineering/Maths/Number_the_language_of_science_by_Joseph-Mazur_and_Barry-Mazur.pdf

22. **every proposition is stated only by means of these signs:** G. Peano (1889) Preface to The principles of arithmetic presented by a new method. In J. van Heijenoort (1967) *From Frege to Gödel: A sourcebook in mathematical logic, 1879-1931* p.85.

23. **a firm structural foundation under what is meant by number:** Peano, *The principles of arithmetic presented by a new method*.

In the twentieth century Thoralf Skolem and later Rafael Robinson demonstrated that the approach of primitive symbols defined solely by axioms has semantic limits, permitting nonstandard models that are significantly different than our conventional intuitive image of what a number is. A. Robinson (1974) *Non-Standard Analysis*.

Here is an example of a nonstandard model for Peano's axioms.

axiom 1:	∞	*the unit*
axiom 2:	$\infty+1$	*the successor to the unit*
axiom 3:	∞	*not a successor to any number*
axiom 4:	$\infty+1 = \infty+1 \Rightarrow \infty = \infty$	*equal successors, equal numbers*
axiom 5:	$\mathbb{N} = \{\infty, \infty+1, \infty+2, \ldots\}$	*induction from unit base*
However	$\infty = \infty+1$	

24. **five primitive propositions in addition to those of pure logic:** B. Russell as quoted in H. Hellman (2006) *Great Feuds in Mathematics* p.164.

25. **and his three primitive ideas to two:** Three set theoretic axioms (a version of finite set theory called GST) are sufficient to fully characterize Peano arithmetic. Informally,

— **Adjunction:** We can put new elements into a set.

— **Separation:** We can form a subset of a set.

— **Extensionality:** Sets are equal if they have the same members.

Separation can be derived from the axiom of Replacement combined with the axiom of the Empty Set. We consider these in Chapter 28.

26. **primitive ideas in Peano's arithmetic are: 0, number, successor:** B. Russell (1920) *Introduction to Mathematical Philosophy* p.5. Online 4/18 at
https://people.umass.edu/klement/imp/imp.html

27. **elegance rests upon a very complicated foundation:** Not only is the mechanism of Peano axioms complicated, it does not even achieve its objective. This from Dehaene (2011) *The Number Sense* p.221:

> While Peano's axioms provide a good description of the intuitive properties of integers, they also allow for other monstrous objects that we are reluctant to call "numbers," but that satisfy the axioms in every respect. These are called "nonstandard models of arithmetic," and they raise considerable difficulties for the formalist approach.

28. **in favor of the structural concept of difference implemented by Accumulation:** It is possible to define a boundary transformation that generates successors. The *replicator boundary* replicates its contents, in effect converting nesting into juxtaposition. Here is an example:

Let   ( ) = o
and   (x) = x ( )   = x o
             (( )) = ( )( )   = o o
           (( )( )) = ( )( )( ) = o o o
          ((( ))) = (( ))( ) = ( )( )( ) = o o o

29. Unit Accumulation which establishes different forms: Composition can be stated with inequalities as easily as with equalities. In a boundary calculus, *difference* (i.e. not-equal) is the primitive concept. It is equality that adds new concept to difference, and what is added by equality is not negation of difference but a capability to transform patterns.

30. definitely describing the addition of the unit 1: Dehaene criticizes induction to infinity as a process. We can apply the successor operation any number of times, but surely not a *non-numeric* (i.e. an infinity) of times. "The circularity of the definition becomes obvious: *Numbers* are what one obtains by repeating the successor operation a finite *number* of times." (p.223). Composition avoids this regress through recursion. We begin with a finite form and remove structure until none remains.

31. the empty system which contains no elements at all: Badiou §1.16.

The quote from Dedekind is from *Essays on the Theory of Numbers* (1901) W. Beman (trans.) §73. Perhaps this is the origin of the incredible difficulty that predicate logic encounters when dealing with an empty set.

32. wholly reject the introduction of measurable quantities: Dedekind p.37.

33. an ability without which no thinking is possible: Dedekind p.32.

Like Peano, Dedekind uses the word *thing* not to identify objects, but rather to identify abstract mathematical entities that have crystallized sufficiently to be considered as discrete, stable and atemporal. *Properties* are inherited from the way that set theory defines elements as unique things.

34. in the contrary case S is said to be a finite system: Dedekind p.63.

35. occupies the place which for Frege is occupied by zero: Badiou §4.13 and §4.15. (Emphasis in original).

36. essence of mathematics lies in its freedom: quote of Georg Cantor in C. Franks (2009) *The Autonomy of Mathematical Knowledge* p.10.

Chapter 23

Diversity

While there is universal agreement on the rules
for calculating with the natural numbers,
there has been a surprising lack of unanimity
concerning what they actually are.[1]
— *John Bell (1999)*

W e'll return now to the development of arithmetic from the structural perspective of Peano by considering three similar axiom systems that each delete specific axioms from Peano's model. The study of **weak systems of arithmetic** is motivated by Hilbert's original goals of constructing the foundations of mathematics from *only* mathematical tools and concepts. Mathematics no longer sought justification of its structure from the world, **truth** was to be determined solely by the internal structure of formal symbol systems. This led to a variety of questions substantively different than those of accuracy, utility or intuition.

Can Peano's axioms support everything that mathematicians might ask numbers to do? What expressive power is lost when we delete some of these axioms? We'll look first at **Presburger arithmetic**, a system so weak that it does not support a definition of multiplication. Then to **Robinson arithmetic**, which can handle addition and multiplication, and does so without the concept of Induction. And we'll end with **Primitive Recursive Arithmetic** (PRA), a system that eschews both the concept of infinity and the use of logic. Our goal is not to describe the hierarchy of expressibility created by these systems, it is rather to explore similarities and differences to James arithmetic.

23.1 All of Finite Mathematics

Harvey Friedman
1948–

Throughout his career, Harvey Friedman has sought to confirm the simplicity and the power of elementary arithmetic.[2] Friedman has proposed that mathematical proof in general needs only a very weak theory, **elementary function arithmetic** or EFA, built from recursive functions and equality. The structure of EFA includes

— the less-than relation, <, to place finite bounds on numbers and operations,

— two constants (0 and 1), to define the base of recursion, and

— three recursive operations (+, x, ^) that define arithmetic.

Friedman's grand conjecture is that

Every theorem published in the *Annals of Mathematics* whose statement involves only finitary mathematical objects (i.e. what mathematicians call an arithmetical statement) can be proved in EFA.[3]

Friedman's conjecture is echoed by Solomon Feferman, under the slogan that *a little bit goes a long way.*

Solomon Feferman
1928–2016

I have come to conjecture that practically all scientically applicable mathematics can be formalized in systems reducible to PA [Peano Arithmetic].[4]

Even Dedekind agreed, although a century earlier. Nothing more than the natural numbers is needed.

Every theorem of algebra and higher analysis, no matter how remote, can be expressed as a theorem about natural numbers.[5]

Friedman's EFA is Primitive Recursive Arithmetic — which we will examine shortly — extended with exponentiation and bounded induction. **Bounded induction** is recursion, taking proof steps from a given number downward to zero, rather in stepping upwards to encompass *all* numbers.

If Friedman and Feferman and Dedekind are right, then *James algebra is sufficient for finite mathematics*. The round container provides both 1 and an implicit 0; the relation of containment provides both less-than, <, and the addition operation; and in combination with the square container the round container provides the operations x and ^. By formulating James algebra as an equational theory, we include the equal sign, and as a bonus have no need for predicate calculus. The Composition Principle supplants induction. In fact, *ensemble arithmetic* is sufficient; James algebra provides, in surplus, the inverse operations which themselves generate rational, real and imaginary numbers.

23.2 Presburger Arithmetic

Presburger arithmetic does not include Peano's axiom that every number has a successor and as a consequence does not incorporate sufficient structure to support the inductive definition of multiplication.[6] Presburger arithmetic is purely about addition; it is the ancient *tally system* without grouping. This is particularly interesting because it is multiplication that calls upon the two James axioms. Addition and equality alone do not require Inversion or Arrangement.

Mojżesz Presburger
1904–1943

We begin with the predicate calculus statement of the Presburger system (Figure 23-1). The existence of a successor has been deleted (Peano axiom 2 in Figure 22-1),

Peano successor
$n \in N \Rightarrow n+1 \in N$

Presburger axioms	*symbolic description*
0 is not a successor	n+1 ≠ 0
equal successors, equal numbers	m+1 = n+1 ⇒ m = n
addition-base	m + 0 = m
addition-step	m + (n+1) = (m + n)+1
induction	P[0] ∧ ∀m (P[m] ⇒ P[m+1]) ⇒ ∀n P[n]

Figure 23-1: *The formal structure of Presburger arithmetic*

while the other Peano axioms remain. The form of induction has been limited from all numbers ℕ to Presburger numbers only; P identifies a member of the Presburger number domain which is an ensemble of tallies. This limitation allows recursive generalization up to any specific number, but it does not take the jump to the infinite extent of all numbers.

Figure 23-2 shows Presburger transcribed into the James system. The comparison exposes this: given Existence (something is not nothing) and the Composition Principle (equal forms can be constructed and deconstructed), nothing further is needed to formally describe addition. In particular, we do not need sets or logic. You might believe that at least we need to say something like *the set of all Presburger numbers*, but this phrase calls upon both sets and universal quantification.

The James version of Presburger arithmetic is simply ensembles of replica indicators constructed from the empty container unit. Removing multiplication has not only removed the square-bracket, it has also removed the need for the two James axioms that permit transformation of forms containing a square-bracket. We have reverted to a *pure tally system*. The one-to-one correspondence of tallies in two different containers provides

Presburger axiom	James equivalent
0 is not a successor	( ) ≠ void
equal successors, equal numbers	composition
addition	composition
induction	composition

Figure 23-2: *Comparing Presburger and James natural numbers*

a definition of equality, while Composition provides all that we need in the way of mechanism to add and delete contents.

The **unit ensemble** arithmetic described in Chapter 2 uses the same representation of whole numbers as does Presburger. Unit ensembles however implement multiplication via substitution of ensembles for units. We must presume the ability to find matching patterns and substitute them as permitted by the axioms in order to manifest change. An **iconic tally representation** of whole numbers has immediately available both addition as fusion and multiplication as substitution. This suggests that structural support of multiplication does not require a definition of multiplication *per se*. Addition is containment; multiplication is substitution. Tallies provide the necessary inductive step size required by Peano.

If multiplication is available to ensemble arithmetic, then it is also available implicitly within Presburger arithmetic, since Presburger numbers are expressed as tallies. Multiplication as substitution exposes an oversight by Presburger possibly attributable to an over-enthusiasm for induction. Induction proposes the separation of mechanism from definition. Presburger arithmetic employs substitution for transformation but fails to acknowledge substitution as multiplication.[7]

The James axioms are anchored solely to the structure of multiplication (i.e. frames), while the property of containers to hold things provides all we need for addition. But recall how cardinality works, via Indication and Replication.

indication
replication

$$A = ([A][o])$$
$$A..._N..A = ([A][o..._N..o])$$

The two James theorems convert a collection of replicas into *the form of multiplication*. The form ([A][B]) also provides **grouping**, there are A groups of B units. The elementary and ancient process of collecting units into groups of a given size *is* multiplication.

Indication is built from Inversion while Replication requires Arrangement. Neither provide an ordering relation. We come to the interesting observation that counting, as opposed to one-to-one correspondence, is introduced solely by the step-wise structure of successor induction. Without counting our steps we can still do cardinal recursion, however induction introduces ordinal counting clothed as the property of well-ordering, the greater-than relation.

Presburger also portends a frailty: there may be numbers that can be reached by multiplication but not reached by addition, in particular by adding 1 indefinitely.

We'll next recover multiplication by reasserting Peano's axiom that every number has a successor. In so doing Raphael Robinson was able to show that induction is not necessary, that from an assertion of the existence of a successor for every number, Induction becomes a theorem.

23.3 Robinson Arithmetic

Raphael Robinson
1911–1995

Robinson arithmetic is a simple axiom system for common arithmetic that does not include the concept of induction.[8] Like Peano, Robinson also incorporates as preamble the axioms that define equality. In fact, Robinson arithmetic

Robinson axioms	symbolic description
zero is not a successor	$n+1 \neq 0$
a number is zero or a successor	$n \neq 0 \Rightarrow \exists m\ m+1 = n$
equal successors, equal numbers	$m+1 = n+1 \Rightarrow m = n$
addition-base	$m + 0 = m$
addition-step	$m + (n+1) = (m + n) + 1$
multiplication-base	$m \times 0 = 0$
multiplication-step	$m \times (n+1) = (m \times n) + m$

Figure 23-3: *The formal structure of Robinson arithmetic*

is the Peano system with the Axiom of Induction removed. Since induction is the workhorse of both Peano arithmetic and common mathematics, it would be beneficial to compare the Robinson axioms to those of the James algebra. We'll find that induction and existential succession are co-defined.

Figure 23-3 expresses the axioms of Robinson arithmetic in common language and using predicate calculus. All variables are presumed to be universally quantified; m and n refer to any number. We have supposedly reached a *simple* system of arithmetic, however the predicate calculus specification includes quantification over sets, logical connectives and equality, all of which add at least a dozen more (hidden) axioms.

Figure 23-4 compares the structure of Robinson arithmetic to that of James algebra, just as Figure 23-2 shows the comparison to Presburger arithmetic and Figure 22-2 shows the comparison to Peano arithmetic. Within the Robinson axioms we can see the principles and axioms of James algebra. The Robinson rules of

Robinson axiom	*James equivalent*
zero is not a successor	$( ) \neq void$
a number is zero or a successor	$( )\ ( ) \neq ( )$
equal successors, equal numbers	*composition*
addition	*composition*
multiplication	*inversion frame*

Figure 23-4: *Comparing Robinson and James natural numbers*

addition are covered by Accumulation and Composition. Multiplication incorporates Inversion and Arrangement. Angle-brackets do not show up since neither Peano nor Robinson address inverse operations.

The recursive definitions of addition and multiplication in Robinson arithmetic can also be expressed as substitution patterns, as illustrated in Figure 23-5. The implicit recursive embedding of symbolic expressions, as described in Chapter 19, requires substitution to unfold the nested applications of each definition. With ensemble arithmetic, the same recursive unfolding can be achieved directly by substitution rules, in effect eliminating both the unnecessary symbolic definitions and the separation of definition from mechanism.

There has, of course, been substantial foundational effort invested in assessing the capabilities of these different *symbolic* formal systems of arithmetic. It is not possible, for example, to prove that addition is commutative having only Robinson arithmetic. Indeed, none of the associative, commutative and distributive laws for addition or multiplication can be proved within Robinson arithmetic.[9] Presburger arithmetic is both complete and consistent, without multiplication it falls just outside of the jurisdiction of Gödel's incompleteness theorem. Multiplication

operation	Robinson	☞	unit ensembles
+ *base*	$m + 0 = m$		$m = m$
+ *step*	$m + (n+1) = (m + n)+1$		$m\ n\ \bullet = m\ n\ \bullet$
x *base*	$m \times 0 = 0$		$(\!(m \bullet void)\!) = (\!(void \bullet m)\!) = void$
x *step*	$m \times (n+1) = (m \times n)+m$		$(\!(m \bullet n\,\vert\bullet)\!)=(\!(m \bullet n)\!)\,\vert\,(\!(m \bullet \bullet)\!)$

$(\!(m \bullet n)\!)$ ☞ *substitute* m *for* • *in* n

$(\!(m \bullet \bullet)\!) = m$

Figure 23-5: *Robinson arithmetic compared to unit ensembles*

permits the construction of Gödel numbering which then facilitates the theorem that declares arithmetic incomplete.

The first two Robinson axioms wrestle with the concept of zero. But as formulated, they are clumsy, perhaps a hangover from trying to build induction on a base that represents nothing.

$$n + 1 \neq 0 \qquad \textit{zero is not a successor}$$

$$(n \neq 0) \Rightarrow \exists m\ m+1 = n \qquad \textit{a number is zero or a successor}$$

Both can be reduced to the simple declaration that no number equals zero, $n \neq 0$

The James concept that *something can be distinguished from nothing* is more than intuitive, it also provides a basis for a theory of representation. Any concept within a symbolic formal system that has a representation *exists*. We cannot infer Accumulation (i.e. the successor concept) from the distinction between something and nothing, but the Composition Principle, combined with the rules of equality, permits us to add 1 and to delete 1. This is literally the successor function at step one. Composition is more general, in that we can add anything to both sides. Adding ( ) yields the successor function, however there

existence

$( ) \neq void$

accumulation

$( )( ) \neq ( )$

is no reason other than convenience to begin with a unit, or to add only units.

composition

$$B \neq void$$
$$A\ B \neq A$$

That is, the successor concept is not strictly necessary. We might presume that it is introduced in order to create a recursive definition of addition and multiplication. Recursion is, of course, just a way to hide a bounded Induction Principle. We could legitimately say that James Composition as well hides recursion, but parallel recursion is sufficiently distant from conventional stepwise induction based on successors that to equate the two would induce conceptual blindness.

In the above formulation, it is possible that B might be *void-equivalent*.

**composition
with void**

$$B = void$$
$$A\ B = A$$

In this case, both inequalities change to equalities. Composition incorporates induction by going underneath the idea of an incremental ladder, to the definition of what it means to be equal. Only void-equivalent forms can escape the Axiom of Accumulation since void-equivalent forms do not degrade an established equality.

Missing from the James formalization is the mechanism of pattern-matching and substitution. These mechanisms are hidden within the Robinson and Peano formalizations as well. In an arithmetic, pattern-matching is one-to-one correspondence of symbolic (or iconic) indicators. Identical patterns, and our ability to discern them, are implicit in the concept of *identity*, A = A. Substitution itself is implicit in our concept of equality.

The Robinson model can take recursive steps due to the assertion of the existence of a successor for all numbers.

**existence of
a successor**

$$n = 0 \ \vee \ \exists m \ n = m+1$$

Robinson set axioms	James equivalent
Empty Set $\exists A \forall x \ \neg(x \in A)$	
The empty set exists.	*Void does not exist.*
Extensionality $\forall A \forall B \forall x \ (x \in A) \Leftrightarrow (x \in B) \Rightarrow A = B$	
Equal sets have the same members.	*Equal forms have equal contents.*
Adjunction $\forall A \forall y \exists C \forall x \ (x \in C) \Leftrightarrow (x \in A) \vee (x = y)$	
A new member can be put into a set.	*Any form can be put into a container.*

Figure 23-6: *Comparing the set theoretic foundation*

This axiom is sufficient to replace induction. The two approaches achieve the same computational results but by different methods. Induction builds successors into the well-ordered sequence required for taking reliable steps, in effect providing a count of the steps. The Robinson model includes nothing to suggest sequential counting. Robinson is weaker than Peano in that there are theorems that it cannot prove. The crux is not being able to show that a successor is different from its predecessor.

cannot prove with Robinson

$0 \neq 0{+}1$

$n \neq n{+}1$

$m{+}n = n{+}m$

How much of set theory is needed in support of Robinson arithmetic? Just three axioms.[13] Figure 23-6 compares the set theoretic concepts to their respective container-theoretic forms. For comparison the predicate calculus representation of these axioms is also shown. The substantive difference is that containment effectively bypasses the predicate logic of Robinson set theory. The Axiom of the Empty Set becomes the Principle of Void.[10] Extension is the Composition Principle; the primary tool for constructing and deconstructing forms and the mechanism that replaces induction. And Adjunction too is at the foundation of the container-based approach: we can put new forms into containers.

axioms in James

$\neq o$

$n \neq n \ o$

$m \ n \ is \ n \ m$

23.4 Primitive Recursive Arithmetic

Reuben Goodstein
1912–1985

Models of arithmetic with induction engage in reasoning that extends into infinity. Primitive recursive arithmetic (PRA), in contrast, uses *finite recursion*. It is PRA that Hilbert conceptualized as finitary arithmetic.[11] While Robinson arithmetic dispenses with induction, it still includes an equally powerful assertion that every number has a successor. Both Robinson and Presburger also include the logical concepts AND and NOT. Earlier versions of PRA incorporate logic, here we are considering Reuben Goodstein's reformulation of PRA that dispenses with logic altogether. Importantly, PRA does not include logical quantification, no claim is made for all numbers, or for the existence of any particular number. Goodstein's arithmetic is thus closer to James arithmetic than the Peano, Robinson and Presburger models. Here is Goodstein's description of his algebraic approach.

> This note outlines a new version of a logic-free formalization of recursive arithmetic known as the equation calculus. In this version the only axioms are explicit and recursive function definitions, and the only inference rules are the substitution schemata.[12]

The general idea of taking valid mathematical steps is called inference. Taking steps via substitution of equals is **equational inference**. And a **schemata** is an inference rule that applies to any valid form in a system.[14]

Substitution Steps

Goodstein included the rules of the equality relation, as do all symbolic equational systems. His three inference rules are presented in Figure 23-7. These rules are formulated using functional language, so that F[a] means the application of an arithmetic function F to the number a, and F[A] is the application of F to expression A.

I. $F[a] = G[a]$ *conclude* $F[A] = G[A]$

II. $A = B$ *conclude* $F[A] = F[B]$

III. $F[0] = G[0]$
       $F[a+1] = H[a,F[a]]$
       $G[a+1] = H[a,G[a]]$ *conclude* $F[a] = G[a]$

Figure 23-7: *Goodstein arithmetic inference axioms*

Unfortunately Goodstein took most of the structure of addition and multiplication as axiomatic. His interest was focused on equational inference.

For our purposes, the functions F and G can be taken to be containment patterns. Goodstein's first axiom is **global substitution**: equality is maintained when one form is substituted for another form, so long as the substitution is global. Using substitution, Axiom I can be written as

$$F[a] = G[a] \; \textit{therefore}$$
$$\textit{substitute } A \textit{ for } a \textit{ in } F = \textit{substitute } A \textit{ for } a \textit{ in } G \qquad \textbf{substitution}$$

In terms of the rules of substitution (specified later in Figure 25-2) Axiom I is the distribution of substitution over equality.

$$(\!(A \; C \; F{=}G)\!) \Leftrightarrow (\!(A \; C \; F)\!) = (\!(A \; C \; G)\!)$$

distribution of substitution over equality

From a structural perspective, this axiom is a simple relabeling: the structure named a becomes the structure named A. Goodstein is however making a distinction between a ground number a and a numeric expression, A. The distinction is artificial since a number *is* a pattern. Due to object/operator confounding, grounds are patterns and the axiom is unnecessary. Its presence stems from the logical perspective that there are objects such as numbers and there are operations such as addition that combine with numbers to generate expressions. From the James perspective, patterns are patterns, and all are accessed by the same pattern-matching algorithm.

Axiom II is a statement of the Composition Principle. It derives classically from Leibniz' Law, the Identity of Indiscernibles. Two expressions are equal only when they share the same properties. Goodstein's axiom asserts that the application of the same function to equal expressions maintains equality.

Axiom III specifies the **mechanism of recursion**. The heart of the idea is the function H, which decomposes a function operating on a successor a+1 into the function operating on a and a memory that stores the sequence of iterative applications. Recursive functions provide quantifier-free induction. Goodstein's recursive functions were relatively novel in the middle of the twentieth century, however *recursive programming* is standard practice in computer science today.[15] An example was presented in Chapter 19 on concurrency.

In Axiom III, F(0) and G(0) identify grounded boundary patterns without variables, the *arithmetic* of the system. The first clause, F(0) = G(0), presumes that we start (or in the case of recursion, *end*) with identical containment structures. The second and third clauses assert that if F and G can be decomposed one unit at a time until both reach the same arithmetic form, then they are same structure within the *algebra* with variables included. This is precisely the strategy of James Composition.

There is an implicit computational link between the decomposition steps and the ground of 0. It is assumed that numbers themselves are grounded at 0, and that we can smoothly take 1 away so long as at least 1 is available. That's why the original distinction between numbers and expressions had to be made. In contrast, the Composition Principle permits reduction of equal forms by whatever equal subforms are immediately available.

There is one other sly presumption hidden in Axiom III: we need a way to combine three assertions into one pattern. There are several equivalent mechanisms to join together expressions that accumulate during computation, such as

— construct a set
— join with logical AND
— assert mutual implication
— construct an axiom with clauses
— put arguments into the same function
— nest function calls
— construct a pushdown automata stack
— put into the same container.

This list suggests that logic and sets and functions and iconic containment are interchangeable mechanisms. None are fundamental.

Iterated Functions

Goodstein's Axiom III incorporates logic since logic has a priority claim on the language of putting expressions together. Traditionally, the accumulation of facts during logical deduction and during equational computation is displayed over time by assembling a sequence of operations, or *steps*. In logic the sequence is a temporal composition of inferences,

$$A \Rightarrow B \Rightarrow C \Rightarrow D$$

inferential steps

In algebra, operations are expressed as a sequence of substitution steps. If we take $(\!(A_{new} \ A_{old} \ E)\!)$ to represent substitute A_{new} for A_{old} in expression E, then substitution steps can be recorded awkwardly as

$$(\!(D_{new} \ D_{old} \ (\!(C_{new} \ C_{old} \ (\!(B_{new} \ B_{old} \ (\!(A_{new} \ A_{old} \ E)\!))\!))\!))\!))$$

sequential substitution

Since each step maintains structural equality, we can also express the accumulation of steps outside of time, such as

$$A \wedge B \wedge C \wedge D$$

timeless conjunction

It's common in both logic and algebra to have many different paths to the same result, so that steps themselves are

structure	James concept	James form
ground	empty container	( )
relation	A contains B	$(B)_A$
operations	inversion frames	(A [B])
transformation	substitution	⟦A B C⟧
equality	composition	{A C} = {B C} ⇔ A = B

Figure 23-8: *James sufficiency within Friedman's grand conjecture*

not necessarily ordered or linear or discrete. Goodstein's Axiom III embodies linear stepwise recursion in its use of the successor function a+1, however the types of recursion that are available are much broader. Goodstein's H function, which embodies both stepwise successor recursion and database storage, is not essential. The structure of H simply identifies an implementation strategy within which intermediate results are accumulated as they become available. Function nesting achieves the same objective using a different implementation strategy. Again there's an awkward notation, the ellipsis is generally not intended for repetition over *depth*:

function composition

$$F[F[.._a..F[0]]] = G[G[.._a..G[0]]]$$

Parallel recursion, as outlined in Chapter 19, for which multiple sequential function applications are replaced by multiple concurrent agents, is also available.

Elementary Function Arithmetic

To come full circle, Friedman's *Elementary Function Arithmetic* is itself a subset of Goodstein's *Primitive Recursive Arithmetic* for which recursion is restricted to finite sums and products. Logic too can be completely replaced by substitution and bounded function composition. As presented in Figure 23-8 James algebra is a conceptual variant within which

- containers provide both ordering and structure
- two structural rules and two boundary types define the arithmetic operations and
- substitution and composition provide mechanism.

PRA includes the capability to define and construct any simple recursive function. Friedman's EFA calls upon that capability by including a recursive *definition* of the exponential function.

$$m^0 = 1$$
$$m^{n+1} = m \times m^n$$

**EFA
exponentiation**

For comparison, the James form of exponentiation recapitulates the *structure* of multiplication

```
m^{n+1} ☞  ( ([[m]][n o]) )
            ( ([[m]][n]) ([[m]][o]) )          disperse
            ( ([[m]][n])    [m]      )  ☞ m × m^n   unmark
```

23.5 Comparing Mechanisms

Figure 23-9 shows the complete axiom system underneath formal arithmetic as defined by Peano. Each of the six formal systems of arithmetic we have considered in this and the previous chapter incorporates a subset of the axioms in Figure 23-9. Each also includes (by the necessity of being able to do computation) equality, substitution and pattern-matching. These three infrastructure mechanisms, combined with the definitions of addition, multiplication and exponentiation are *sufficient* for arithmetic. Presburger, EFA and PRA incorporate finite processes. The Robinson and Peano systems both include logic and sets, and sufficient mechanism for infinite recursion. However, in the shadow of **pattern-matching**, inference, induction and function composition can all been seen as evolutionary variants.

The central organizing principle across the finite varieties is to establish a base such as 0, and then to deploy

FORMALIZED ARITHMETIC

propositional calculus

$A \Rightarrow (B \Rightarrow A)$	simplification
$((A \Rightarrow (B \Rightarrow C)) \Rightarrow (A \Rightarrow B) \Rightarrow (A \Rightarrow C))$	transitivity
$(\neg A \Rightarrow \neg B) \Rightarrow (B \Rightarrow A)$	transposition
$(A \wedge (A \Rightarrow B)) \Rightarrow B$	modus ponens

predicate calculus

$P(t) \Rightarrow \exists x\, P(x)$	existential generalization
$\forall x\, P(x) \Rightarrow P(t)$	universal instantiation

arithmetic of numbers

$m = n \Rightarrow (m = k \Rightarrow n = k)$	equality
$n+1 \neq 0$	Peano
$m+1 = n+1 \Leftrightarrow m = n$	Peano
$n + 0 = n$	+ base
$m + n+1 = (m + n)+1$	+ recursion
$n \times 0 = 0$	x base
$m \times n+1 = (m \times n) + m$	x recursion
$P(0) \vee \forall n\, (P(n) \Rightarrow P(n+1)) \Rightarrow P(n)$	Peano

Figure 23-9: *The complete axioms of elementary arithmetic*

successive substitutions into an expression recursively until the base is reached. It appears that both sets and logic are evolutionary precursors developed in the early twentieth century and are not essential for formal arithmetic itself. The infrastructure of predicate logic and set theory is certainly necessary to conduct a full mathematical investigation of what we mean by the arithmetic of numbers, however this infrastructure is not essential to formally define the *common* arithmetic that is used by culture and society.

The iconic axioms of James algebra set it apart from the other foundational models of arithmetic expressed in string notation. James arithmetic is spatial and container-based while the other five formal systems are, at least in notation, linear and string-based. Unlike Peano arithmetic, Robinson arithmetic includes addition and multiplication within its axioms. Like Peano arithmetic it postulates a successor relation that identifies the next number. James arithmetic resembles Robinson's in that neither includes induction. They differ in that James arithmetic does not include the successor function.

The linear structuring mechanisms of grouping and ordering, as well as the ordering relation >, are replaced by containment. Sets and quantification and domains move to the metalanguage that we use to talk about containment structures. Domains become an unnecessary refinement since all "things" are patterns. Yes, we can identify types of patterns, again as metalanguage via interpretations. Finally perhaps the most fundamental change is the reduction of the symbols 1 and 0 to an empty container.

Theory of Strings

There is one more hidden mechanism. String-based languages must necessarily include the *axioms of string construction*. These include a definition of the empty textual string and operational rules for **concatenation**. Strings are limited to an alphabet consisting of specific different typographic characters, and a language that consists of all the words that can be composed by con-catenation of characters. The empty string is the identity element, binary concatenation is associative but not commutative. The theory of strings can be replaced entirely by the operation of putting forms into a container. Spatial "juxtaposition" is by definition putting into a container, without concepts of ordering or grouping or arity or proximity or priority.

empty string
" "

concatenate
"a" "b" ⇒ "ab"

James pattern-matching, although it may be implemented by a serial computer using a string-processing algorithm, does not incorporate a theory of how strings are processed. Algorithmic processing was introduced by Turing with his linear, tape-oriented Turing machine. Since then parallel tapes, each implementing serial string processing, have been shown to be equivalent to a single tape. *Iconic parallelism* differs substantively from multiple copies of strings being transformed concurrently, as described in Chapter 29 by the distinction network architecture.

Reflection Monsters

Reflection permits us to entertain valid James structures that do not obey the conventional Peano definition of a number. To establish a base for recursion/induction, a common axiom for the arithmetic of natural numbers is that zero is not a successor to any number:

0 is not a successor $n+1 \neq 0$ ☞   n o $\neq$ *void*

To violate this axiom, we might say that there *is* a number for which zero is a successor.

0 is a successor $n+1 = 0$ ☞   n o = *void*

                                                     n   = <o>   ☞ -1

In effect this terrible axiom takes away the ground upon which induction stands. This is not a problem for James numbers since *void* grounds both o and <o>.

We can continue along this disruptive path, not undermining but rather extending what a number is. Let's violate the axiom that every number is either zero or a successor.

0 or a successor $n = 0$ or $n = m+1$

We can produce a repugnant number that is neither zero nor a successor by this assertion,

neither 0 nor a
successor $n + n = 1$ ☞   n n   = o

type	logic	☞	James	prototype form
negative numbers				
	∃n n + 1 = 0	☞	n o = *void*	<o>
rational fractions				
	∃n n + n = 1	☞	n n = o	(<[oo]>)
irrational roots				
	∃n n x n = 2	☞	([n][n]) = oo	((([oo]]<[oo]>))
imaginary numbers				
	∃n (n x n) + 1 = 0	☞	([n][n]) o = *void*	((([<o>]]<[oo]>))
				(((J]<[oo]>))
J *base #*				
	∃n (# ^ n) + 1 = 0	☞	(([[#]][n])) o = *void*	[<o>]

Figure 23-10: *James inverses*

Clearly n ≠ 0. If n = m+1 then we find

$$m+1 \ + \ m+1 \ = \ 1$$

which just gets us into deeper trouble. The Indication Theorem provides a way to construct this mystery number. We'll mark and collect the ns.

```
      n          n     =     ( )
([n][o])([n][o]) =     ( )              mark
([n][oo])        =     ( )              collect
[n][oo]          =     void             cover
[n]              =     <[oo]>           move
      n          = (<[oo]>)   ☞  1/2    cover
```

Figure 23-10 shows the conventional axioms that bring the inverse numbers into existence. Of course, these new numbers are incipient within the James boundary forms. There is an unexpected catch with logical quantification. By phrasing these axioms in terms of existence, *there exists an n such that*, we are required to provide the choice that n = 0 *or* it is a number defined by an

---

arithmetic operation. This is a hangover from requiring that induction have a ground case, even though we have taken that ground away by asserting the repugnant axioms. *Void* provides the concept of termination as ceasing to exist, without the necessary existence of a terminal ground.

23.6 Remarks

Mathematical concepts — even the most elementary ones like the concept of number — continue to change over time.[16] When mathematical rigor fell into question during the late nineteenth century, identifying the foundations of the discipline became the paramount objective of the mathematical community. From this fervor grew the theories of numbers, sets and logic. Metamathematics sought to provide rigorous foundations at the extreme cost of isolating mathematics from all other disciplines. Mathematical questions changed substantively, from finding solutions for applications, to defining groups of related mathematical structures, to confronting non-numeric forms such as infinity and infinitesimals, and finally finding rest with the concept of *decidability*. A question is decidable if an algorithm exists that can determine whether it is TRUE or FALSE. Regardless of purpose, can a specific mathematical questions always be answered? What are the inherent limits of specific systems and structures? We will next explore the idea of formality itself. Just what are the capabilities and the limitations of the mathematical approach? What is the meta-structure of formal systems in general?

Endnotes

1. **opening quote:** J. Bell (1999) *The Art of the Intelligible: An elementary survey of mathematics in its conceptual development* p.47.

2. **identify the simplicity and the power of elementary arithmetic:** Friedman holds the Guiness Book record as the world's youngest professor, as a Stanford Assistant Professor of Philosophy at age 18.

3. **can be proved in EFA:** Wikipedia entry (4/24/16) *Elementary Function Theory.*

4. **applicable mathematics can be formalized in systems reducible to PA:** S. Feferman (1997) Does mathematics need new axioms? Online 4/18 at http://math.stanford.edu/~feferman/papers.html

5. **can be expressed as a theorem about natural numbers:** R. Dedekind (1901) *Essays on the Theory of Numbers* W. Beman (trans.) p.35.

6. **structure to support the inductive definition of multiplication:** R. Stansifer (1984) *Presburger's article on integer arithmetic: remarks and translation.* Technical Report 84-639. Dept. of Computer Science, Cornell University.

7. **fails to acknowledge substitution as multiplication:** In describing how to generate exponential numbers via substitution into the tally system, Bernays fully specifies multiplication in ensemble arithmetic:

> We start from the number 10, which...we represent by the figure, 1111111111. Let z be an arbitrary number, represented by an analogous figure. If in the representation of 10 we replace each 1 with the figure z, there results, as we can see intuitively, another number-figure, which for purposes of communication is called "10 x z".

P. Bernays (1930) The philosophy of mathematics and Hilbert's proof theory. P. Mancosu & I. Mueller (trans.) p.21. Online 12/18 at http://www.phil.cmu.edu/projects/bernays/Pdf/philmath.pdf

8. **does not include the concept of induction:** R. Robinson (1950) An essentially undecidable axiom system. *Proceedings of the International Congress of Mathematics 1950* p.729-730.

9. **laws for addition or multiplication can be proved within Robinson arithmetic:** Robinson arithmetic is "weak" only from the perspective of a

string-based representation. From an iconic perspective commutativity, associativity and consequently distributivity *should not* be provable because they do not rise to the status of concepts within iconic form. Weakness in Robinson arithmetic is due to failure of linear notation rather than failure of proof. Analogously, arithmetic cannot prove that the sky is blue.

10. The Axiom of the Empty Set becomes the Principle of Void: Rather than having the Empty Set a member of every other set, and rather than having the Empty Set a common occurrence, James *void* is a strict non-participant, an unnameable and an unmentionable. However within their own formal systems, both the empty set and *void* are *everywhere*.

11. PRA that Hilbert conceptualized as finitary arithmetic: W. Tait (1981) Finitism. In W. Tait (2005) *The Provenance of Pure Reason* p.21-42.

12. the only inference rules are the substitution schemata: R. Goodstein (1954) Logic-free formalizations of recursive arithmetic. *Mathematica Scandinavica* 2 p.247-261.

13. in support of Robinson arithmetic? Just three axioms: A. Tarski (1953) Undecidable theories. *Studies in Logic and the Foundations of Mathematics*

14. rule that applies to any valid form in a system: Schemata are usually considered to be an infinite collection of specific axioms. We can avoid this call to infinity by saying that Goodstein schemata apply to *constructed* expressions.

15. recursive programming is standard practice in computer science today: In the mid-1930s several research directions coalesced around the definition of *computable functions*. Church and Kleene's lambda calculus and recursive function theory, Turing's effective computing machines, and Herbrand's equational recursive functions all identified the same class of functions that can be described by algorithms.

I spent a decade writing only recursive code, no sequential iteration and no loops. Recursive structures can be *verified* as functioning correctly, and have the advantage of being little modular computational engines.

16. continue to change over time: A. Heeffer (2007) Learning concepts through the history of mathematics. In K. François & J. Bendegem (eds.) (2007) *Philosophical Dimensions in Mathematics Education* p.88.

Chapter 24

Formalism

Thus mathematics may be defined as the subject
in which we never know what we are talking about,
nor whether what we are saying is true.[1]
— Bertrand Russell (1918)

The objective is to explore a simple alternative, a proof of principle if you will, that numeric mathematics is not necessarily about numbers nor is it necessarily abstract nor is it inherently complicated.[2] We have introduced three different types of mathematical perspective:

— an intuitive proto-theory, *ensemble arithmetic*,

— an iconic formalism incorporating that proto-theory, *James algebra*, and

— a metatheory about how the formal theory should work, *iconic mathematics*.

Following Hilbert's innovations, Kleene made fundamental contributions to the foundation of metamathematics.

Stephen Kleene
1909–1994

Metamathematics must study the formal system as a system of symbols, etc. which are considered wholly objectively. This means simply that those symbols, etc. are themselves the ultimate objects, and are not being used to refer to something other than themselves. The metamathematician looks at them, not through and beyond them; thus they are objects without interpretation or meaning.[3]

Metatheory is a theory *about* the formal system and not about any interpretation of the formal system. Thus the metatheory cannot reach into an intuitive interpretation for guidance. *A metatheory is purely structural.* However the iconic approach breaks down the distinction between proto-theory and theory by using "symbols" that cannot escape their meaning. This naturally leads to a very different kind of metamathematics.

The elimination of meaning from representation freed formalists to assume that how a concept is written does not impact what the concept means. This in turn permitted the assumption that the iconic notations of Peirce, Frege, Venn and even Euclid were at best only syntactic variants that contributed nothing to understanding, and at worst were sources of error and confusion.

The *sentential* style is propositional logic, particularly that type of reasoning for which conclusions are implied by statements that are clearly either TRUE or FALSE. Here's computer scientist Mark Greaves.

> For a particular set of theories which encode some of our highest standards for correct reasoning — the theories of expression and proof which are operative in geometry and technical logic — the representations which are currently sanctioned are uniformly sentential. This tradition is so pervasive that it is rarely explicitly commented upon...the overall sentential style is typically presented as if there were no sensible alternative.[4]

Disagreements and controversies that exist within conventional metamathematics are not addressed nor resolved by boundary math techniques, other than by looking the other way. The questions of metamathematics — closure, consistency, completeness, conciseness — are of a different type than those encountered while traversing the chasm between symbolic and iconic thinking, so much so that any comparison may turn out to be inappropriate.

In Chapter 28, we'll examine the formal perspectives of implicational and equational logic in order to identify points of comfort and points of departure between the conventional and the boundary foundations of the arithmetic and algebra of numbers. The significant weakness of classical approaches to the construction of axiom systems is that they overlook *computational dynamics*. In order to *use* a theory, it is necessary to manipulate representations. The tools and techniques of logic, set theory and algebra, however, were each developed before the invention of silicon computation, which we will explore in the next chapter.

I've attempted to avoid engaging in an exploration of the various philosophies of mathematics. The well known varieties of thought the arose at the beginning of the twentieth century — logicism, formalism, and intuitionism — appear to be rather quaint from the perspective of iconic computation. Each was making claim about what mathematics and validity should be, but with the advent of category theory, probabilistic proof, automated reasoning, ultrafinitism and iconic representation, the belief that mathematics could be built upon a single foundational principle has necessarily been abandoned in favor of embracing multiple orthogonal perspectives, all of which are valid. Still, experienced mathematicians see deep and astonishing connections between apparently disparate styles of mathematical thinking (i.e. logical, numeric, geometric, algebraic, topological), perspectives that have been proven to work for the wide array of solved and unsolved mathematical problems. The expert opinion is that mathematics must be thought of as an ecological unity, a densely connected network of dynamic relations.

24.1 Metamathematics

Hilbert's goal for metamathematics was to justify mathematical structure independently of its application. Theoretician Javier Leach states succinctly: "Formal mathematics has declared a kind of autonomy from even the empirical sciences."[5] James algebra too can be taken to be independent of its application to the arithmetic of numbers, as a study of the specific structural characteristics of bounded spaces consisting of an inside, an outside and a delineating boundary. However the metamathematics of boundaries is different from the metamathematics of formal symbol systems in two very distinct ways. The first is visually apparent, icons carry their meaning structurally while symbols are explicitly divorced from their meaning. Boundary icons illustrate the structural meaning of distinction and containment.

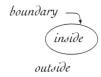

The second difference is somewhat surprising. Conventional metamathematics takes the arithmetic of whole numbers as an intuitive foundation, while arithmetic is an *interpretation* of boundary forms. The great formalist Hilbert recognized that tally marks were sufficiently obvious to intuition so as not to require formal verification.[6] Here is Mark Greaves again:

> However, for the case of the basic axioms of arithmetic, Hilbert pointed out that when the referents are interpreted as being about counting relationships between extralogical signs of a certain type (marks of the form |, | |, | | |, etc.), then the statements of mathematics can be assigned enough content so that we can intuitively judge them to be true or false without the requirement of formal mathematical proof.[7]

The technique introduced by Gödel of designating sentences in logic by specific large finite numbers has altered the evolution of logic to converge with the evolution of natural numbers. Conventional metamathematics is inseparable from mathematical logic, the native language chosen to express metamathematical truths. Gödel numbering converts logical expressions into natural numbers, deeply connecting the logic and structure of mathematical proof to the natural numbers.

Computation is a metamathematical conundrum. Semiconductor gate logic and software programming codes are themselves exceptionally large finite binary numbers acting upon other large binary numbers. Closer to the silicon, computation is synchronized electric currents passing through a maze of open or closed doors. Nonetheless the electronic choreography behaves as a *formal system*, obeying strict rules of transformation with transitions that can be associated both with massively parallel sequences of pulse modulations and with large binary numbers. Underneath every process on the global internet is an incomprehensibly large natural number, changing with unimaginable rapidity. We might even say that the "Gödel number" of a streaming 4K digital movie is precisely the unique sequence of binary digits that encode the behavior of the interface between digital and analog (i.e. the pixel display device).[8]

Another conundrum is that there is no satisfactory notation for real numbers. Unlike rational fractions, we can write down only a few real numbers, primarily those with names acquired through application, for example $\sqrt{2}$, π, e, the golden ratio Φ, and Feigenbaum's constants ∂ and α. Boundary forms, under the exponential/logarithmic interpretation of inversion frames, can express these irrational numbers, but a lawless irrational cannot be expressed without explicit instructions about how to construct (at least some of) it. And yes, if explicit instructions are possible, then that irrational number is not lawless. No operational arithmetic can encompass the entire domain of a countable infinity within finite resources. This observation is a linchpin of Gödel's incompleteness theorem: No matter what numeric structure we may wish to examine, there will always be numbers outside of that method of description. No matter what structural axioms we might formulate, there must be numbers not defined by or accessible by that system. There is essentially no difference between potential and actual infinity.

Finally, an objective of boundary math is to demonstrate that, although predicate calculus and set theory are absolutely necessary for advanced mathematics, they are potentially destructive for mathematics education. Put bluntly, the metaphysical foundation of Platonic mathematics is divorced from the psychological foundations of learning. The disconnect, the absence of meaning within symbol systems, is precisely the feature that allows meta-mathematics to study itself, while disallowing students in schools from understanding it.

24.2 Formal Systems

Common to almost every mathematical school of thought is the idea of a **formal system**. A formal system is a complex web of laws, precedents, preferences, beliefs and trusts. More specifically, it is a consensual agreement to follow explicit structural rules for constructing and transforming strings of tokens. Formal systems require a clear and unambiguous set of definitions, representations, constraints and transformations, as well as a clear and concise mapping from structure to meaning. We have all seen an example of a formal system in primary school: the arithmetic of whole numbers. However few have seen the rules that define how the symbols themselves must behave, the **rules of formal systems**. Just like conventional notation accepts strings of tokens as foundational, the iconic approach accepts finite spatial forms. The laws and goals of formalism itself identify the common ground.

Metaphysical Style

The original Platonic world-view saw mathematics as perfect, existing in a sort of heaven that was far more perfect than this world. Platonic reality exists independently of human minds, making it impervious to rational negotiation. In the Perfect World it is OK to discover wondrous creatures that cannot possibly coexist with us on Earth. These creatures bless us, when we strictly follow their rules, with things like Eternal Truth, Infinite Divisibility, Infinitesimal Near-Nothing and Universal Knowledge.

Most of the late nineteenth century metamathematicians, particularly Hilbert, sought to ground Eternal Knowledge in the natural numbers of the Earth. Constructivists beginning with Aristotle and in the modern era with Kronecker insisted that mathematical fantasy creatures cannot just be proved to exist somewhere within potentia, they must also be actively constructed so that we all can see them. Nominalists said: Come on, folks, to be grounded means grounded to the earth, to the ground. There is nothing abstract there, it is all here with us. Lately the Ultrafinitists will not tolerate even a hint of forever or a thought of unbounded plentitude. *Even whole numbers can get too big.*

Leopold Kronecker 1823–1891

Brian Rotman makes the point quite emphatically, mathematics must be grounded in physical reality. Any objects, such as the set of natural numbers or any single irrational number, that call upon actual or potential infinity are constructions of the mind, and are thus grounded in belief rather than consensual proof. Mathematician Verena Huber-Dyson's commentary on these Platonic creatures:

> Since we cannot get to them by ANY realizable constructivist method in a finite amount of time, then they cannot be said to "exist". According to Rotman, such concepts as the irrationals (and as infinity itself) ought to be regarded as theological abstractions.[9]

Objects

For an object to acquire a symbolic form, a *representation*, the object needs to hold still long enough for us to identify it as an object rather than a process. Unique objects can be collected into sets, and most folks are willing to presume that an infinity of objects can be collected into one set. Objects then are chimera that can morph across physical and virtual realities. They must be stable and unambiguous enough to be deemed an object yet accessible and common enough so that we can easily come up with an infinity of them.

You may be seeing some structuralism slipping in. We can imagine and talk about no end of objects, but it is the representation of the objects and the transformation of the representations that defines the entire game. Objects are co-defined by the network of permitted transformations of their representations. It is not only that a domain of objects has two way transformation paths that connect members of the domain, it is also that the functional pathways between objects themselves define what a unique object is. We define truth, or at least consistency, as staying on a permitted path, and we vigorously limit the range of representations to be exactly within the permitted syntax or the rules of structure.

Representation

With representation, the iconic and symbolic perspectives clash, as do the structural and interpretative perspectives. First, our interpretation of objects is converted into a representation. There are many techniques of representation, from words to text, to symbols, to icons, to drawings, to photographs, to movies and videos, to computer games and augmented realities. The symbolic perspective is to consider only strings of tokens drawn from a finite collection of distinguishable squiggles. Some folks specify that the string, or strings, can go on forever, as in the case of the decimal expansion of a real number or an infinite series of terms. If this is the case, then there are mathematical objects that cannot be directly represented by strings. The ellipsis in the decimal expansion of π as 3.14159... requires a leap of faith.[10]

There is a body of rules and conventions that guide the conversion of an object into a representation. These are generally not made explicit. First of all, math does not tolerate ambiguity, so any agreed upon representation must be by consensus. Everyone must also agree about exactly what a symbol refers to. New symbols must always be defined, of course, and all definitions must be unambiguous and non-contradictory. In the case of structure, permitted transformations must be unambiguous and explicit. Changes must be implemented only by substitution that does not change intention. And no infinite processes are permitted. The possibility of change is finite.

There are some rules that put dubious constraints upon the scope of representation. *Every* concept under consideration must have a symbolic form. Even the blank space between two words is defined typographically as a character. The core idea of string representation is that the meaning of a particular string is independent of its referent, while the structure enforced in the shuffling and transformation of strings covers the possible relationships between actual referents. Yes, the strings are meaningless but their context within other strings is not.

We find meaning by mapping forms to objects and concepts. Nominating another string language as the semantics or meaning of a first string language is a common symbolic technique. The meaning of the symbol $\wedge$, for example, is the word "and". The meaning of a high level software computer instruction is the binary string of machine language that it compiles to. As we look toward the iconic however, syntax and semantics meld. A void-based calculus cannot be symbolic.

The complexity of *symbolic* systems arises out of two seemingly innocuous activities: **free replication** of labels and **rearrangement** of configurations of labels. A presumption of string languages is that symbols are free and can be freely replicated to any extent.[11] This is *the source of symbolic complexity*, unavoidable yes but not a feature to be sought after. Rearrangement, of course, is defined by the axioms of a system.

One deep problem arising from symbolic representation is that it encourages an object-oriented viewpoint at the cost of a focus on process. For example, the symbolic expression 3 + 4 joins two numeric objects by a process of addition, but the result of the process itself is partitioned into a different step and into a different space. We isolate process by saying 3 + 4 ⇒ 7. Objects maintain their identity while processes act to change the appearance of objects. The fusion model of addition is slightly better. Three fused with four, •••|••••, is closer to a process perspective. The objects themselves are redefined by fusion, from wholes to parts: •••|•••• ⇒ ••• ••••. However, it is substitution that best exposes the object bias of symbolic expressions. In contrast, **tally multiplication**, implemented by substitution, makes every unit a process.

We have been using **double-struck tortoise shell brackets** as a notation for the substitute operation.

substitution ⟦A C E⟧ ☞ *substitute* A *for* C *in* E

The *process* of substitution yields a new form, but unlike fusion, the new form generated by substitution changes the original form, so the representation of the process does not resemble the representation of the result. This is an instance of the general problem of how to represent and record *change*. For example,

$$⟦A \ Y \ (X \ Y \ Z)⟧ \Rightarrow (X \ A \ Z)$$
substitute A *for* Y *in* (X Y Z) *yields* (X A Z)

Here the structure of the process does not match the structure of the result. Compare that to 1/3 or to $\sqrt{2}$, for which the processes (divide 1 by 3, take the root of 2) share the same structure as the result (the rational number 1/3, the irrational number $\sqrt{2}$). Converting $\sqrt{2}$ to its infinite decimal expansion, $1.414...$, does not eliminate the process representation. It merely substitutes an infinitely complex polynomial process for the process symbol $\sqrt{}$.

$$\sqrt{2} = 1 \times 10^0 + 4 \times 10^{-1} + 1 \times 10^{-2} + 4 \times 10^{-3} + \ldots$$

Expressing a real number as a decimal expansion is, rather perversely, changing a succinct symbolic token into the most complicated process description we can have, one that is *always* expressed as a finite component augmented by a call to an infinite continuation.

Underlying these observations is the rather dramatic neglect by formalism of the structure and capabilities of human language. Just because we can rigorously select and define a system of symbols, that still does not free us from how thinking and language work within human perception and cognition. Mathematics does pursue an ultimate abstraction, but it takes an inhuman degree of Platonic isolationism to believe that abstraction can escape cognition or that thinking about abstraction can escape the physiological determinants of how thinking works. Perhaps it is possible to completely escape physical reality, but it takes divine intervention to escape the cognitive reality perceived by our sensory organs. Science and Philosophy professor Timothy Lenoir observes:

Timothy Lenoir
1948–

> Thought, including abstract thought such as mathematical reasoning, rests on metaphors and diagrams derived from repeated and deeply layered patterns of body movement.[12]

Truth

Arising from the bedrock of formal systems *as a philoso-phy*, Boolean algebra defines how the concepts of TRUE and FALSE work in conjunction with the logical connectives of propositional calculus. It is at this very early stage that James algebra departs from conventional metamathematics. It is possible to identify common roots, the shared fundamental concepts such as structure, variable, equality, demonstration and interpretation. Divorced from the roots of logic and sets, each of these shared concepts takes on a substantively different meaning.

> **Structure** is spatial rather than sequential.
>
> **Variables** stand in place of arbitrary containment structures.
>
> **Equality** is defined by permitted transformations.
>
> **Transformation** occurs by pattern-matching and substitution.
>
> **Demonstration** occurs by a rule-based process of successive constructive transformation.
>
> **Meaningless form** is generated by void-equivalent construction and deletion.
>
> **Semantics** maps from typographic delimiters to configurations of physical containers.
>
> **Interpretation** associates mathematical concepts with configurations of distinctions. A *numeric interpretation* maps configurations of containers onto numeric concepts.[13]

What do these shifts of concept imply for our understanding of the foundations of numbers and of mathematics? They accumulate into something new: **iconic formality**.

As it turns out very few people, and very few mathematicians, are interested in the foundations of mathematics. Foundations was a big topic a hundred years ago, but in the early twentieth century the study of foundations drifted into quite challenging symbolic logic (proof theory, model theory, complexity theory). Even though mathematics is purported to rest upon logical proof, mathematical foundations have evolved over the last fifty years away from logic and into theories of algebraic mapping (category theory, topos theory).[14] Rigor is also exceedingly tedious for most people. The implementation of rigor is now clearly the responsibility of computation and silicon hardware.[15]

24.3 Axiomatic Systems

Metamathematics examines the structure of and relationships between **axioms**. An algebra is an axiomatic system in which valid transformations are certified to maintain the equivalence classes of different structural patterns. Incestuously, equality is also defined by the same axioms. We must consider the **grain-size** of the axioms, their relative **efficiency**, their **ease of use** and their **intuitive credibility**. And here is where set theory and predicate logic and even universal algebra have failed. In striving to meet the desirable structural conditions such as completeness and consistency, they are each without aesthetic appeal. (The colloquial standard that I have been applying is simply: Can grade school students easily understand it?)

Susan Stebbing, in 1931, made a distinction between two types of axiomatic thinking.[16] The first, *formalism*, creates simplicity by staying rigorously within syntax. There is nothing simpler than the axioms of a system because there is nothing else but the system. This puts postulates and theorems at the same level, and often it is possible to swap them around, proving one from the other.

Stebbing's second type of axiomatic construction has the intent of shedding light upon the meaning of mathematical objects such as numbers. *Principia Mathematica*, for example, does not engage in metamathematics, in the analysis of the symbols that convey its ideas. Symbolism is anchored in meaning and meaning is determined by the significance of the symbolic structures. The *logical* approach presumes that logic itself has meaning, a presumption that became deeply rooted within ancient Greek thought when Aristotle established the first laws of rationality. We have presented James algebra from this perspective, finding simplicity within the form of containment. That simplest of meaning is the act of distinction, of differentiating inside from outside. In this sense, we are interpreting in two directions, outward toward the mathematical complexity of the natural numbers, and inward toward the ultimate simplicity of the contents of an empty container. This perspective too respects Aristotle by acknowledging that arithmetic is a relative late-comer to formal mathematics.

Scope of Metamathematics

Metamathematical concepts vary depending upon one's school of thought. All of the schools of thought, of course, are deeply intertwined. Much of the representational structure can be cross-translated between these schools of thought, but it is difficult to reconcile the ways of thinking. The following sections are not intended to provide formal proof, just reasonable observations. The content bears more of a resemblance to informal conceptual demonstration rather than to proof, making apparent a general framework rather than a network of strictly derived structural details.

Focusing on *logic*, we might ask about

— the **closure** of the transformations
— the **independence** of the axioms
— the **consistency** of the results of applying transformations
— the **completeness** of the axioms to generate all possible forms, and
— the **decidability** that specific forms can be effectively identified and transformed.

Focusing on *algebra*, we might ask about

— the **equivalence classes** generated by the transformations
— the **symmetries** (group structure) of the objects and operations of the algebraic system
— the applicability of available **interpretations**, and
— the existing **morphisms** or mappings between systems.

Focusing on *computation*, we might ask about

— the **computational effort** it takes to identify a specific pattern
— the **unification** of variables
— the **convergence** of substitutions and sequences of substitutions to reach a single result
— the **data structures** that best express the language and its transformations, and
— the **parallelism** available during transformation.

Focusing on *education*, we might ask about

— the **intuitive sensibility** of the axioms
— the **elegance and simplicity** of the system
— the **learnability** of the concepts
— the **semiotics** of the representations, and
— the **neural substrate** that might justify a particular mode of thought.

Focusing on *boundary mathematics*, we might ask about

— **object/operation** unity
— the **absence** of properties we have called *void*
— the **independence** of contents
— the **multidimensional** nature of notation
— the illusory **void-equivalent forms**
— the **pervasiveness** of bounded space
— the **permeability** of boundaries, and
— the **absence** of logic, sets, functions, numbers and familiarity.

Gödel form

$$\exists n \ (n \neq 0) \ \text{☞} \ 2^{13} \times 3^{2^{27} \times 3^{25}} \times 5^{2^9 \times 3^{2^{15} \times 3^{2^{27} \times 3^{25}}} \times 5^{23}}$$

boundary form

```
(([[2]][13])
([[3]]([[2]][27])([[3]][25]))
([[5]]([[2]][9])
    ([[3]]([[2]][15])
        ([[3]]([[2]][27])([[3]][25]))
        ([[5]][23])))))
```

Figure 24-1: *Gödel numbering in conventional and James notations*

Arithmetization

Kurt Gödel
1906–1978

As a foundation to his work on the consistency of mathematical systems, Gödel developed a technique called arithmetization to convert symbolic text into numbers. Basically he coded each symbol of any selected formal system with a unique *natural number*, called a **Gödel number**. When symbols are strung together, they form the axioms and the expressions of the system. Gödel numbers can also be combined so that statements in any string-based formal system can be associated with a unique natural number. Transformation within a formal system can be converted into the structural properties of Gödel numbers. With this technique, as Kleene observes, by "talking about the correlated numbers instead of the formal objects, metamathematics becomes a branch of the arithmetic of natural numbers."[17]

This is both obvious (formal systems are so rigidly defined that they may as well be numbers) and astounding (whatever you have to say in mathematics you can say using finite natural numbers). Although simpler coding systems have been devised, Gödel used prime numbers raised to different powers to assure uniqueness. For fun, Figure 24-1 shows the Gödel number for the statement that there is a number that is not zero.[18] It *is* a large number. The figure also shows what this number would look like in James notation.

The motivation for Gödel's work, and for most of the foundational work at the turn of the twentieth century, was to remove the concept of continuity from mathematics. Continuity is very difficult to work with, since it throws us immediately into infinity. Half and half again and again and again just can't keep getting smaller, *ad infinitum*. Continuity cannot be implemented as a computation. And then that creature *quantum mechanics* was also raising its head. The physical universe is chunky.

Lakoff and Núñez identify five components of the program to make math discrete.[19]

— build calculus on discrete arithmetic
— build math from discrete symbol strings
— build logic from symbols
— reduce math to symbolic logic
— convert space to a collection of points

For a while, at least until the twenty-first century, it appeared that the incompleteness (or inconsistency) of arithmetic was restricted to the very exotic huge numbers that Gödelized rather abstract self-referential assertions, and could thus be relegated to obscure philosophy. However, in 1977 the Paris-Harrington theorem identified a problem in common number theory that was beyond the capability of the Peano axioms.[20] Then in 2011 Harvey Friedman found "concrete mathematical incompleteness".[21]

The challenge was to find a relatively simple finite problem that can be stated within the axioms of Peano arithmetic but cannot be proved or disproved using Peano axioms, thus demonstrating that the Peano axioms are either incomplete or inconsistent. Imagine that you have

find the
sub-graph
((()))

(()()()(()))
((()))(()())
(()(())((())))
(()(()(()()))
((())()(()()))

a large but finite collection of finite containment forms using only one type of container. That is, a collection of well-formed parenthesis structures. Within this potentially huge structure can you find a form that contains another specific form as a substructure? Can you assure that such a relationship between parenthesis forms can be found? Friedman's result is that you cannot assure it and you cannot not assure it. What does this mean? Perhaps that the values that mathematics has established for itself have changed. Perhaps Wittgenstein was right, modern mathematics is permeated with insidious ideas.

24.4 Mathematical Logic

Conceptually, the integrity of a set of axioms depends upon the *completeness* and *independence* of the axioms and the *consistency* of axiom interaction. These concepts have been developed exclusively to address the behavior of string-based symbolic forms, so we must reconsider the meaning of each concept within the context of a void-based spatial calculus. Void-equivalence makes understanding the integrity of a boundary system much easier than that of a symbolic system. And a *computational model* is also very useful.

Here are the conventional logical meta-properties. Each property is a constraint upon available types of transformation paths. A collection of axioms is

— **closed** only when all operations result in a structurally valid form.

— **independent** only when it is impossible to derive any one axiom from the others.

— **consistent** only when an axiom does not change the value (equivalence class) of the form.

— **complete** only when the value of an arbitrary form can be determined by the axioms.

— **decidable** only when there is an algorithm that can determine the value of any form.

These concepts are not independent. For example, if a system is undecidable, then necessarily it must include either forms that create contradiction or forms that cannot be transformed. Gödel's result, that useful formal systems are either **inconsistent** or **incomplete**, is a natural consequence of failure to be able to specify precisely how we can represent and reduce any given form. If we do not have *computability*, then formality itself begins to evaporate.

A **ground form** is a form that no longer reduces, what we have been calling a **stable** form. Finite systems usually have only a few ground forms determined by axioms. In propositional logic, for example, every form is expected to reduce to either TRUE or FALSE. In Peano arithmetic forms are expected to reduce to a natural number, but for numeric algebras, unfortunately, there are an infinity of ground forms. To make matters worse, when subtraction is introduced, there is another infinity of negative ground forms. When division is introduced there is another infinity of fractional forms and one exception, division-by-zero. When continuity is introduced, we find a new type of infinity that is incomparably larger than the previous infinities.

Closure

When a system is closed, transformation does not generate new types of things. For example, every second grade student knows that this is not OK:

$$3 + 4 = cat$$

For our purposes *number* itself is an interpretation of configurations of containers. From a computational perspective substitutions permitted by the axioms do not generate forms that are outside of the domain of containment forms. And there are definitely non-numeric James forms. Within our default interpretation, [ ] is negative infinity, not a number. (<[ ]>) is divide-by-zero, a forbidden non-number.

In fact every reduced form that incorporates an empty square-bracket is outside of the closure of numeric forms. Fortunately the only non-numeric "unit" is [ ], so we will simply make an exception for it. The James language can be interpreted as numbers plus a version of infinity. This exception will later get us into trouble and in Chapter 42 we'll have to deal with some indeterminate forms, forms that we *cannot* know what they mean.

There is a different, boundary perspective on closure. Every form has an outer boundary. Nothing from outside of the outermost boundary can enter into a computation or a representation. Since all represented forms are con-figurations of containers, James forms are *literally closed*. Crossing a boundary changes the intention of a form. Let's make that a premise using both words and symbols.

semantic containment

Closed by containment
Forms do not cross distinction boundaries without permission.

To express generality, we will need an outer boundary shape to represent *any* of the three James boundaries, ( ), [ ] and < >. We've been using curly braces, { }, to stand in place of any arbitrary simple (singly nested) stable (maximally reduced) James boundary. Given that A and B are not *void*,

$$\{A\ B\} \neq A\ \{B\}$$

A cannot escape its outer boundary without changing meaning, regardless of the type of boundary. As well, boundary transformations are semantically closed since they each generate a possible physical configuration of containers. This makes the James axioms closed by inspection.

All boundary forms have an innermost empty container, a **unit ground**. Thus the Composition Principle can be used both destructively (recursively) and constructively (iteratively), making finite iteration/recursion available as a proof technique.

The *only* relation is between a container and one of its content forms. The mutual independence of content forms is a consequence of the definition of containment: the space within a container has no properties. Therefore composition and decomposition of forms maintains closure. Again calling upon the curly brace to stand in place of any simple boundary,

$$\{A\ C\} = \{B\ C\}\ \textit{only when}\ A = B\ \textit{and}\ C \neq [\ ]$$

composition

Independence

To have axioms that are mutually independent is an **aesthetic**, like reducing a fraction is believed to be a good idea even though reduction can lose semantic information. Independence is very handy for transformation since it reduces the number of available transformation paths.

One way to phrase the concept of independence is to ask if any particular axiom can be constructed from the others. The only possibility is if two axioms address the same types of boundaries. However

reflection
$A\ <A> =$
$[\ ]<[\ ]>$ *indeterminate*

— Reflection removes only angle-brackets and adds only void-equivalent forms.
— Inversion removes and adds only inversion pairs of round- and square-brackets.
— Arrangement removes and adds only replicas of existent variables within Inversion frames.

inversion
$([A]) = [(A)] = A$

arrangement
$(A\ [B\ C]) =$
$(A\ [B])\ (A\ [C])$
$[[\ ]]$ *undefined*

The only possible interaction would be between Inversion and Arrangement. With any combination of the pattern variables being *void*, Arrangement condenses into Inversion or into an identity. Thus the difference between the two rests upon the existence of instances of each of the three variables. That is, Arrangement as a rule requires variables, whereas Inversion does not. Inversion is purely about inversion boundaries, Arrangement is purely about variables. These two rules apply to different structures and are therefore *independent*.

Another way to think about independence is to construct axioms that structurally cannot interact. In particular, void-equivalent forms are independent of all other forms simply because they can be deleted or added without changing whatever a form may mean. Both Reflection and Inversion identify void-equivalent structure. Closely related to the *irrelevance of nothing* is the idea that there are no relations between the various contents of any container. Each outer container enforces independence among the forms that it contains.

Consistency

Within the conceptual system of logic, consistency asserts that it is not possible to demonstrate both an expression and its negation. Computationally, consistency means that there are no transformation sequences that can bifurcate into contradictory end-points. That is, no transformation sequences change the logical equivalence class of a form. From a boundary perspective, consistency means that no forms cross a boundary without (axiomatic) permission. Fundamentally no transformation will convert a unit into *void*, or into a different type of unit.

unit existence

( ) ≠ *void*

[ ] ≠ *void*

< > = *void*

Consistent by existence

The axioms do not make existent forms void-equivalent, and vice versa.

Void-equivalence guarantees no impact, so Inversion and Involution are safely consistent. The only possible difficulty might come from Arrangement. Can Arrangement change the equivalence class of a form?

inversion frame

(A [B])

Arrangement both rearranges and replicates. The axiom replicates the inversion frame (A [...]), which incidentally replicates the frame-type A. Like independence, consistency is at issue only when all three Arrangement variables exist. Since on the left B and C have the same outer container, they are mutually independent. Their separate occurrence on the right does not introduce a change in equivalence class since there is no boundary relation that has been crossed. The only remaining potential difficulty is if replicating A may impact the class of a form. Here is where the concept of an *inversion frame* is relevant. All the frames of the Arrangement axiom are of the same type, so that the transformation is consistent over frame-type.

Completeness

Logical completeness means that a symbolic axiom system is capable of proving any expression either TRUE or NOT TRUE. Computationally, a transformation path exists that connects *every* expression separately to its equivalence class. Completeness for an iconic system means that all possible forms can be constructed (or deconstructed) via the axioms.

Can we reduce all existent forms to their stable ground form? Yes, by applying the Composition Principle in the deconstructive direction. Are there forms that cannot be constructed? Here we need to separate consistency (which is about contradiction) from completeness (which is about possibility). Both Composition and the James axioms allow construction from a base while maintaining value. That is what the equal sign within these rules means. Disregarding equality, Existence serves as an implicit Axiom of Foundation, asserting that ( ) can be brought into existence only at the cost of a change in value. Disregarding consistency, Existence asserts that ( ) can be created anywhere in place of *void*, at the cost of a change in value. Since *void* is pervasive, all possible *numeric* James forms can be constructed by successively replacing *void* by ( ). Since all forms are composed of marks, wherever a mark is needed there is a *void* to support its construction. Can we identify all void-equivalent forms? Since deconstruction is trivial, i.e. there are no choice points, any form that does not *delete* directly is not void-equivalent.

Consistency asks if we can always determine the equivalence class of a given form, while completeness asks whether we can find all forms within a given class. In the approach of logic, every possible expression is either provable or not. In the iconic approach, every possible form is either constructible or not. But we have begged the question: "possible form" *means* "constructible form". The dilemma of logical expressions is that there are presumed to be an infinity of them. This is where finite constructibility can provide reasonable bounds: let's presume that there are no forms that are larger than our universe. The constraint of reasonable boundedness saves us from the worry of being surprised by some form outside of our possible reference that may violate completeness.

Here we have fundamentally changed the intention of symbolic completeness, which is proof from the axioms that all forms can be shown to belong to some equivalence class. Symbolic completeness does not concern itself with arbitrary construction. Construction is given, the question is knowing what has been constructed. In a distinction-based regime, there is no question about what has been constructed. We are distinguishing existence from *void*, not truth from non-truth.

⟪11⟫
includes
7+4
1+2+3+5
16–5
77/7
(4x5)/2 + 1
√121

A common conventional technique to demonstrate completeness is to reduce an arbitrary form to its canonical structure, and then to show that the canonical form has a property that permits determination of value in all cases. A **canonical structure** is a skeleton shape that all forms can be transformed into. Natural numbers, for example, are constructed so that any combination of numbers with the operations + and x can be reduced to a single natural number. This is what Peano's axioms address by calling upon induction. The definitions of addition and multiplication are such that they lead to a single number by pecking away at a composite expression one unit at a time. The rules of syntax assure that no form can be constructed that cannot be decomposed.

A canonical James form would be one with no void-equivalent subforms and with Arrangement applied to disperse as much as possible. This would leave all existent forms with singular frame contents, however inversion frames themselves may be recursively embedded. Reduction to the minimal number of labels using collect rather than disperse can result in different "minimal" forms. Forms with minimal variable references are not necessarily unique. For example, there are three symmetric ways to collect this maximally dispersed form:

$$([A][B])([A][C])([B][C]) \Rightarrow (A \times B) + (A \times C) + (B \times C)$$
$$([A][B\ C])([B][C]) \Rightarrow (A \times (B + C)) + (B \times C) \qquad \text{collect B C}$$
$$([B][A\ C])([A][C]) \Rightarrow (B \times (A + C)) + (A \times C) \qquad \text{collect A C}$$
$$([C][A\ B])([A][B]) \Rightarrow (C \times (A + B)) + (A \times B) \qquad \text{collect A B}$$

Any of the variables A, B, and C can stand in place of arbitrarily complex forms, so that in principle there is no procedure to assure that collecting prior to computation will yield a "simplest" form. We either have to accept that some ways of writing down an arithmetic problem can lead to excess work, or that it takes excess work to find the simplest route through a computation. That is to say, canonical structure is inefficient while efficient structure is not canonical. This choice is usually avoided in conventional proofs by ignoring the question of efficiency. The dilemma of course is that infinite domains may have expressions that require infinite effort to reduce. Within finite constraints useful mathematical systems are necessarily incomplete and not necessarily closed.

There is another deep problem: the range of possible interpretations of a symbolic system can be so wide that most formal systems work not only for their intended interpretation (numbers in our case) but also for "nonstandard" models, for conceptual systems that have nothing to do with the intended purpose. We encounter this, for example, in Volume III where an object that we can call "infinity" shows up embedded within James numbers. There we will see that James algebra is necessarily incomplete, since there are forms that are non-numeric and forms that are inherently *indeterminate*.[22] Yes, [ ] is a conundrum. Our focus on structure has been one of syntactic completeness. **Semantic completeness** involves providing a model, or interpretation, of the syntactic structures. Iconic contain-ers, of course, have that model built in. The combination of both syntactic and semantic completeness implies that for-mal manipulation of structure maintains semantic validity, that is, the formal axiom system maintains value under all possible interpretations. However, James algebra includes **indeterminate forms** that cannot be interpreted, as does common arithmetic. Multiplying A by 0, for example, removes the concept of numeric value from the "variable" A.

$$A \times 0 = 0$$
A *is indeterminate*

Decidability

The criteria that logic imposes upon communication are quite severe. **Computational decidability** is the most severe yet, since it requires that there be an effective method by which value can be determined. For example, if I believe that the value of a particular gem is $5 and you believe that the same gem is worth is $50, we may have a serious problem doing commerce. We need a way to mutually agree upon the same value for the gem. But agreement is just the start. We need to define an *algorith-mic* procedure that will in all cases resolve our differences. Effective methods are by definition algorithmic, so decid-ability is inherently a computational rather than a logical criterion. It is a late comer to metamathematics, and a tacit acknowledgment that logic itself has computational roots.

Here's the conceptual coup. If there is no way to decide upon the value of an arbitrary form, then a system is quite limited. *Pragmatism* must enter at some point. The theoretical problem is that pragmatism exits almost imme-diately. If we add so little to logic as equality and one other binary relation, then logic itself is undecidable. Robinson arithmetic, for example, is undecidable.[23] James forms are decidable if we consider the value of a form to be its physical manifestation. This shifts the question of numeric decidability to the interpretation. The advantage of physical forms is that they specifically exclude the concept of infinity. This severely limits pure mathematics, so we might adopt what appears to be a reasonable compromise. James algebra applies to a limited domain of mathematics, that part without infinities. In the worst case, decidability is available by searching the finite collection of possible forms. In essence, infinite structures are not pragmatic. In specific, James forms with [ ] innermost are excluded from a numeric interpretation.

24.5 Algebraic Logic

Algebraic logic uses an algebraic approach based on equality rather than inference. The technique of proof changes from logical deduction to transformation via substitution of equals for equals. The PRA and EFA axiom systems described in Chapter 23 are examples of algebraic systems, as is James algebra. In algebraic logic

— the primary connective is *equals*
— axioms define *patterns* that can be transformed
— transformation and proof are by *substitution* guided by axioms
— variables identify *constructible* forms

A variable stands in place of any possible form. A variable nested within a form is constrained by its context. Since equational logic expresses implication quite nicely in two directions, we can build propositional logic with only the ideas of **equality** and **substitution** within configurations of NOR relations. Algebraic logic dovetails with constructive computational techniques, leading to systems that require only pattern-matching and substitution by rule to maintain equality of patterns. Truth becomes confounded with Equivalence.

The algebraic concept of an equivalence class defines as ground a specific set of forms that reduce no further. Commonly, we think of the different equivalence classes of numbers just to be the numbers themselves. Each number is a ground form. But this idea gets sticky when we think about the number 1/3, because the representation says that it is *not* reduced, the division sign remains. We have returned to the old question: is 1/3 one number or two? Are we looking at the object or the transformation network?

Binary Worlds

Binary forms require only two equivalence classes, say TRUE and FALSE. To prepare logic to be a **generic operational subsystem** (a *metatool* if you'll permit a stretch in language) that provides rigor across all types of objects and all domains, **variables** will represent arbitrary domains and thus represent *many* equivalence classes rather than two. So as not to loose the discrimination power of logic, it's 0/1 perspective must be independent of the equivalence classes of objects. The equal sign immediately takes on two responsibilities, 0/1 to maintain classification of equations as equal or unequal, and A = A to maintain equivalence classes.

A calculus of distinction maintains difference, A ≠ B, to partition forms into their classes. This results in a constraint-based perspective that eliminates impossible classes instead of assigning a singularly correct class to each form. **Boundary logic** itself was developed extensively prior to the idea of applying boundary techniques to the arithmetic of numbers.[24] There's a very significant difference within the 0/1 perspective. Here's an analogy: if we need to know which of two bags holds lunch, we need only *one label*. In a purely binary realm of classification such as truth-value logic, it's possible to label one class (TRUE for example) and not label the other. Pragmatically, if we are looking for something, we do not need to track where it is not. In a sense TRUE forms are of interest while NOT TRUE forms are irrelevant. Indeed, in boundary logic only TRUE forms maintain existence; NOT TRUE forms are void-equivalent.

Algebraically, should we need both binary values, we have the *variable* which stands in place of either. And if computation is sufficiently efficient, we need store only one of the equivalence classes, say 1. And if we store only what is of interest, we don't even need to label the single equivalence class. The ability to retrieve is a sufficient label. So if we see representation as a dynamic, then we do not need logical distinction at all. Logic itself (binary discrimination) is stored in the dynamic transformation of a database. Equality maintains transformational consistency.

Boundary logic replaces the singular logical NOR relation with a different single relation, contains. In the process it abandons the ideas of logical implication and truth. We end up with a system that like propositional logic has one binary relation and like algebra has axioms that give permission to make structural changes to forms while maintaining equality. But it requires no other concepts and no other mechanisms. James algebra is not a logic, its interpretation is numeric. And in its void-based form it is also not equational, as was demonstrated in Chapter 17.

Our mathematical foundations are a complex web of interconnected concepts and systems. To simplify the web of mutual definitions, it is necessary to remove equality from the top of the pyramid and place it at the foundation. Thus, for James algebra, equality of form is defined explicitly by the transformations permitted by axioms. Boundary equality does *not* have the properties of symmetry, transitivity, and reflexivity, not because it has other opposing properties but because the properties themselves are placed within a different process, that of transformation. The equals sign becomes simply an indicator that we have not left a particular equivalence class. It is the *application of transformations* that is reflexive, symmetric and transitive, as shown in Figure 24-2. The arrows in the figure are no longer logical implication arrows, they are transformation permission

property	assertion	transformation
identity	A ⇔ A	A can-change-to *itself.*
symmetry	A ⇔ B	A can-change-to B, B can-change-to A
transitivity	A ⇔ B ⇔ C	A can-change-to B, B can-change-to C
		C can-change-to B, B can-change-to A
		A can-change-to C, C can-change-to A

Figure 24-2: *Transformation as a kind of equality*

arrows, with substitution being the only mechanism of transformation. Permission is underwritten by patterns manifest in axioms. Constructive boundary mathematics thus retains the algebraic techniques of substitution to maintain equality but eliminates the concept of truth in favor of the ability to construct while following structural rules. Equality becomes confounded with Composition, while the void-based techniques confound equality with existence.

24.6 Remarks

Formalism is simply following unambiguous, finite symbolic rules while refraining from thinking about what the symbols may mean. Formalism, minimally, is being a computer. So it is appropriate next to explore computation.

Endnotes

1. **opening quote:** B. Russell (1918) *Mysticism and Logic and Other Essays* Ch 5: Mathematics and the Metaphysicians. Online 8/18 at https://www.gutenberg.org/files/25447/25447-h/25447-h.htm Here's the broader context:

> We start, in pure mathematics, from certain rules of inference, by which we can infer that if one proposition is true, then so is some other proposition. ...If our hypothesis is about anything, and not about some one or more particular things, then our deductions constitute mathematics. Thus mathematics may be defined as the subject in which we never know what we are talking about, nor whether what we are saying is true. People who have been puzzled by the beginnings of mathematics will, I hope, find comfort in this definition, and will probably agree that it is accurate.

2. **nor is it necessarily abstract nor is it inherently complicated:** I have attempted in this chapter to skim the technical surface of several deep formal disciplines. The primary motivation is to demonstrate the feasibility of iconic form for expressing and studying common arithmetic. The particular choice of James algebra is driven by a desire to render arithmetic in a simple enough format to preserve the time honored Additive Principle. A secondary motivation for this chapter is to explore some selected technical details underlying this choice. The net result is a chapter that at times overlooks some technical details and that asks you, the reader, to tolerate rapidly changing models and metaphors in order to gain a wider perspective on the implications of thinking formally about containment relations.

3. **not through and beyond them; thus they are objects without interpretation or meaning:** S. Kleene (1952) *Introduction to Metamathematics* p.64.

4. **typically presented as if there were no sensible alternative:** M. Greaves (2002) *The Philosophical Status of Diagrams* p.2.

5. **a kind of autonomy from even the empirical sciences:** J. Leach (2010) *Mathematics and Religion* p.68.

6. **tally marks were sufficiently obvious to intuition so as not to require formal verification:** Chapter 2 formalizes tally marks as *ensembles*.

7. **true or false without the requirement of formal mathematical proof:** Greaves p.186.

8. **the behavior of the interface between digital and analog (i.e. the pixel display device):** The behavior of each display pixel is encoded by a binary number that is at least 32 digits long, providing 256 options for each of red, green, blue, and transparency. There are about 50,000 pixels per square inch, about 20 million on the screen, each changing 120 times a second. That puts the binary number of an HDTV streaming movie somewhere around 10^{15} bits long, and the number of different possible movie encodings at $2^{1,000,000,000,000,000}$.

9. **irrationals (and as infinity itself) ought to be regarded as theological abstractions:** V. Huber-Dyson (1998) On the nature of mathematical concepts: Why and how do mathematicians jump to conclusions? EDGE conversation 2/15/98. Online 8/18 at https://www.edge.org/conversation/verena_huber_dyson-on-the-nature-of-mathematical-concepts-why-and-how-do-mathematicians

10. **the decimal expansion of π as** 3.14159... **requires a leap of faith:** Equations that have an ellipsis on one side and a specific object on the other, such as

$$1 + 1/2 + 1/4 + 1/8 + \ldots = 2$$

are self-contradictory. They express a *type error* by equating a non-number with a number.

11. **symbols are free and can be freely replicated to any extent:** Many systems comfortably begin with "Let there be an infinity of variables."

12. **diagrams derived from repeated and deeply layered patterns of body movement:** T. Lenoir (2008) Machinic bodies, ghosts, and paraselves: confronting the singularity with Brian Rotman. Foreword to B. Rotman (2008) *Becoming Beside Ourselves* p.xxv.

13. **maps configurations of physical containers onto numeric concepts:** The shift from notational to physical containment is important since it underscores that elementary mathematics is inherently physical rather than abstract.

14. **theories of algebraic mapping (category theory, topos theory):** F. Lawvere & S. Schanuel (2009) *Conceptual Mathematics 2nd edition*.

15. **the responsibility of computation and computer hardware:** A single rare error in a silicon chip is sufficient to trigger a massive hardware recall. Although there is a software development community focused on formal verification, they are largely ignored except for mission critical systems such as missiles, radiation machines and space probes. By marketing convention the responsibility for software errors is usually transferred to the customers.

16. **distinction between two types of axiomatic thinking:** L. Stebbing (1931) Postulational Systems and *Principia Mathematica*. In *A Modern Introduction to Logic*. Online 8/18 at http://www.naturalthinker.net/trl/texts/Stebbing,LSusan/PostulationalSystems.html

17. **metamathematics becomes a branch of the arithmetic of natural numbers:** Kleene p.246.

18. **there is a number that is not zero:** Kleene p.255.

19. **five components of the program to make math discrete:** G. Lakoff & R. Núñez (2000) *Where Mathematics Comes From* p.261.

Distinctions are discrete, inside or outside, a binary choice. However, a semipermeable distinction allows forms on the outside freely to be inside as well. If we were to label outside as 1 and inside a 0 then semipermeability permits 0 to include 1, reminiscent of a superimposed quantum state.

20. **number theory that was beyond the capability of the Peano axioms:** J. Paris & L. Harrington (1977) A mathematical incompleteness in Peano arithmetic. In J. Barwise (ed.) (1982) *Handbook of Mathematical Logic*. Online 8/18 at https://www.karlin.mff.cuni.cz/~krajicek/ph.pdf

The problem is within Ramsey theory which involves associating a property (a coloring) with small groups of natural numbers and then finding specific groups with the given property.

21. **found "concrete mathematical incompleteness":** H. Friedman (2013) Concrete mathematical incompleteness. Online 8/18 at http://cage.ugent.be/programFriedman/slides/MathInc083113.pdf

22. **forms that are non-numeric and forms that are inherently *indeterminate*:** This issue is also rampant within numeric arithmetic. 1/0 is the archetype non-numeric expression. Another example is the lawless real numbers that cannot be *described*, much less evaluated.

23. **Robinson arithmetic, for example, is undecidable:** R. Robinson (1950) An essentially undecidable axiom system in *Proceedings of the International Congress of Mathematics 1950* p.729-730.

24. **applying boundary techniques to the arithmetic of numbers:** G. Spencer Brown (1969) *Laws of Form*, Bohmeier Verlag Edition 2009 Appendix 4 *An algebra for the natural numbers* (1961).

Chapter 25

Computation

Arithmetic is numbers you squeeze from your head
to your hand to your pencil to your paper
till you get the answer.[1]
— *Carl Sandburg (1993)*

We have examined logic and algebra, two of the elementary symbolic systems of mathematics. We'll visit set theory in Chapter 27, and revisit logic and functions with a more critical analysis in Chapter 28. Each of these axiomatic systems was developed prior to the invention and ubiquitous presence of digital computation. Our theme is that the **foundations of mathematics** have been substantively redefined by digital convergence and pervasive computation.

Formal approaches carefully identify both the domain under consideration and the explicit representations permitted to stand in place of domain objects. Transformation rules permit symbolic expressions to be rearranged without loss of meaning. Underneath every formal system is a presumption that like forms can be identified, that **pattern-matching of structure** is a given capability. Transformation via **substitution of patterns** is fundamental to almost every mathematical system whether it be algebra or logic or set theory or geometry. Since almost every step of a formal proof involves a substitution, we will stretch to say that

*Pattern-matching and substitution are
at the foundation of mathematics.*

What we are seeking is an adequately rigorous and conceptually friendly foundation for thinking about simple mathematical structures in general and about elementary arithmetic in particular. The fantasized formal rigor that brings with it a promise of Eternal Truth is difficult and arduous to achieve, is largely at a grain size that is not suitable for human mental capabilities or for human lifetimes, and is terminally disconnected from all of the essential characteristics of physical reality. Mathematical verification is turning toward computer implementations that accurately process formal minutia billions of times faster than do humans, and with several orders of magnitude fewer errors. Once we take the plunge into computational rigor, mathematics becomes **computational mathematics** rather than conceptual mathematics. Pure mathematics for the most part relies on broad brush strokes, using a paint of incredibly detailed and tightly interwoven symbolic structures. Conceptual proof relies upon deep intuition and a multitude of established theorems to provide the freedom of a terse explanation. However a fundamental difficulty is that conceptual mathematics lacks a physical basis. Silicon computation, although physical only in its manifestation as electronic signals, is sufficient to provide pragmatic grounding for abstract concept.

25.1 Symbolic Computation

The advent of **symbolic computation** has been a tectonic shift for mathematics. Computation is not about numbers any more, it is about patterns of symbols. Computation is synonymous with symbolic transformation. Common mathematics is not so much about truth and proof as it is about form and transform. Mathematical logic has evolved from a focus on consistency and independence and completeness of sets of axioms to a focus on decidable and effective computational processes: an evolution from implication to implementation.

A symbolic regime can manipulate the symbol π without knowing that "π" stands in place of a real number. This is, incidentally, a necessary shift since the real number π has no finite representation as an exact number. The trouble with the raw symbol π is that it shows you nothing about what π is or how it is structured internally. Like all symbols, it is devoid of meaning without some additional context. In contrast

$$\pi = (J/2\ [J])$$

$$J = [<(\ )>]$$

$$J \ \text{☞} \ \log_{\#} -1$$

$$\pi \quad \text{☞} \quad (\ ([[<(\ )>]]<[(\ )(\ )]>)\ [[<(\ )>]]\ )$$

$$\text{☞} \quad \#^{\#^{((\log\log_{\#}-1)\ -\ (\log_{\#}2))}\ +\ \log\log_{\#}-1}$$

shows us a great deal about what we mean by the symbol π. The James form of π is an explicit set of instructions about how to compute the value of π given the interpretation we have placed on the three types of brackets. There is a catch, we need to understand how J works.

This chapter addresses in detail what it means to change form by obeying axioms. The modern algebraic idea of a category is very much like what in computer science is called an **abstract data structure**. Elementary advanced algebra overlaps considerably with intermediate computer programming.

Methods

Transformation of a representation rests first on an ability to identify the symbols within the transformation template and then to match them with symbols within the expression being modified. Most axioms are **context-free**, the symbols in the context of a potential substitution do not interact with the substitution itself. Axiom sets are designed to avoid many problems that would make pattern-matching unreliable. Patterns must be explicit and unambiguous. Transformations are independent of one another, so that transformation sequences can accumulate in steps. Operations are designed to be closed so that all expressions in a language reduce to explicit ground objects. Each ground object defines an equivalence class of expressions, while the ground objects themselves are archetypes for expressions within an equivalence class.

A matrix of constraints on formal structure assures both clarity and consistency. Ambiguity and contradiction are eliminated by severe constraints on the types of appropriate transformation rules. Symbols themselves must not dynamically change in meaning. Rule-based transformations must maintain value as the structure of an expression changes. Transformations can be combined into handy stable sequences called **lemmas**. Finally, no changes are permitted without an explicit rule in support.

The Axiomatic Principle
What is not explicitly allowed is forbidden.

All of these structural constraints were developed prior to the advent of silicon computation, so that people with pencil and paper might be able to understand and manipulate symbolic form. Mathematical proof used a **procedural model**. In the procedural model a proof consists of a series of steps determined by a human. Each step is constrained by a pattern transformation rule that specifies instructions to be followed. *Let, substitute, consider.* It was very common to appeal to a collection of steps taken by another person and validated by the community. These bundles of steps are **theorems**, and validated theorems constitute the assemblage of mathematical knowledge. The introduction of high level programming languages beginning in the 1950s was to change that. Rigor got too difficult for humans, rigor got out of hand.

The modern **declarative model** presumes an adequate computational engine that can implement a *search and simplify strategy*. We give the engine a representation of the problem and instruct it to seek an answer. In the declarative model, the engine not only provides the mechanism for mathematical transformations it also assures the integrity of the metamathematics, that is, *the rules of the substitution game*. The engine chooses and implements a set of techniques, often with guidance from the human user, to construct a sequence of transformations that constitutes **proof**. We take the rigor and correctness of the implementation for granted. In this century, wondering about the correctness of the engine is analogous to wondering about the correctness of hardware wires and transistors of last century. There is a well-known catch: often the engine produces a series of steps that are too long or too detailed for a human to follow.

In lieu of the algebraic properties of consistency and completeness, computation imposes constraints on the process of transformation. We will describe what it means to be a pattern, what it means to match a pattern, and what it means to change a form. In James algebra, *all forms are patterns*. Forms without variables are exact patterns, for example <[<( )>]>. Mathematically these forms are objects within the arithmetic of containment patterns. Forms with variables constitute the language of the algebra.

James algebra stays within the domain of containment relations. Even though a cat can fit into a box, a cat is not a form. Neither is a box, although both cat and box have an inside and an outside. The abstraction of boundary forms is that *only* inside and outside is relevant, that is all that's required by a contains relation. We do not need to associate the contents of each container with a set of objects. We do not need to associate pattern transformations with logical implication. And we do not need symbols that require interpretation to have meaning. Elementary arithmetic and algebra can be formulated as patterns of physical and manipulable containment structures.

Patterns

The capability to match symbolic structures is implicitly assumed in most mathematical systems, but it is far from trivial computationally. Substitution is usually hidden in the equal sign and in the cognitive deliberations of a supra-computational Agent that we might call the Mathematician. From the algorithmic perspective, however, we must specify precisely what a pattern-matching engine should and can do. We can readily pass off the task of finding equal forms (i.e. using the equal sign) to the computer. Computers look for equivalent data structures in different parts of memory. **Structure sharing** is compiling identical structures into the same memory location. With a declarative programming language, the computer will take care of all the work to find patterns and to apply substitutions, but we do need to provide guidance about the context of symbolic substitutions for cases in which

- a specific transformation matches more than once
- the same transformation matches different parts of the same form
- different transformations match parts of the same form
- the result of a transformation again matches an available transformation
- a transformation might be beneficially applied in two different directions.

Just like conventional algebra has developed around the manipulation of strings of characters, computational pattern matching has been developed around strings of binary digits. Both imitate written, or at least typed, language for which words are patterns of typographic characters. The word house, for instance, is a pattern consisting of five characters. Were we to google house, the search engine would identify the five characters as a pattern, and then (via an index that maps words to their respective webpages) return to us a listing of the URLs that contain the pattern house in text. The process is entirely syntactic, the search engine does not know what we might be looking for by typing house, whether it be a query about houses for sale, or activities at the White House, or a State House of Corrections, or the antihero of the television show House, or the electronic dance sounds of house music. That is why we need to type in other words to a search engine to differentiate all the variations of meaning associated with house.

If we were interested in words that rhyme with house, though, we would not succeed simply by typing ouse. That request would first take us to the River Ouse in England, or to the alternative spelling of ooze, or to all the people whose last name is Ouse. A pattern-matching engine however includes special typographic variables that match *any* character. Typing ?ouse, for example, would return us not only house, but also mouse and douse and louse, as well as possibly others. It would not return blouse or spouse or grouse since the pattern-matching symbol ? will match only one character. It is too inconvenient to have to type ??ouse, so pattern-matching engines include other special symbols that match one or more characters (but not blank spaces). For a pattern to return both house and spouse, we might type $ouse. We would not see sprouts or dowse or the mathematician Gauss because we have asked for an exact match of the letters ouse.

Mathematica

The programming language *Mathematica* includes three types of pattern variables (Figure 25-1). These variables match expressions rather than characters, appropriate for an algebraic engine. The underbar identifies a type of pattern while the preceding letters provide a name for the matched pattern. In James terms, Mathematica pattern-variables allow us to label a single form (one underbar), the contents of a container (two underbars), or

name_

the contents of a container as well as unit containers that have no contents (three underbars). Pattern-variables can be embedded within larger expressions as constraints. A specific label or containment structure returns only those expressions that match the label or structure within the specified context. For example, should we wish to identify opportunities to clarify a single form, we could enter

$$([A\_])$$

The label A will store a single form without the explicit inversion boundaries. Alternatively to identify the other string-based form of clarify, we would need a different explicit pattern.

$$[(A\_)]$$

Should we wish to identify applications of Void Inversion only, we would specify[3]

$$([\ ])$$

If we wanted to assemble one or more forms within an inversion boundary but exclude Void Inversion we would employ the double underbar

$$([A\_\_])$$

And if we wanted possible applications of clarify regardless of contents, we would specify

$$([A\_\_\_])$$

Similarly all candidate patterns that support the collect transformation match the pattern

$$(A\_\_ [B\_\_]) (A\_\_ [C\_\_])$$

Here the explicit brackets are constants within the pattern, they define the constraints imposed by boundaries.

To implement a transformation, Mathematica provides several different versions of replacement, also shown in Figure 25-1. We can specify the collect transformation as

collect   *form* /. (A__ [B__]) (A__ [C__]) $\Rightarrow$ (A [B C])

pattern variable	*binds to*
name_	one form
name__	one or more forms
name___	zero, one or more forms

replacement instruction	*effect*
form /. rule	apply a specific rule to a form
form /. rules	apply a set of rules once to all subparts of a form
form //. rules	apply a set of rules repeatedly to all subparts of a form

Figure 25-1: *Mathematica pattern variables and replacement strategies*

The ReplaceAll operator, /., takes care of all the details about finding appropriate replacements within a given form, determining the order of replacement and optimizing the replacement steps and strategy. The *continued* ReplaceAll operator, //., keeps on applying transformations to results until no changes occur.

There are several subtleties to pattern specification. For instance the collect pattern above identifies inversion frames two at a time rather than all at once. To collect four frames, the collect transform would run three times.

```
(A [B]) (A [C]) (A [D]) (A [E])
(A [B C]) (A [D]) (A [E])              collect
(A [B C D]) (A [E])                    collect
(A [B C D E])                          collect
```

However, this is a matter of efficiency rather than computability, a dimension of computation that is the speciality of a mathematical branch of computer science called **automata theory**. Pattern-matching identifies candidates for transformation, while automata show us how to implement a collection of pattern rules such as the James axioms.[4]

It is difficult to apply the results of computational complexity theory and automata theory to James forms
because classical computational theory, like other formal
systems in mathematics, is string-based. The theoretical
efficiency and the low-level implementation efficiency of
James algebra provides fundamental guidance for the
design of the structure of its axioms.[5]

We must also distinguish between the different uses of
identifiers that stand in place of configurations of containers. The letter A might stand in place of a particular
form, say <[<( )>]>, in which case A is a label. We would
say that A is *bound* to <[<( )>]>. Unbound variables are
usually considered to be **universally quantified**, which
means that they stand in place of *any* form. Logical quantification becomes confounded with existence within an
active database. That's one of the reasons it is necessary
to make sure that a form is clearly defined to be a single
bounded object. The other important but hopefully obvious point by now is that *void* is not a form. Void-equivalent
forms are deleted.

a form

(A B C)

not a form

A B C

Another technicality is that a variable may be free to
stand in place of a diversity of structural objects other
than forms. For example the *free variable* A might stand
in place of a number or a picture of a cat or a collection
of similar patterns. This is usually handled by separating the formal language from the interpretation or by
extending the formal language to include numbers and
pictures of cats. An *abstract algebra* permits arbitrary
domains, but axiom systems are usually designed for
specific domains such as logic or numbers.

Concreteness

The existent database defines the universe of discourse
and therefore takes the place of the predicate calculus concept of logical quantification. The fundamental
change of perspective brought on by powerful declarative

computation (which is now acquiring the name AI) is that the database is not a listing of instances, it is a collection of the currently computed instances together with the transformation rules that permit all expressions within the domain of discourse to be generated. An unbound label refers to any and all expressions without invoking quantification. Rather, the computational context defines and permits valid expressions to be brought into existence within a **knowledge base**.

One fundamental idea of representation is that properties that apply to all components of an expression or form can be *lifted* to become properties of the entire configuration. Since the property of existence is global, for example, it does not need to be a property attributed to variables or to assertions. In fact, global properties can be lifted out of James algebra entirely and placed in the interpretation.

No James forms are numbers. All James patterns and transformation rules refer to configurations of containment. It is the physical and representational configurations of containers that can be read as numeric objects and operations. This is a subtle point. ooooo is not 5, it is precisely those empty containers sharing the same implicit outer container. "5" is the name of the cardinality of the units in the container. Thus ooooo is not constrained to behave as if it were 5. The *mapping* of forms to numerics assure that form transformation maintains connection to numeric computation. To make the contrast clear, [ ][ ][ ][ ][ ] is also not 5, nor does it map to the concept 5 under our interpretation. In the domain of the Unify axiom, 5 = 1.

( )( )( ) ☞ 3

[ ][ ][ ] ☞ 1

25.2 Pattern Substitution

Substitution includes several structural identities that define its behavior in any algebra. Figure 25-2 shows these structural and value-preserving symmetries, as discussed in Chapter 2. Transformations are applied by matching the structure on one side of a rule, and then substituting the other side. When labels align, a symbolic transformation is valid. When patterns align, an iconic transformation is valid. When variables are present, patterns are **unified**, a pattern-matching generalization of direct substitution described in the next section.

Here, the substitute operation is represented by double-struck tortoise shell brackets.

$$(\!(\text{PUT FOR INTO})\!) \quad ☞ \quad \textit{substitute } \text{PUT } \textit{for } \text{FOR } \textit{in } \text{INTO}$$

— The INTO-form is the structure that is being changed by the substitution.

— The PUT-form is the structure that is being substituted into the INTO-form, in the process changing the structure of the INTO-form.

— The FOR-form is the substructure within the INTO-form being replaced by the PUT-form.

The rules of substitution maintain the equivalence classes of forms. The behavior of substitution is often bundled with the definition of equality as "substitute equals for equals". This however is only one of the invariants of substitution, the one that maintains value but not structure. In Figure 25-2 the four categories of substitution provide different types of filters on transformation processes.

— *Structural invariance* rules maintain identity.

— *Replacement* suppresses contradiction.

— *Substitution equality* suppresses transformation error.

— *Void-substitution* manages database integrity.

Substitution is a logical rule of inference. This rule can be formatted as distribution of substitution over equality; it is labeled **into-equality** in Figure 25-2.

into-equality $\qquad (\!(\text{A C E=F})\!) \Leftrightarrow (\!(\text{A C E})\!) = (\!(\text{A C F})\!)$

Substitution maintains both equality and inequality. Whether a substitution is valid or not is determined by transformation axioms that allow that particular

STRUCTURAL INVARIANCE

⟦A E E⟧ = A	**global substitution**
⟦A A E⟧ = E	**self substitution**

REPLACEMENT

⟦A C E⟧ = E	*given* A = C	**value maintenance**

SUBSTITUTION EQUALITY

⟦A C E⟧ = ⟦B C E⟧	*given* A = B	**put-equality**
⟦A C E⟧ = ⟦A D E⟧	*given* C = D	**for-equality**
⟦A C E⟧ = ⟦A C F⟧	*given* E = F	**into-equality**

VOID-SUBSTITUTION

⟦*void* C E⟧ ⇒ *delete* C *from* E		**delete**
⟦A *void* E⟧ ⇒ *construct* A *within* E		**construct**

Figure 25-2: *Substitution*

substitution. Equality not only has relational properties, when it is used within predicate logic it comes also with its own rules of inference. The relational properties of equality (reflexive, symmetric, transitive) belong to the algebraic way of thinking, while the substitution properties trace their roots to the computational way of thinking. In a substitution-based approach that does not include logical operators such as AND, OR, NOT and quantification[6], it is more appropriate to consider substitution as a systemic technique rather than as a *logical* inference rule.

One common type of substitution is called **replacement**. The rule of replacement maintains equality when any pattern within a form is replaced by another pattern so long as the two patterns are equal.

replacement

If A = C *then*
substitute A *for* C *in* E = E

For example, let's take the two equal patterns defined by Arrangement, labeled A and C, and an example form E:

A = C

A = (D [G H])　　　　　C = (D [G])(D [H])
E = (A [M])

We can create a valid equality by replacing every occurrence of A within E by C.

E = (A [M]) = (C [M])

Specifically

substitute

((D [G H])[M]) = ((D [G])(D [H])[M])

Replacement is very common in pattern matching. We have a subform within E that matches the pattern on one side of a permitted transformation, and we replace that subform by the other side of the transformation pattern. This process is commonly called **match-and-substitute** (although it is replacement that is occurring). Since capital letters stand in place of arbitrary structure within a pattern, match-and-substitute can implement any unambiguous formal transformation.

Computer scientist Joseph Goguen strongly connects the process of substitution to modern *category theory*. The axioms that define substitution in Figure 25-2 "define neither more nor less than **categories**....In particular we will say 'morphism', 'map' or 'arrow' instead of 'substitution'".[7]

Unification

Computation addresses equations that have symbolic, but not necessarily numeric, structure. In computer science, **unification** is a fundamental algorithm for logical reasoning and for symbolic pattern-matching. Unification is *constraint-based reasoning*. Two different expressions containing variables can be made equal by finding an appropriate substitution for the variables that results in equal expressions. For example, the simple linear equation

$$2n + 5 = n + 6$$

can be solved conventionally by algebraic manipulation of the equation to isolate the variable n, arriving at n = 1. The equation can also be solved by finding a **unifier** *that makes both sides equal*, in this case the substitution of 1 for n.

$$⟦1 \ n \ (2n + 5 = n + 6)⟧ \ \Rightarrow \ 2 + 5 = 1 + 6$$

Here is a James algebra example. We are seeking the structure of form A that will unify (i.e. make equal) both of the forms that incorporate it.

Find A *given*   [(A)(B)]   *and*   [([A] B)(o)]

A unifier for these forms is A = o. More precisely, substituting o for A in each form makes them equal.

$$⟦o \quad A \quad [(A)(B)]⟧ = ⟦o \quad A \quad [([A] B)(o)]⟧$$

[(o)(B)] =	[([o] B)(o)]	replace
[(o)(B)] =	[(B)(o)]	clarify

Incidentally, in this example, the form of B is irrelevant, A = o unifies for all structures that B might represent. Since B is arbitrary, the most succinct way to unify the two forms is to use B as a void-equivalent unifier, B = *void*:

Find A *when* B = *void*, *given:*
        [(A)(B)]   *and*   [([A] B)(o)]

	[(A) o] = [([A])(o)]	B = *void*
	[(A) o] = [A (o)]	clarify
Let A = o	[(o) o] = [o (o)]	replace

In this case it is difficult to solve for A using algebraic techniques. For example, with Equality Reflection from Chapter 18, we can get the replicas of A on one side of the equation, but then they are difficult to combine.

[(A) o] = [A (o)]		
(A) o = A (o)		cover
(A)<A> = <o> (o)		move

For comparison, here is the above unification example transcribed to numeric algebra.

Solve for A: $\log_\# (\#^A + \#^B) = \log_\# (\#^{\log_\# A + B} + \#)$

$$\#^A + \#^B = A\#^B + \#$$

In these types of exponential equations, it is conventional to assign the constant e to the arbitrary base #.

$$e^A + e^B = Ae^B + e$$
$$A = 1$$

Unification maintains all possible options for solution by mapping variables to other similarly constrained variables. The unification process does not assume an interpretation, numeric or otherwise. It is a purely structural technique based solely on substitution.

Boundary Subtleties

Boundary representation incorporates some implicit conventions that must be made explicit to a computational pattern-matcher. The symbolic description of a pattern-based transformation rule needs to identify four different types of structure.

RULE

$3 + 4 \Rightarrow 7$

explicit

$3 + 4$

contextual

$+ 3 + 4$

incidental

$2 + 3 + 4$

forbidden

$2 \times 3 + 4$

— *explicit*: necessary structure that must be present

— *contextual*: structure that is contextually necessary but not changed

— *incidental*: structure that is incidental to the transformation and not changed

— *forbidden*: structure that when present blocks a transformation.

Explicit structure is explicitly present in a rule. Contextual structure is present in a rule but passes through a transformation unchanged. Incidental structure is not present in a rule and is passed through a transformation unchanged. Forbidden structure is present in a rule and causes a rule application to fail when it is found in the form being transformed.

Applications of Arrangement, for example, are independent of other forms within the context. This feature is a
direct consequence of the independence of contents. To
express this feature to a symbolic pattern-matcher, we
would need a generic pattern variable X___ to stand in
place of any and all incidental structure that is irrelevant
to the identification of patterns within rules. The triple
underbar is an instruction to apply the label X to this
superfluous structure, which may consist of zero, one
or many independent forms. They will be temporarily
stored under the nominated label A without change. Thus
Arrangement would be expressed as

$$X_{---} (A_{--} [B_{--} C_{--}]) \Rightarrow X (A [B]) (A [C])$$

Note that the double underbar specifies that *at least
one* form in the place of A, B, and C must be present. If
there are no forms in the location of A, the Arrangement
rule will not trigger but Inversion will. If either B or
C are not present then there is no available application
of Arrangement, and if both B and C are not present,
then Dominion will trigger. Even this specification has
some subtleties. The variable B cannot bind to all of the
forms within the square-bracket since that would leave
no available forms to bind with C. Built into the pattern
matching algorithm are many structural judgments that
a human might take for granted.

inversion
([B C])
dominion
(A [ ])
stable frame
(A [B])
arrangement
(A [B C])

One final notational elaboration is that transformations
are insensitive to depth of nesting. We can apply the same
transformation mechanism to every container regardless
of depth of nesting. That is, every container is a locally
outermost container. Again this is a direct consequence
of the independence of contents.

25.3 Rewriting

Applying a sequence of substitutions in order to reduce or
transform an expression is called **rewriting**. When rewriting is applied to strings of symbols it is appropriately

called **string rewriting**. Container configurations are *graphs*, so James algebra uses **graph rewriting**. There are many strategies for rewriting and some potential difficulties. The primary motivation though is quite different than solving mathematical equations, because computer science is interested in the *efficiency* of sequences of substitutions while mathematics is interested in the *possibility* of transforming one expression into another. The axioms of the James system are still subject to the concerns of logic (consistency, completeness, etc.) and the concerns of algebra (equivalence classes, mappings, etc.), but we are adding new concerns that address the **processes of transformation** by substitution.

A primary concern is whether or not there are unique stable forms. Do the James axioms provide sufficient power and clarity to take any form and reduce it to a consistent simple form? If this is the case, we would say that there is a **normal form** for equivalence classes within the James algebra. Normal forms allow us to apply reduction rules in a quite straight forward manner. Unfortunately, the normal form of a given expression might increase the size of the expression exponentially. When a reduction to normal form exponentially increases the replicas of variables within an expression, the process is non-polynomial (NP). The gain of normalcy is lost in the clumsiness of the normal form. Normal forms are great for proving properties of a transformation system, but they are not necessarily a benefit for finding efficient transformation sequences.

If reducing *every* arbitrary form within an axiomatic system is easy, then the system is trivial. Useful systems *must* include difficult reductions. Descriptively powerful transformation processes are necessarily complex. The complexity associated with Arrangement is that the most effective direction of application is unclear. There is not a consistently preferred direction that leads to a minimal form, rather direction of application depends upon context. Arrangement is the only James axiom that entails

```
                    ([o][<o>]) ([o][<oo>])

  ([o][<o><oo>])   collect        <([o][o])><([o][oo])>   promote
  ([o][<o  oo>])   join           <([o][o])  ([o][oo])>   join
  <([o][ o   oo ])>  promote      <([o][o oo])         >   collect
```

Figure 25-3: *Convergence of boundary transformations*

complexity, a feature that leads to very efficient transformation sequences. But having three different types of
boundaries potentially increases the risk of undesirable
features such as the lack of a unique normal form. There
is even the risk of contradictory results.[8] For the James
algebra, we will come across a quite interesting complexity: the system itself is very well behaved, but the
interpretation can step outside of the domain of numbers,
as is the case of zero and infinity.

Confluence

A rewrite system that fails to converge on a signle form
exhibits **lack of confluence**. There is a potential issue
when two different transformations can be applied to the
same form. Each will create a different transformed form,
and the question is whether or not those varieties will
eventually converge to the same resultant form. In the
example in Figure 25-3 two different transformations are
immediately available, collect and promote. Taking each
path results in two structurally different forms. However,
by continuing to apply available transformations, the two
different forms converge to become the same form. The
original form is confluent; the form has the *Church-Rosser
property*. In a **confluent system**, every form and every
selection of transformation paths results in the same terminal form. Confluence implies that there is a **unique
normal form** to which transformations converge.

*Alonzo Church
1903–1995*

$$(a \times -b) + (a \times -c)$$

$a \times (-b + -c)$	collect	$-(a \times b) + -(a \times c)$	promote
$a \times (-(b + c))$	join	$-((a \times b) + (a \times c))$	join
$-(a \times (b + c))$	promote	$-(a \times (b + c))$	collect

Figure 25-4: *Convergence of algebraic transformations*

The form in Figure 25-3 converges, but not to a minimal form. Confluence assures that the normal form can be found; it makes no assurance about how easy that may be. We applied collect in both of the reduction sequences in the figure but ignored a simpler path of immediately applying Indication.

$$([o][<o>]) \ ([o][<oo>])$$

unmark	<o>	<oo>
join	<o	oo>

Conventional arithmetic is confluent. The normal forms are the numbers, but the transformation paths to reach a single number can vary. Figure 25-4 shows a numeric example similar to that in Figure 25-3.

For James forms, any application of Inversion or Reflection is confluent because of void-equivalence. Since there is a map from James arithmetic to conventional arithmetic, and conventional arithmetic is confluent, so are the numeric forms within James arithmetic. However, the normal forms for an algebra that includes Distribution are not necessarily efficient, since Distribution can increase rather than decrease complexity. An example in James algebra

$$[([A][B]) \ ([B][C]) \ ([C][D])]$$

collect	$[([B][A \ C])([C][D])]$	$[([A][B])([C][B \ D])]$

[([A][[([Q][P R]) ([R][S])]]) ([[([P][Q]) ([R][Q S])]][C]) ([C][D])]

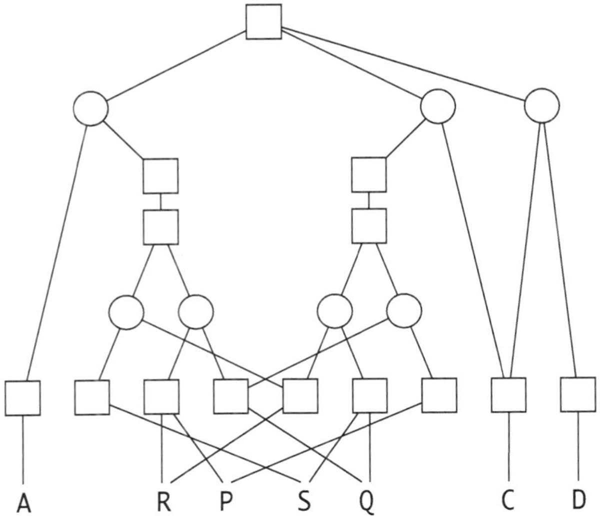

Figure 25-5: *A tangled arrangement structure*

Here there are two different paths for applying collect. Reducing in the direction of collect does not converge into a normal form. Applying in the direction of disperse does converge, however this direction increases the number of variable replicas. In the example, the dispersed form on top has six variable references, whereas both collected forms have five variable references. The difficulty is that each variable may itself be very complex, so multiple references can be costly to manage. It also does not suffice to keep track of variable labeling, because each variable (B for example) might itself have different structural varieties. For example consider these two equal but different varieties of B:

B = [([Q][P R])([R][S])] = [([P][Q])([R][Q S])]

If we substitute these two structural varieties of B into different locations of B within the above example, you can begin to see how tangled these arranged forms can get. Figure 25-5 shows the distinction network for this tangled

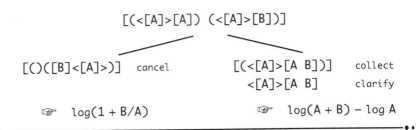

$$[(<[A]>[A]) (<[A]>[B])]$$

$[()([B]<[A]>)]$ cancel $[(<[A]>[A B])]$ collect
                                  $<[A]>[A B]$ clarify

☞ $\log(1 + B/A)$ ☞ $\log(A + B) - \log A$

Figure 25-6: *Divergence of James algebraic transformations*

Arrangement structure. The network itself transforms multiple textual references into visually tangled network connections.

There is another potential complexity: a reduction system may contain infinite reduction sequences. We have avoided this issue by requiring that the container language be physically constructible. A finite system that is confluent is called **convergent**.

Ambiguity

Rewrite ambiguity can occur when two or more rules can be applied to transform the same form. Figure 25-6 provides an example in which both cancel and collect can be applied, each resulting in an equivalent but structurally different algebraic expression. Fortunately, cancel is void-equivalent, so it's easier to see the advantages of the left path.

Whenever there is rewrite ambiguity, there is a potential for **computational intractability** (NP complexity). Intractability does not mean that a computation cannot be completed, it means that as a form grows in size, the time to find the best reduction path increases exponentially. Therefore it will be possible to increase, say, the depth of nesting in a form to a point where it would take longer than a person's lifetime (or indeed longer than the universe has existed) in order to find a reduction path. Any time a reduction provides a choice that is essentially a guess, that reduction is intractable. The choice of which forms to collect is an example of such a guess. As mentioned earlier, almost all significant computational problems are intractable.[9]

With the prevalence and indeed unavoidability of computational complexity, void-equivalent transformations are a blessing. Because of Arrangement, complexity is unavoidable, but because Arrangement is the only source of complexity, the number of necessary guesses during a reduction are small (relative to other systems). Both James and algebraic transformations are intractable, however the void-based approach of James forms provides a technically *simpler* way to do arithmetic and algebra than does the symbolic approach. And that suggests an educational question: why do we teach unnecessarily complex math to children?[10]

Finally, as was observed in Chapter 19, graph rewriting can occur in parallel. Each node (each boundary) can identify local structure that permits local application of reduction rules. The parallelism is *strong*, which means that global organization and coordination are not necessary. Usually though, some type of global strategy is needed to achieve minimal forms. Parallel graph reduction introduces plenty of technical implementation details, not the least of which is that true fine-grain parallelism requires a processing unit for each boundary.[11]

25.4 Implementation

A goal for implementing James algebra is to be able to verify all transformations within these volumes. There is *no computer code included here* cause of the absurd detail that is necessary.[12] This section on the implementation of software algorithms is included for two reasons. It's a reminder of the tremendous effort it takes a student to read, understand and compute with string-based arithmetic and algebra. Recall that it takes a dozen or so years of training to learn symbol processing while each of us is young and cognitively malleable. The three Rs (readin', writin' and 'rithmetic) are poetically considered to be the subject matter of schooling, at the cost of learning that may come from our physically grounded bodies.

The second reason is to emphasize the antipodal differences between pure math and computational computer science. The two converge in the mathematical concept of *complete verification* that is needed to rigorously prove a theorem. This type of rigor is available only within a computational implementation. Yet the conceptualization and scope of pure mathematics is beyond description in terms of an effective computing procedure. It is this strange dialectic between machine and cognition that makes both fields most entertaining, and as well most frustrating due to the severe difficulty of understanding the technical challenges of both fields.

Software

An implementation of James algebra requires three distinct software components:

— *parsers* to change input strings into forms

— *transformation engines* that apply pattern-matching and substitution guided by axioms

— *control structure* to establish goals and manage transformation paths.

Each component is basically control logic and a pattern-matcher immaculately synchronized at both the hardware and the software levels. Some of the elementary pattern-matching tools and control structures provided by *Mathematica* are described in Section 25-1; Figure 25-7 shows the *Mathematica* patterns for the James axioms.[13]

Inversion

clarify1	F___ ([A___]) R___	⇒ F A R
clarify2	F___ [(A___)] R___	⇒ F A R
enfold1	A__ ⇒ ([A])	
enfold2	A__ ⇒ [(A)]	

Reflection

cancel	F___ A__ M___ <A__> R___	⇒ F M R
create	F___	⇒ F A <A>

Arrangement

collect	F___ (A__ [B__]) M___ (A__ [C__]) R___
	⇒ F (A [B C]) M R
disperse	F___ (A__ [B_ C__]) R___ ⇒ F (A [B]) (A [C]) R

Figure 25-7: *Mathematica transformation rules for James algebra*

Here is the challenge of implementation. Imagine having to stoop to the lowest levels of communication, below meaning and intention, below sequence and grouping, down to *individual characters* that can be typed. Each character has an 8-bit binary name. Massive strings of binary digits, that's the currency of the machine level and that's what drives coders to look for others who have already taken care of some of the intimate details. Decades ago computer pioneers who had some idea of what a person might want a machine wrote **compilers**, code that translates across languages, from machines to characters to instructions to programming languages to high-level languages. For many of the new methods of computation and verification embodied in James algebra, however, most of the underlying mechanism must be built from scratch. A significant difficulty with the implementation of iconic and void-based algorithms is that existing computer languages are poorly suited for creation/deletion actions. Almost every computer language is string-based, so we must deal also with each of the *notational accidents* mentioned throughout these volumes. It is here that *Mathematica* is extremely flexible, but still not iconic.

The job of the input parser is to convert string language into the data structures enlisted to represent James forms. We can label the character [by its shape "[".
The visual appearance connects us to its binary appearance 01011011 that is recognized by the machine.[14] In reading an input string with delimiters, we'll need to find the matching], identified not only as "]" but also as the next set of eight bits that matches the] pattern. This inspires the parser strategy of looking until we *first* find an ending bracket such as "]" and then backing up to find the first matching opening bracket. The string accumulated by backing up now needs to be labeled and the label inserted in place of the bracketed form. This label locates the contents of the James bracket. When that is done for all brackets and for all grounds, we have essentially a distinction tree that can be sewn together bottom up by matching leaves and then shared structure to get a **distinction network** (dnet).

01000101 ☞ A
11101101 ☞]

The goal of expressing forms as dnets is so that we can suppress the native string language of the typewriter and think in terms of the native language of James forms. To be clear, James forms are not in the memory of the computer; what is there is determined by the architecture of the hardware, its association with the machine-level input language (i.e. just what does 01011011 signal?) and with the software compiler that is negotiating between the two.

Abstract Data Structures

Next we will need the control structure to apply the axioms, with an added complexity that the tools for transforming James forms also need to be built out of the native tools of the general purpose supporting computer language. The **abstract data structure** is code that manages the James language on top of a conventional programming language, in effect screening the concepts of boundary math from the vulgarities of lower-level computer languages closer to machine language. *Mathematica* is a wonderfully supportive language, but its native mode is, you may have guessed it, string processing.

We'll need explicit transactional policies about the outermost container. How to handle *void* presents significant challenges. *Void* is *everywhere* throughout a form, it is the background substrate of all existent forms. *Void* cannot be represented explicitly, but it still must have a transactional presence whenever void-substitution is applied and whenever an illusory void-equivalent form is encountered or constructed. This issue, like *void* itself, is manifest throughout every proof sequence.

And how should parallelism be handled if we are using a conventional sequential machine and operating system? Many folks for example, when writing about Spencer Brown's void-based logic say that commutativity is "implicit". For them it is a rule, one that Spencer Brown did not feel motivated to write down. Rearrangement of sequences of characters however is an artifact of the implementation level, not of the James abstract data structure. A fundamental axiomatic policy (If it is not explicitly allowed, it is forbidden) does not permit the addition of "implicit" structure. The James native language is a distinction network, not a string of textual delimiters. Dnets are described in Chapter 29.

Matching Explicitly

If we are to use the *Mathematica* string-based pattern matcher, it will not only need to know the *essential* pattern of a transformation, it will also have to be informed about the *contextual* forms needed for the transformation, the *incidental* forms that do not interact with the transformation, and the *forbidden* forms that will block a transformation. So instead of implementing Reflection as

cancel   A_ <A_>   ⇒   *void*

where A_ stands in place of one form, we need to say

mathematica cancel   F___ A__ M___ <A__> R___   ⇒   F M R

where F, M, and R identify any incidental strings in the same context as A and <A>. We need three (F, M, R) rather than one to tell a sequential string pattern-matcher that the intervening incidental structure can be anywhere. We need to allow A (and F and M and R) to consist of more than one form, thus A__ rather than A_. We need to allow for the possibility of no intervening forms, thus three underbars for the pattern-variables that collect the non-participants. We need to apply Reflection to the *nested contents* of each container both outside of the current form being processed and inside the forms being bypassed as incidental to the current form. We need to keep on applying Reflection to the result until it no longer applies. This then leads to several implementation strategies that preprocess forms to give the pattern-matcher an easier task. Ignoring the incidental structure and presuming that the pattern-matcher will continue to look for a pattern until instances no longer remain, we still have several choices for Reflection. For example this preprocessing pattern will make the contents of each angle bracket singular.

split   <A_ B__>   ⇒   <A><B>

Another computational improvement is to arrange forms in order of depth of nesting to assure that outside candidates for matching are found before inside ones, that is:

reorder   <A__> A__   ⇒   A <A>

The important observation is that the arrangement of forms for processing is *independent* of the rules of James algebra.

Compiled Forms

Parsing applies primarily to algebraic transformation and not to storage and computation of arithmetic facts. Parsing might also introduce more efficient encoding for accumulating numbers such as depth-value rather than tally marks. Once raw numbers are translated into digital base-10 numbers, computation is easy cause there's a calculator built into the hardware circuitry controlled by assembly-level code. So all numeric arithmetic can be reduced or removed first.

All the syntactic grounds will need to be listed. These are the leaves of a graph representation. They include two character sequences such as "[]" which will trigger Dominion, "<>" which is deleted, and "()" which is turned into 1 (as is o). And we'll need an index of all the specific names whether they be A or result387B. We may as well find the character pairs ([, [(, <<,]),)] and >>, and delete them too, in pairs, as soon as they are matched, in effect precompiling Inversion and Involution.

There are equally specific and ugly details about specifying and locating patterns that match Arrangement and an early decision whether or not to standardize with collect or with disperse.

Bridging Equality

Within a void-based strategy, the bridge transformation is applied whenever an equal sign is encountered, so that the goal of each void-based form is for it to be *deleted completely* when the equality is TRUE. During a void-based reduction, the sequence of transformations needs choreography, not for efficiency but to avoid *cul de sacs*. For example, here's the void-based proof of the Promotion theorem that verifies a suspected equality.

A = B ☞
A <B> = *void*

	(A [<B>]) = <(A [B])>
bridge	(A [<B>]) <<(A [B])>>
unwrap	(A [<B>]) (A [B])
collect	(A [<B> B])
cancel	(A [ ])
absorb	*void*

In this example, frames need to be collected prior to deletion via Reflection. The choice of collect rather than disperse is not difficult since only Reflection and Dominion are available to achieve deletion to *void*. The void-based methodology is very supportive of convergence. The challenge is in *construction* from *void*, since the diversity of choices makes blind search extremely difficult. Guidance about which forms to create is fortunately provided by existent forms within a context. It is never necessary to create a form that does not somehow interact with existent forms.

Discovery

How might we proceed to discover the Promotion Theorem given only one-half of an equality, say (A [<B>]) above? We need an *algorithm*, not an insightful discovery. We need to create a void-equivalent structure: if a variable is to be included only Reflection is available. For example, an algorithm might explore the four different contexts marked by the subscripted at-signs in the following form.

construction locations
$$(A \quad [\quad < \quad B> \quad])$$
$$@_1 \quad (A \ @_2 \ [@_3 \ <@_4 \ B> \ ])$$

Location $@_1$ is relevant only if we intend to apply Arrangement, so it supports a frame as a natural candidate. Dominion provides a frame for any *void-equivalent* form. Here $@_5 = void$.

emit
$$(A \ [\ @_5 \ ]) \ (A \ [<B>])$$

This form must interact with <B> to be useful. We might consider creating B <B>.

$$\text{(A [B <B>]) (A [<B>])} \qquad \text{try create}$$

Disperse has no direct effect so this line of reasoning does not look productive. There is another way to generate void-equivalent frames, this time directly by Reflection.

$$Let\ @_1 = \text{(A [}@_5\text{])<(A [}@_5\text{])>}$$
$$\text{(A [}@_5\text{]) <(A [}@_5\text{])> (A [<B>])} \qquad \text{try create}$$

To be useful for a pattern-match, the reflected form must have A as the frame type and must include B within the frame contents. <B> is undesirable since it would accumulate so we might try B as the frame content.

$$Let\ @_5 = \text{B}$$
$$\text{(A [B]) <(A [B])> (A [<B>])} \qquad \text{try create}$$

All of the action will be in the choice of Arrangement, however here there is only one choice to collect.

$$\text{(A [B <B>]) <(A [B])>} \qquad \text{collect}$$

Now B <B> cancels and Dominion absorbs, leaving

$$\text{(A [   ]) <(A [B])>} \qquad \text{cancel}$$
$$\text{<(A [B])>} \qquad \text{absorb}$$

This sequence of algorithmic reasoning has demonstrated the Promotion theorem by discovery.

$$\text{(A [<B>])} \quad \Rightarrow \quad \text{<(A [B])>} \qquad \text{promote}$$

We have not explored the other three locations for creation of void-equivalent forms. None permit Arrangement, so we know that none are relevant.

For a more extensive demonstration, look at the derivation of the quadratic formula in Chapter 18. It too requires only one application of create. That demonstration illustrates another unsurprising technique, the ability to *label* subforms in order to focus algorithmic exploration.

Control

The central design challenge is a control structure which must choose to apply transformations in one of two directions. It is easier to let the control structure access a small number of transformation patterns than it is to incorporate theorems into the tool set. The proofs within these volumes have illustrated that it is rarely necessary to apply Inversion in the constructive direction. That usually happens only when we are aligning the James form with a standard interpretation. The application of Inversion, Dominion and Reflection in the deletion direction are obvious choices. The constructive application of Reflection is a powerful technique almost always guided by existent subforms within the problem, while Dominion permits the introduction of any arbitrary form. That leaves only Arrangement as a challenge to the control structure.

reflection
$void = A <A>$

dominion
$void = (A [ ])$

involution
$A = ([A])$

The design of control code to *explore* possible theorems and transformations is more complex that code to *verify* the existence of valid transformation paths, primarily because exploration requires an evaluation criterion that determines whether or not a step is worth taking. This approach is rather like a chess playing program which must choose one move out of several and does not see the end-game. The judgment can always be tentative, as a *what-if* exploration, which leads us only into efficiency questions.

One dominant feature of code specification is that standard mathematical notation is predominantly a record-keeping device. All the decisions are left to the human Agent who is creating the records. Thus programmed control structure is usually quite elaborate since it needs to take the place of all of the discretionary choices of the Agent. This is one reason why the computational perspective is so important, it is intolerant of human error and misjudgment. And incidentally this is the same reason that a mathematical system benefits for being simple and intuitive.

25.5 Remarks

We have traced the development of formal systems from Hilbert's seminal insights to the growth of modern computational proof. Like any comparison across diverse academic disciplines, there are vast conceptual differences between the practice of pure mathematics, of logic and of computation. However in this century they have become thoroughly interwoven. Silicon computation does not recognize academic silos, nor is it committed to respect human compartmentalization or human achievement.

Perhaps just as profoundly, modern computation does not necessarily distinguish differences in media. Text, photos, video and sound each appeal to different human sensory systems. However, digital convergence converts all media to strings of binary signals, with the capability of processing billions of bits concurrently within silicon circuitry and cycling billions of times per second sequentially. Electronic technology is rapidly moving outside of human comprehension in many forms of human endeavor.

Computational theorem proving and artificial intelligence both rely extensively upon pattern-matching, substitution and unification. The challenge is to *locate* patterns, so **guided search** is a primary contributor to computational complexity. The extreme of search strategies is currently being implemented in deep learning AI systems, which break up data structures across literally thousands of subprocessors that reinforce and inhibit one another while finding patterns that match those of a learning set of examples. The result of this type of process is classification schemes that *do not match* human categorical or abstract thinking yet still achieve desired goals such as prediction, visual identification, strategic planning, and extra-human performance.

With an overview of the history of and issues around the definition of number in hand, we can next step into criticism, in particular, why reduce logic and sets and functions to pattern? Pattern-matching as the foundation of mathematics, at least of mathematical computation, provides access to higher dimensions of form, finite concreteness of meaning and powerful new techniques that capitalize upon treating nothing as if it does not exist.

Algorithmic thinking at first appears to be distant from the processes of mathematical discovery. However computation has only made apparent a level of complexity within symbol processing that has always been implicit in mathematical notation. Human cognition brings great skill to pattern-matching but that skill does not necessarily meet the inhuman standards of rigorous mathematical proof. We have been ignoring the details because they are far beyond our capabilities. In this digital age AI engines are excellent at identifying patterns, whether they are symbolic or iconic or spatial. But there is a different catch. The conceptual language that AI systems use to organize the patterns they find are *unintelligible to humans*. We gain power over detail only by giving up our ability to explain AI decisions. This situation is not unlike an attempt to explain the structure of dreams.

Endnotes

1. **opening quote:** from a children's poem by American poet Carl Sandburg *"Arithmetic"*. C. Sandburg (1993) *Arithmetic*.

2. **we would need a different explicit pattern:** From the perspective of a symbolic string representation, ([A]) and [(A)] are two distinctly different patterns. It takes an iconic approach to appreciate that they are the same pattern viewed from different perspectives.

3. **identify applications of Void Inversion only, we would specify:** There is little to no motivation to label a void-equivalent form. Instead the form is deleted since it can be reconstructed whenever it may be needed.

4. **implement a collection of pattern rules such as the James axioms:** Silicon implementation is improved by the use of huge numbers of very efficient, atomic steps. It is often advisable *not* to include lemmas. Brute force is usually a better silicon reduction strategy than is the subtlety provided by many shortcut theorems. It is better, for instance, to collect frames two at a time and to do so repeatedly than to craft a specialized pattern that would discern the number of matched forms to be collected.

W. Bricken (2008) Simplicity rather than knowledge *AI Magazine* **29**(2) p.41.

5. **fundamental guidance for the design of the structure of its axiom:** I believe that boundary math does not impact the fundamental theorems of complexity theory, however it does change the asymptotic efficiencies.

6. **logical operators such as** AND, OR, NOT **and quantification:** Primitive recursive arithmetic, described in Chapter 23, is an example of a system that uses substitution but not logic.

7. **we will say 'morphism', 'map' or 'arrow' instead of 'substitution':** J. Goguen (1988) What is unification? (Emphasis in the original.) Online 8/18 at http://citeseerx.ist.psu.edu/viewdoc/summary?doi=10.1.1.16.9221

8. **There is even the risk of contradictory results:** The computational language in this section is largely a rewording of the constraints on *logic* systems. Normal forms are canonical forms. Unique forms are non-contradictory. Stable forms are consistent.

9. **almost all significant computational problems are intractable:** Because of intractability, computer scientists have invested tremendous effort both studying the nature of computational complexity and learning how to effectively solve easy toy problems.

10. **why do we teach unnecessarily complex math to children:** Yes, I know it is because of our cultural heritage, and yes, I'm in no way suggesting that we should abandon conventional arithmetic.

11. **true fine-grain parallelism requires a processing unit for each boundary:** R. Plasmeijer & M. van Eekelen (1993) *Functional Programming and Parallel Graph Rewriting* Ch.14.

12. **cause of the absurd detail that is necessary:** As an example, there is an ancient language for specifying string patterns to be extracted from longer string patterns, called a **regular expression**. *Ancient* cause it was developed by Kleene in the early 1950s. There was a dark ages of computing when people had to talk the language of the machine. Regular expressions served that purpose in the early seventies, before the idea of a person actually owning a computer existed. Back then there were experts who developed arcane dialects and many of those dialects are still with us today. A premiere example is the URL (Uniform Resource Locator), which tells machines where to find other machines. No human should ever see a URL.

Even sophisticated software tools like *Mathematica* still read regular expressions. One reason is that the task of specifying arbitrary string patterns is itself quite complex. So as an example here is a regular expression specification that extracts top-level curly-brace forms from a string description not unlike those used in this volume.

```
\{(?:(?:\{(?:(?:\{(?:[^{}])*\})|(?:[^{}]))*\})|(?:[^{}]))*\}
```

13. **shows the Mathematica patterns for the James axioms:** These patterns lack the control structure that would determine when each transformation should be applied. Create is particularly sensitive to the application context.

14. **01011011 that is recognized by the machine:** The encoding standard is called ASCII, and the binary number is 91 in decimal. 91 is a unique but meaningless assignment, after 90 other typographic characters that are apparently more important got their number.

Chapter 26

Postsymbolism

All of life is imbued with nonsymbolic communication....
A book is a book as an object prior to being a book that
can be decoded as a bearer of symbols.[1]
— Jaron Lanier (1989)

Mathematics has *schools of thought*. The traditional
categories are **pure** mathematics and **applied**
mathematics.[2] I'm from a third school of thought, computer science. **Computation** is mathematics without
infinities, which excludes most of what a pure mathematician does. It is intensely practical, we are after all
trying to get machines to do interesting things. James
algebra is designed for a computer to implement.

Mathematical content and technique have changed so
rapidly over the last fifty years that the concerns and
contributions of Frege and Peano and Hilbert and Gödel
seem antiquated at best. We have not even considered
the revolution in contemporary mathematics initiated by
Grothendieck (and many others) that has fundamentally
changed what advanced math is. Nor have we integrated
the algorithmic work initiated by Turing (and many others). This chapter continues in a relatively narrow vein,
considering only one small addition to the structure of
mathematics, a change that is already fully underway

Alexander
Grothendieck
1928–2014
Fields Medal 1966

Alan Turing
1912–1954

during the first two decades of the twenty-first century. **Postsymbolic math** is mathematics that recognizes the formal structure of non-textual forms.

What cognitive limitations are imposed by the choice of a particular style of representation? What are the costs of attempting to separate the content of a communication from the method of its transmission? Does formulating our criteria for clarity, proof and efficiency in terms of linear strings of symbols limit our capabilities for understanding the concepts that these strings supposedly represent? Could it be that what we consider to be rational and logical thought is burdened by approaches to communication that are excessively narrow?

A theme is that the representation of formal thought is a design choice, one that strongly interacts with both content and cognition. Reading the book is not isomorphic to seeing the movie.[3] Symbolic techniques support an ancient Greek belief that formal thinking is entirely cognitive, that sensation has no place within the rigor of mathematics. Iconic techniques support a postsymbolic perspective that **cognition is embodied**, that rigor arises from its biological and physiological context. A screenplay is expanded into a movie by enriching its sensual elements: sound, light, action! In reducing a movie to its readable text, sensuality retreats into the imagination, an enrichment of a different kind but one that weakens rigor by removing the validation of experience.

26.1 Contemporary Mathematics

Contemporary mathematics is not only lacking a foundation, it is adverse to the simplicity imposed by a foundation of any type. Logic and algebra and geometry have been woven into a tapestry that provides a rich diversity while also providing exciting glimpses of a richer unity. The time honored metaphor of a plethora of balconies overlooking a central town square, providing a diversity of perspectives on a singular center, has been inverted. Mathematics is now a grand hotel with a plethora of balconies each looking out in a different direction. The hotel's core, the elevator shaft, provides a way to reach each of the rooms, but only as a method of traversal, not as an organizational principle. Abstract mathematics has transcended the *concept* of a foundation, rendering Russell's and Brouwer's and Hilbert's dreams as ancient history.

Fernando Zalamea, in his philosophical study of contemporary mathematics, summarizes recent growth as

> a complex dialectic that delineates both the movement of concepts/objects (the functorial transit between the algebraic, the geometric, and the topological) and the relative invariants of form (cohomologies). At stake is a profound mathematical richness — a richness that vanishes and *collapses* if one restricts oneself to thinking in terms of elementary mathematics.[4]

Logic, set theory, algebra and geometry are each in themselves idealizations that apply false partitions within advanced mathematics, and critically, they also do not provide a ground for understanding. Zalamea sees the bulk of modern philosophy in mathematics as rehashing centuries old debates that themselves have been replaced by radical innovation.

Shaking the Ground

We're not exploring in this chapter the specific axioms of James algebra so much as an iconic approach to understanding the classical mechanisms of mathematics. Two features enable boundary math to contribute to the vision of a new basis for math education:

— Iconic form is fundamentally different than symbolic expression since it accommodates our physical senses.

— The available mapping of James forms to conventional expressions provides a metamathematical bridge.

In this and the following two chapters we will focus upon the *comparative* characteristics of different foundational axiom systems. And it is here that boundary math may appear to be most outrageous, partly because it violates so many of the presumed and established rules of how mathematical representation works, partly because such violations may appear to be arrogant or disrespectful or incompetent, and partly because comparing a new and different experimental approach to a culturally established pillar of wisdom will necessarily appear to be comparing a trickle to a river. Boundary math lacks the depth and diversity of a field that has been evolving over millennia. It both borrows and mirrors, while at the same time being audacious enough to suggest that for elementary mathematics to be complete, computation and experience are equally as important as abstraction. And incidentally, if Zalamea and his contemporaries are correct, we are but dancing on graves of the already departed.

26.2 Postsymbolic Math

Iconic form is **postsymbolic**. It enlists images and experiences as glue to repair the disconnection of words and textual symbols. The container is perhaps the smallest step away from words to icons. Certainly, apart from *emoticons*, containers as textual delimiters are the only iconic forms available on a conventional typewriter. Typographic characters do not support a meaning of their own.[5] They are building blocks for words but do not individually contribute to the meaning of a word. Only the first few whole number digits have retained even a ghost of the image of their former selves. Parentheses in contrast overtly separate inside from outside both textually and visually.

The construction of mathematics (and our tacitly symbolic understanding of mathematics) from *strings of tokens* is somewhat a reaction to the separation of algebra from geometry in the nineteenth century. Math historian Israel Kleiner observes that "mathematics evolved for at least three millenia with hardly any symbols."[6] Iconic notation was widely used by Peirce, Frege, Venn and other founders of formal arithmetic at the turn of the twentieth century, but by the 1950s the currency of mathematical expression was typographic. I suspect the construction of the syntax/semantics barrier gave false security that all structural concepts could be stringified. The operation of juxtaposition (aka concatenation) created *de facto* sequences of symbols, while spatial ensembles were completely ignored. Here's Brian Rotman:

> Within the Platonist program, this alphabetic prejudice is given a literal manifestation: linear strings of symbols in the form of normalized sequences of variables and logical connectives drawn from a short, preset list determine the resting place for mathematical language in its purest, most rigorously grounded form.[7]

Origins

Euclid's *Elements* was the primary mathematics textbook throughout Western history until the mid-eighteenth century. Although Euclid introduced the axiomatic method, his content was geometric structure without the inclusion of number as measurement. Geometry yielded to algebra in the 1800s, and algebra to logic at the end of that century, although only for a few decades. The enthusiastic exploration of logic led not only to monumental symbolic efforts

Bertrand Russell
1872–1970

Alfred North
Whitehead
1861–1947

such as Whitehead and Russell's *Principia Mathematica*, but also to iconic techniques such as Venn's diagrams, Hasse's ordering diagrams, Frege's concept script and Peirce's existential graphs. The mutual heresy of these pioneers was to advocate concepts embedded in spatial arrangements rather than in strings of tokens. Ancient Greece scholar Reviel Netz observes:

> Mathematical diagrams may well have been the first diagrams. The diagram is not a representation of something else; it is the thing itself. It is not like a representation of a building, it is like a building, acted upon and constructed.[8]

Peirce

Charles S. Peirce
1839–1914

Charles Sanders Peirce is recognized as America's greatest philosopher, having made foundational contributions to formal logic, semiotics and the entire panoply of philosophy (ethics, ontology, metaphysics, …). Peirce makes the case that *spatial visualization is the native vocabulary of rational thinking*. To Peirce, formal structure was a geometric not a textual property. Geometric properties can be observed directly. Therefore, the process of thought is directly observable in the structure and transformation of iconic forms of logic. This structure is obscured by textual expressions, since text cannot directly represent some essential concepts of iconic logic. Worse, text obscures the process of rational thinking by hiding its spatial structure behind essentially arbitrary tokens. Here is Peirce's commentary on his pioneering development of iconic logic:

> I dwell on these details which from our ordinary point of view appear unspeakably trifling, — not to say idiotic, — because they go to show that this syntax is truly diagrammatic, that is to say that its parts are really related to one another in forms of relation analogous to those of the assertions they

represent, and that consequently in studying this syntax we may be assured that we are studying the real relations of the parts of the assertions and reasonings; which is by no means the case with the syntax of speech.[9]

The question is whether or not diagrams and images can convey the same formal information as strings. Venn developed his diagrams with set theory in mind; Peirce developed his existential graphs with logic in mind; Hasse developed his diagrams with partial orderings in mind. But with the development of metamathematics in the first half of the 20th century, these iconic techniques were ignored or rejected as insufficiently formal, which lead to a general disregard for the attempts by Venn, Peirce, Frege and others to incorporate the expressive power of spatial forms into formal mathematics. Peirce philosopher Randell Dipert observes:

John Venn
1834–1923

Helmut Hasse
1898–1973

> We should also give some hard thought to the difficult question of how much conceptual progress is made by symbolism and symbolic rigor alone.... The recent history of logic has appeared to value any, and sometimes quite shallow and unenlightening, symbolisms and axiomatizations and tended to dismiss any non-symbolic historical account (for example those of Aristotle or Ockham) as so much empty verbiage.[10]

Constructivism

Arend Heyting, student of the founder of the intuitionist school of logic L.E.J. Brouwer, contributed to turning constructivism into a formal system with rules slightly different than classical logic. Heyting's idea that all mathematical objects should be shown to exist, rather than just being inferred, essentially calls for algorithmic proof. Within *intuitionism* Truth gives away to Justification, allowing for context within logical expressions. In order

L.E.J. Brouwer
1881–1966

Arend Heyting
1898–1980

double negation

$\neg\neg A = A$

to reach toward a mathematics built upon what is obvious rather than obscure, **constructive logic** eliminates the Law of Double Negation, which is equivalent to eliminating one of Aristotle's grounding principles of logic, the Excluded Middle,

excluded middle

$$A \lor \neg A = \text{TRUE}$$

The *meaning* of an expression is no longer anchored to a truth-value, a first step toward iconic form in which meaning can be associated with physical circumstance. Heyting's perspective combines constructive existence with meaning accessible to intuition, leading the way for anchoring mathematics within diverse experience rather than within a binary evaluation. Heyting:

> *A mathematical construction ought to be*
> *so immediate to the mind and its result so clear*
> *that it needs no foundation whatsoever.*[11]

For some, mathematical thought has always been post-symbolic. Here's Einstein:

> Words and language, whether written or spoken, do not seem to play any part in my thought processes. The psychological entities that serve as building blocks for my thought are certain signs or images, more or less clear, that I can reproduce and recombine at will.[12]

Iconic Formality

Saunders Mac Lane
1909–2005

Kurt Reidemeister
1893–1971

Stephen Wolfram
1959–

Richard Feynman
1918–1988

Since the iconic approach incorporates types of structure that are simply not available within a string-based notation, spatial formalism is an asset rather than a liability. Today diagrammatic mathematics permeates modern formal systems. Premiere examples include Saunders Mac Lane's **category theory,** Reidemeister's **knot invariants,** Conway and Wolfram's **cellular automata**, and **Feynman diagrams**. The recent acceptance that human thought must have a physiological basis is essential to the recognition of iconic form as mathematical structure. Wittgenstein emphasizes the relation between thinking and language. Other modern theorists have integrated the Platonic realm with the physical body, particularly

— Stanislas Dehaene (neurological substrate of numbers)
— John Horton Conway and Richard Guy (mathematical games),
— Benoit Mandelbrot (fractal geometry),
— George Lakoff and Rafael Núñez (embodiment of arithmetic), and
— Brian Rotman (mathematical communication and belief)

Stanislas Dehaene 1965–

John H Conway 1937–

Benoit Mandelbrot 1924–2010

George Lakoff 1941–

Brian Rotman 1938–

As well George Spencer Brown and Louis Kauffman are of special importance to the development of iconic mathematics and James algebra.

Although it appears as though James forms are symbolic in that they stand in place of putatively abstract concepts, the intention of an iconic system is that *representation looks like what it means*. This step is unique for several reasons.

— James forms have a physical as well as a representational manifestation.
— The physical manifestation can be read as concepts and be interpreted as numbers.
— The conceptual basis of James forms differs from that of numeric expressions.
— What James forms represent is not what numbers represent.
— Containment is not counting.

It is challenging to isolate one or two facets of boundary mathematics that deviate from conventional arithmetic. The change in perspective is *systemic* rather than local.

We have already highlighted many of these conceptual shifts.

— Arithmetic is about physical experience. It is not abstract.

— Formal rigor is not incompatible with direct experience.

— Iconic forms provide their own meaning.

— Reliance on strings of symbols limits the perspectives of mathematics.

— Void-equivalence eliminates meaningless form.

At the same time, boundary mathematics maintains rigorous formality. It is neither a psychological nor an educational technique. It is a collection of axiomatic systems that share common characteristics. *Formality* is an essential aspect of computational math. Only computational demonstration is sufficiently rigorous to meet the formalist criteria for mathematical veracity.

accumulation

$\bullet\ \bullet \neq \bullet$

Hilbert

$1 = |$
$2 = ||$
$3 = |||$
$n = |\cdot\cdot_n\cdot\cdot|$

Frege

0 *exists*
$1 = \#0$
$2 = \#1$
$3 = \#2$
$n = \#(n-1)$

Peano

0 *exists*
$1 = 0'$
$2 = 1'$
$3 = 2'$
$n = (n-1)'$

Zermelo

$0 = \{\ \}$
$1 = \{0\}$
$2 = \{1\}$
$3 = \{2\}$
$n = \{n-1\}$

vonNeumann

$0 = \{\ \}$
$1 = \{0\}$
$2 = \{0,1\}$
$3 = \{0,1,2\}$
$n = \{0,\ldots,n\}$

Incremental Numbers

Each whole number is an accumulation of the numbers that precede it. Different formal models generally differ by the way in which accumulation is achieved. Hilbert describes numbers specifically as tally marks, as intuitive signs so obvious that they come prior to logic and prior to inferential definition. Frege defines numbers conceptually: 0 is the number of objects that are not identical to themselves; 1 is the number of things that are 0; 2 is the number of things that are either 0 or 1. Peano generates natural numbers by assuming both 1 and the successor operation, +1. The next number is the successor of the prior number. Ernst Zermelo, an originator of set theory, conceived of the natural numbers as the successive nesting of sets. Rather than incrementing, the successor function converts an existing number into a singleton set. VonNeumann's set theoretic successor constructs the union of the prior and the current number. The empty set { } has zero members, while the set of the empty set {{ }}, has one member, and {{ }, {{ }}}, the set of 0 and 1, has two members. Frege and vonNeumann build numbers from the collection of all numbers before them. Peano and Zermelo do not. In all cases, each number has its own unique structure.

Ernst Zermelo
1871–1953

John vonNeumann
1903–1957

Paul Benacerraf observes that these definitions are mutually contradictory.[13] For Zermelo, the number 5 is a set with one member, for vonNeumann is it a set with five members, for Frege it is five conceptual differences, for Peano it is five unitary increments and for Hilbert it is five identical tallies. Boundary arithmetic identifies 1 as a distinction, ( ). The emptiness inside serves as 0 but it is actually *nothing*. Then like Hilbert and like other tally systems, numbers grow in magnitude by the expedient of not permitting condensation.

The complexity of numbers themselves depends on the choice of foundational approach. Zermelo gives us the whole numbers; vonNeumann gives us the ordinal numbers. Cantor journeys all the way to actual (rather than potential) infinity. His definition of an infinite set is something that can be grasped as a whole. Modern theorists as such Badiou see the entirely of countable numbers as a structured whole. Numbers themselves are a unity. No single number makes sense without reference to all other numbers. You can tell a unity because it has a boundary rather than an unlimited expanse. This leads us to our current structural definition of a James number:

> *A number is a reduced James form*
> *that contains a round unit, ( ),*
> *and does not contain a square unit, [ ].*

Mathematics Education

The approach we are exploring is not intended to simplify or to modify the edifice of mathematics itself. We are not challenging professional mathematics, but we are challenging unprofessional mathematics education. The central question is whether or not there is a conceptually simpler approach to mathematical ideas that might benefit the 99.9% of people who do not engage in advanced mathematics, and the two-thirds of Americans who literally hate math.[14] As I tell my students, it is most likely that what they hate is *not* mathematics. Math is a tool, and it's hard to hate a hammer. What they hate is the experiences imposed upon them in the name of mathematics education. What they hate is the disrespect.

Until a student becomes a math major, in upper-division college, math teachers usually do not mention sets or logics or varieties of algebras. Yes, set theory and logical deduction and functional analysis are useful mathematical systems for students to know, but the fact is these mathematical skills are not taught in K-12 anyway. Some aspects of foundational thinking are embedded implicitly into math education but none are taught *as* math education. Making the ground upon which a learner stands implicit leads to confusion rather than to understanding. It's like asking a carpenter to built the walls of a house without having a cement slab to stand upon.

Even **group theory**, the conceptual mechanism underneath modern algebra, is not taught as high school algebra. Seeing symmetry is vital. Intuitive understanding of symmetric form is vital. But these conceptual skills are not in the K-12 mathematics curriculum. Group theory is an upper-division college course for math majors. Category theory, until very recently, was reserved for graduate school. Yet we still teach algebra with specifically selected group theoretic algebraic structures implicitly embedded as the *rules of algebra*. These rules provide a rather antiquated perspective on algebra. Useful in some circumstances but positively destructive to the growing understanding of young students. This is simply because these rules are taught as symbolic behavior, while students for the most part are learning about human behavior.

The Rules of Algebra (the familiar concepts of commutativity, associativity, zero, inverse and arity) pervade elementary and secondary mathematics education, perhaps due to a belief that these concepts somehow explain how arithmetic works. But prior to the introduction of symbolic forms, *preschool* mathematics emphasizes interactive manipulation, embodiment rather than abstraction of concepts. The tension between these two approaches "is a fundamental and unavoidable challenge for school mathematics."[15] The lesson of the Additive Principle is that the symbolic concepts that classify the arithmetic of numbers as an Abelian group are not the same concepts that have defined numbers throughout their evolutionary history.

Research in mathematics education recognizes the necessity of multiple modes of representation and multiple theoretic perspectives, placing mathematics learning in a pluralistic human context.[16] In contrast Hilbert's Program, the formal agenda of mathematics, removes from the operations of mathematics gross intuition, psychological necessity, physical interaction and concrete manipulation.[17] In support of Hilbert, here's mathematician Herbert Weyl: "We now come to a decisive step of mathematical abstraction: we forget about what the symbols stand for."[18]

Hermann Weyl
1885–1955

The symbolic model of arithmetic trades the visual and physical intuition that arises from direct experience for memorization of the rules of manipulation of structured strings of abstract tokens that explicitly divorce representation from meaning in order to protect rigor. The goals of advanced mathematics do not necessarily align with the needs of novice learners nor with the objectives of mathematics education.[19] Educator James Kaput is directly critical of the emphasis of form over content, and attempts to steer mathematics education toward representational

James Kaput
1942–2005

diversity.[20] The advent of computer graphics and web-based **virtual manipulatives**[21] has reinforced visual and manipulative techniques at all levels of math education, but arithmetic itself is still characterized by a single symbolic theory (algebraic group theory) to the exclusion of other conceptualizations of number.

26.3 Simplifying Foundations

Modern descriptions of natural numbers invariably enlist axioms that embed *sets* to identify domains and equivalence classes; predicate *logic* to provide connectives, quantification, and relations; and *functions* to enable transformations and invariants. What would numbers look like, indeed how would we be able to conceive of their structure without sets, logic and functions? What would a mathematical foundation that was calibrated, for example, for ease of understanding and teachability look like? Mathematician Alexandre Borovik states the case elegantly: "We cannot seriously discuss mathematical thinking without taking into account the limitations of our brain."[22]

The goal is to construct an iconic system that does not require the foundational axiomatic theories of sets, logic and functions. This does not mean that we abandon all mathematical concepts, just the dominant prepackaged component systems that currently serve as conventional foundations. We will keep the binary contains relation, the concept of equality, and the mechanism of pattern-matching and substitution constrained by pattern transformation rules. These features may be characterized as *algebraic*. In the following two chapters we will explicitly eliminate set membership, logical quantification, logical inference, induction and functional thinking. This makes James algebra challenging to talk about, so we will relax a bit and use conventional mathematical concepts in the metalanguage to converse *about* iconic concepts and to compare iconic structure to conventional structure. An experiential system though, in the final analysis, is characterized by actions rather than words.

A primary use of **set theory** is to provide standardized conceptual tools that can describe mathematical systems. The effort has been from its inception controversial. Apparently benign axioms lead to difficult to accept consequences.[23] Set theory itself is built upon the language of **predicate calculus**, aka first-order logic. A primary use of predicate calculus is to provide tools that can describe structural invariants across functions, relations, domains of objects and techniques of proof. The functions and relations of predicate calculus vary, depending upon the kind of mathematical structures we seek to describe. However quantification and logical inference are shared across almost all types of mathematical systems to describe domains and transformations.

The difficulty is, bluntly, that it might be imperative to quarantine these tools since many are toxic to the non-professional and most are represented by language that has grown to be outside of general human comprehension. It takes Russell and Whitehead, in *Principia Mathematica*, 345 pages to construct a sufficient groundwork of symbolic logic to introduce the concept One as "the class of all unit classes." This One requires on the order of 50,000 symbols.[24]

As symbolic form burgeons, newer mathematical approaches such as cellular automata and chaos theory are coming to the conclusion that complexity is just a whole lot of simplicity. In the 1920s, Frank Ramsey (and Bertrand Russell) made the case for simple mathematics. Here's Ramsey:

Frank Ramsey
1903–1930

> So in saying that every thing in whose existence we have reason to believe is simple, I mean that there are no classes, complex properties or relations, or facts; and that the phrases which appear to stand for these things are incomplete symbols.[25]

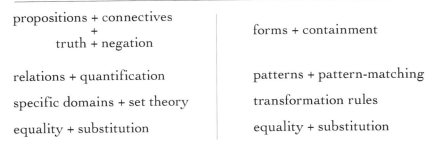

FORMAL MATHEMATICS

established	*boundary*
propositions + connectives + truth + negation	forms + containment
relations + quantification	patterns + pattern-matching
specific domains + set theory	transformation rules
equality + substitution	equality + substitution

Figure 26-1: *Deconstruction of formal mathematics*

For another contrast, we take as both axiomatic and obvious that a closed curve has an inside and an outside. This observation in mathematics is called the Jordan Curve Theorem: Every simple closed planar curve separates the plane into a bounded interior region and an unbounded exterior. Using the HOL automated theorem-prover, Thomas Hales completed the proof of the Jordan Curve Theorem, but at the cost of its simplicity.

The formal proof of the Jordan curve theorem in HOL-Light consists of 138 definitions, 1381 lemmas, and over 44,000 proof steps spread over 59,000 lines of computer code. There are approximately 20 million primitive logical inferences in this proof.[26]

The iconic perspective is that the problem is *symbolic representation*, not the nature of closed curves.

Mapping

The foundational theories of mathematics are designed to accommodate all mathematical ideas and notations. Naturally they have come into being, primarily in the twentieth century, through extensive study by the greatest mathematical minds of our time. Our goal here is far

group theory	☞	*James algebra*
commutativity		independence of content
associativity		independence of content
additive identity		*void* n
multiplicative identity		Indication ([n] [o])
additive inverse		Reflection n < n >
multiplicative inverse		([n]<[n]>)
distribution		Arrangement

Figure 26-2: *Conventional algebraic axioms and James axioms*

more modest: to design an adequate formal system that is simple enough to convey some basic ideas to naive minds. Thus we are pursuing a system that is visual and manipulable, that has only one binary relation, and that does not need the support of other foundational systems.

Figure 26-1 compares a hierarchical deconstruction of mathematical foundations to analogous components within the James system. Threaded throughout the objects of math are mappings between objects. The most common of these is the **function**, a relation between the inputs and outputs of a process or a transformation. The group theoretic structure of functions is compared to the mechanisms of James algebra in Figure 26-2. Functions themselves are objects of study in mathematics, leading to the concept of a **morphism**, or a structure preserving map between mathematical structures. **Structure preserving** means, roughly, that the objects and the transformations between two systems align. Recently the study of morphisms has led to the more abstract approach of **category theory**, in which the objects of study are mapping systems themselves. The premier example of a category is the *category of sets*, which includes collections of unique objects and the functions that relate them. Mathematician Barry Mazur:

A category is a mathematical entity that, in the most succinct of languages, captures the essence of what a mathematical theory consists: objects of the theory, allowable transformations between these objects, and a composition law telling us how to compose two transformations when the range of the first transformation is the domain of the second.[27]

Proof

There are two other great themes within mathematics: proof and interpretation. The simple perspective on **proof** is that it is following rules to get from one form to another. Since proof can be accomplished by different systems of transformation (logic, algebra, pattern-matching) deductive reasoning is not an essential component.

An **interpretation** is a mapping between symbols and relations. Presumably, symbols are arbitrary, we can represent the concept of five by 5, by *cinq*, or by a hand with fingers spread open. Technically functions map symbols to other symbols, ones that we have perhaps a better understanding of. Mathematics seems to have a difficult time bridging the gap between the symbolic and the concrete. Indeed, we are using the word *interpretation* to mean a formal mapping between container forms and mathematical expressions composed of arithmetic symbols.

An entirely different use of interpretation is to assign *meaning* to symbols, where we are strict to maintain that meaning exists only in the physical world. The plus symbol might be interpreted to assert that we should put two things together, given that the things themselves are concrete rather than symbolic. 3 + 4 does not tell us to put together the two squiggles 3 and 4. It tells us to put together 3 and 4 *of something*. For elementary arithmetic that something is tallies, what we have been calling indications. Here we also have the option of converting container configurations to arrangements of physical containers, so that the meaning of (( )), for example, is a physical container residing within another physical container. We might even say that when we see physical containers as mathematical relations we are interpreting the physical as something virtual.

The current postsymbolic challenge is to provide a proof of principle that it is possible to describe significant mathematical systems without symbols and without the tools that enforce a symbolic conceptualization. Our working example, James algebra of containers, can certainly be described symbolically, and we have done so by implying that the contains relationship is a *logical relation*. But which aspects of the core concept of a *distinction* rely upon the infrastructure of sets and logic, and which are more accurately conveyed by *physical* containment? Can the relationship between a container and its contents be described without calling upon predicate calculus?

26.4 Doing without Symbols

Symbolic exposition dominates mathematics, especially foundational mathematics. Educators rationalize the frustration they visit upon students trying do math "in their heads" rather than with their eyes and fingers and bodies by claiming that mental math is both necessary and good for you. Presumably it helps the development of rational thinking. There is absolutely no evidence to support this. Most math teachers who express their distress publicly say that they love math, and that something is dreadfully wrong. The subtext of an exploration of iconic math is, of course, that one thing that is dreadfully wrong is *symbolic* math. Tristan Needham, in his ground-breaking textbook *Visual Complex Analysis* makes this appeal:

When one opens a random modern mathematics text on a random subject, one is confronted by abstract symbolic reasoning that is divorced from one's sensory experience of the world....The present book openly challenges the current dominance of purely symbolic logical reasoning by using new, visually accessible arguments to explain the truths of elementary complex analysis.[28]

It is not difficult to find professional mathematicians and educators who are disturbed by the requirements that symbolic math has put on student learners. Here's math educator Norman Wildberger:

> I am confident that a view of mathematics as swimming ambiguously on a sea of potential Axiomatic systems strongly misrepresents the practical reality of the subject...at no point does one need to start invoking the existence of objects or procedures that we cannot see, specify, or implement.[29]

Historical Context

Plus, +, the first widely used sign in arithmetic, originated in the West in the middle of the fourteen century. At that time algebra was written out in words. The words gradually morphed into shorthand symbols. From a book by Leibniz scholar Louis Couturat:

> The symbols now in use for the operations and relations of arithmetic mostly date from the sixteenth and seventeenth centuries; and these "constant" symbols together with the letters first used systematically by Viète (1540-1603) and Descartes (1596-1650), serve, by themselves, to express many propositions.[30]

Couturat emphasizes that Leibniz sought an iconic system of notation for his universal language, "by providing an ideography, in which the signs represent ideas and the relations between them directly (without the intermediary of words)."[31] Here's Leibniz:

But it will be appropriate for the signs to be as natural as possible, e.g. for one, a point, for numbers, points.... The whole of the writing will therefore be made as if of geometrical figures and like pictures, just as the Egyptians once did and as the Chinese do today.[32]

Today, formal mathematics is expressed almost exclusively as strings of symbols. Successive transformation of strings generates the structure of proofs. The rules of string formation and transformation provide the syntax of mathematics. However, as Joseph Goguen observes, our actual notation for arithmetic is mixed.

With Arabic numerals, the use of 1 for "one" is iconic (one stroke), but the others are symbolic; using the blank character for "zero" would be iconic.... When an operation like + is associative, it is usual to omit parentheses; thus we write a+b+c instead of (a+b)+c or a+(b+c).... Dropping parentheses is iconic of the fact that it doesn't matter where they are; spread sheets also exploit this. Using 0 for the identity of addition is only symbolic, but using 1 for the identity of multiplication is indexical.[33]

Goguen concludes

Perhaps mathematics could only get started through the iconic notation of its earliest achievements. And certainly hiding that iconicity is harmful to students trying to learn mathematics.[34]

Semantics

If mathematics is to stand alone, without reliance upon other more concrete disciplines, then the concept of semantics, of a tie to reality, is irrelevant. Mathematician Edward Nelson expresses the structuralist viewpoint,

The role of syntax in mathematics is not to express semantic truths (because there are no semantic truths in mathematics to express). Mathematics is syntax, and syntax is mathematics itself.[35]

Nelson continues, "What is real in mathematics is simply formulas and proofs themselves, as strings of symbols."[36]

If we are to take this view seriously, then James algebra is *not mathematics*. But over the last few decades, diagrammatic mathematics has been widely accepted within many sub-disciplines of mathematics (as discussed in Chapter 1). The whole numbers are on a particularly firm iconic foundation. The numeral 3 is the label for Leibniz' conceptualization of *numbers as points*, a label for the icon •••.

Collatz function

If n *is even,*
  f(n) = n/2
otherwise
  f(n) = 3n + 1

There are also severe foundational questions when one considers the definition and implementation of arbitrary symbolic specifications. Symbolic "rules" that appear to define sets or truth-valued logical expressions or functions can be arbitrarily incomprehensible, or undecidable or ambiguous. There are simple mappings such as the Collatz function that are believed to behave chaotically during iterated recursion. (There is no known proof that iteratively feeding the Collatz function back into itself always terminates at 1.) There are structural questions that are unanswerable, for example: What is the longest sequence of 7s in $\sqrt{2}$? And questions that seem answerable but may take longer than the age of the universe to compute. For example, find the next pair of twin primes greater than a googolplex. Many famous unproved theorems (e.g. the Riemann hypothesis) may not be provable. Well-formed algorithms may not terminate, or a well-formed result may be too large to record within the resources of the known universe. We are left having to acknowledge that whatever foundation we choose, whatever definition of all the numbers we adopt, we may still find ourselves in unknown territory.

But here is a bold suggestion: those ambiguities may be associated with our use of language rather than with our use of natural numbers. Penelope Maddy attributes the difficulty of learning numbers for toddlers to learning *number words*, acquisition of a linguistic rather than mathematical skill. She quotes cognitive scientist Paul Bloom:

> It is not that somehow children know that there is an infinity of numbers and infer that you can always produce a larger number word. Instead, they learn that one can always produce a larger number word and infer that there must therefore be an infinity of numbers.[37]

By admitting that mathematics is a human endeavor, we may not be able to avoid symbolic confusion. But perhaps some of these types of confusion can be avoided by iconic and behavioral communication.

Embodiment

Postsymbolic math is embodied rather than abstract. There is a deeper alienation: symbolic representation denies that our eyes and our bodies and our thoughts are grounded in experience. Using symbolic tokens to convey structural ideas is neither intuitive nor natural. Symbols drastically increase cognitive load, we must memorize their meaning. String representation requires structural redundancy that is both technically inaccurate and cognitively misleading. We impose commutativity on addition to create symbolic addition but natural addition occurs in space as fusion, with no sequential first and second objects. And for most learners, symbolic systems engender insecurity since they ask for a mode of learning that has no biological or evolutionary basis.

Acceptance and memorization of concepts that have no possible basis in experience helps to undermine understanding. Young learners and their teachers appear to have little choice but to believe what they are told, that symbolic mathematics supports out-of-body experience, that it takes one to unreachable infinities, and that it denies common sense by expressing its ideas in generally incomprehensible strings of arcane symbols.

26.5 Remarks

In Chapter 27 and Chapter 28 we'll explore the rationale for avoiding the abstract formalism that now accompanies mathematical foundations. The mechanisms of set membership, logical conjunction and function composition are each equivalent to one another and to the act of physically putting things into containers. The binary connectives of logic and the arity-dependent composition of functions are to some extent not in place to clarify mathematics, but rather to limit operations to two arguments at a time. It is not that sequential thinking is in error, or that it was inappropriate to evolve through the various phases that lead to formalized thinking. It is just time to move on to newer models that include newer concepts such as parallel composition, pattern-driven transformation and iconic form. The next two chapters review the reasons to abstain from building the foundation of mathematics on logic, sets and functions. We'll then explore the implication of making mathematics more than strings of symbols.

Endnotes

1. **opening quote:** J. Lanier (1989) Communication without symbols. *Whole Earth Review* 64 p.118-119. Online 8/18 at http://www.jaronlanier.com/jaron%20 whole%20earth%20review.pdf

Not only is Lanier credited with coining the term *virtual reality*, his company VPL was the first to build a virtual reality system. Lanier's intention is to be able to explore direct non-mediated communication. To my knowledge in the cited article he is also the first person to use the term *postsymbolic communication*. In J. Lanier (2017) *Dawn of the New Everything* p.298 he writes:

> Consider that people have been innovating ways of connecting with each other since the dawn of the species. From spoken language tens of thousands of years ago, to written language thousands of years ago, to printed language hundreds of years ago, to photography, recording, cinema, computing, networking; then to virtual reality, and eventually to what I hoped my talk might provide a glimpse of: postsymbolic communication — and then on to what I could not imagine.

2. **traditional categories are pure mathematics and applied mathematics:** The old joke is that a pure mathematician is embarrassed if someone finds a use for his work, while an applied mathematician is embarrassed if no one finds a use.

3. **the book is not isomorphic to seeing the movie:** And a blank canvas is worth a thousand unspoken words.

4. **collapses if one restricts oneself to thinking in terms of elementary mathematics:** F. Zalamea (2009) *Synthetic Philosophy of Contemporary Mathematics* p.179.

5. **Typographic characters do not support a meaning of their own:** There are conventions that endow individual characters with meaning, such as adding an 's' to make a noun plural or replacing a '.' with '!' for emphasis.

6. **evolved for at least three millenia with hardly any symbols:** I. Kleiner (1991) Rigor and proof in mathematics: A historical perspective. *Mathematics Magazine* 64 p. 291-314. Online 8/18 at https://www.maa.org/sites/default/files/ pdf/upload_library/22/Allendoerfer/1992/0025570x.di021172.02p0031c.pdf

7. **the resting place for mathematical language in its purest, most rigorously grounded form:** B. Rotman (2000) *Mathematics as Sign* p.55.

8. **it is like a building, acted upon and constructed:** R. Netz (1999) *The Shaping of Deduction in Greek Mathematics* p.60.

9. **which is by no means the case with the syntax of speech:** C. S. Peirce (1909) MS 514 "Existential graphs"

10. **(for example those of Aristotle or Ockham) as so much empty verbiage:** R. Dipert (1995) Peirce's underestimated place in the history of logic: A response to Quine. In K. Ketner (ed.) *Peirce and Contemporary Thought: Philosophical Inquiries* p.34.

11. **and its result so clear that it needs no foundation whatsoever:** A. Heyting (1971) Disputations. In P. Benacerraf & H. Putnam (1983) *Philosophy of Mathematics 2ed* p.70.

12. **signs or images, more or less clear, that I can reproduce and recombine at will:** Einstein, quoted by K. Devlin (2006) The Useful and Reliable Illusion of Reality in Mathematics. *Toward a New Epistemology of Mathematics Workshop*, GAP.6 Conference 2006. Online 8/18 at https://web.stanford.edu/~k-devlin/Papers/Berlin06.pdf

13. **these definitions are mutually contradictory:** P. Benacerraf (1965) What numbers could not be. In P. Benacerraf and H. Putnam (eds.) (1983) *Philosophy of Mathematics 2nd ed.* p.272-294.

14. **the two-thirds of Americans who literally hate math:** See, for example, M. Burns (1998) *Math: Facing an American Phobia*, and S. Tobias (1993) *Overcoming Math Anxiety.*

15. **a fundamental and unavoidable challenge for school mathematics:** J. Kilpatrick, J. Swalford & B. Findell (eds.) (2001) *Adding It Up: Helping Children Learn Mathematics* p.74.

16. **places mathematics learning in a pluralistic human context:** J. Greeno & R. Hall (1997) Practicing representation: learning with and about representational forms. *Phi Delta Kappan* 78 p.1-24. Online 4/18 at http://www.pdkintl.org/kappan/kgreeno.htm

17. **psychological necessity, physical interaction, and concrete manipulation:** M. Greaves (2002) *The Philosophical Status of Diagrams.*

18. **we forget about what the symbols stand for:** H. Weyl (1941) *The Mathematical Way of Thinking.*

19. **nor with the objectives of mathematics education:** M. Donovan & J. Bransford (eds.) (2005) *How Students Learn Mathematics in the Classroom.*

We do not need to understand how an electronic fuel injector works in order to drive a car. Knowledge of the electronic fuel injector is not even essential to understanding how a car works.

20. **steer mathematics education toward representational diversity:** J. Kaput (1987) Representation systems and mathematics. In C. Janvier (ed.) *Problems of Representation in the Teaching and Learning of Mathematics* p.19-26.

It is quite appropriate here to view representational diversity in a wider, cultural sense. Karen François comments:

> Traditional mathematics [curriculum] is strongly directed towards the performance of techniques and has little to do with the study of mathematics as a historical and cultural product nor with the underlying cultural values.

K. François (2007) The untouchable and frightening status of mathematics. In K. François & J. vanBendegem (eds.) (2007) *Philosophical Dimensions in Mathematics Education* p.14.

21. **computer graphics and web-based virtual manipulatives:** P. Moyer, J. Bolyard & M. Spikell (2002) What are virtual manipulatives? *Teaching Children Mathematics* **8**(6) p.373.

Funded primarily by the National Science Foundation, many of these interactive learning tools are available online. For example,

Utah State University (1999) National library of virtual manipulatives at http://nlvm.usu.edu/en/nav/index.html; and

D. Clements (1999) Concrete manipulatives, concrete ideas. *Contemporary Issues in Early Childhood* 1(1) p.45-60. Online 8/18 at http://www.gse.buffalo.edu/org/buildingblocks/Newsletters/Concrete_Yelland.htm

22. **discuss mathematical thinking without taking into account the limitations of our brain:** A. Borovik (2007) *Mathematics under the Microscope: Notes on cognitive aspects of mathematical practice* p.vi. Online 8/18 at http://eprints.ma.man.ac.uk/844/1/covered/MIMS_ep2007_112.pdf

23. **benign axioms lead to difficult to accept consequences:** The Axiom of Choice, for example, facilitates the Banach-Tarski paradox, in which a single solid object can be disassembled into specific pieces and then reassembled into two of the same object with the same size.

24. **This One is on the order of 50,000 symbols:** A. Mathias heard this estimate and decided to verify the number. He deconstructed the structuralist definition of the number One from the Bourbaki school by identifying each symbol and expanding it to its most primitive definition. Going back to the very basics of symbolic definition, as if communicating in binary with a computer, he calculated that One would takeover 4.5 trillion symbols to define. A. Mathias (2002) A term length of 4,523,659,424,929. *Synthese* **133** p.75-86.

25. **phrases which appear to stand for these things are incomplete symbols:** F. Ramsey (1922) Truth and simplicity. *British Journal for the Philosophy of Science* (2007) 58 p.379-386.

26. **approximately 20 million primitive logical inferences in this proof:** T. Hales (2007) The Jordan curve theorem, formally and informally. *The Mathematical Association of America Monthly* 114 p.883. Online 8/18 at https://pdfs.semanticscholar.org/70ab/0431a8d59e1cd9147b54c5e99883a54190a1.pdf

27. **when the range of the first transformation is the domain of the second:** B. Mazur (2007) When is one thing equal to some other thing? Online 4/18 at http://www.math.harvard.edu/~mazur/preprints/when_is_one.pdf

28. **visually accessible arguments to explain the truths of elementary complex analysis:** T. Needham (1999) *Visual Complex Analysis* p.vii.

29. **the existence of objects or procedures that we cannot see, specify, or implement:** N. Wildberger (2005) Set theory: should you believe? Online 10/18 at http://web.maths.unsw.edu.au/~norman/views2.htm

30. **serve, by themselves, to express many propositions:** L. Couturat (1905) *The Algebra of Logic* L.G. Robinson (trans. 1914). From the Preface by P. Jourdain p.i.

31. **the relations between them directly (without the intermediary of words):** Couturat p.ii.

32. **just as the Egyptians once did and as the Chinese do today:** L. Couturat (1901) *The Logic of Leibniz* Ch 4. p.18. footnote 101 quoting Leibniz (§90; Phil., IV, 73; Math., V, 50). Online 8/18 (in French) at https://babel. hathitrust.org/cgi/pt?id=ien.35556036601318;view=1up;seq=1

33. **using 1 for the identity of multiplication is indexical:** J. Goguen (1993) On notation. In. B. Magnusson, B. Meyer & J-F. Perrot (eds.) *TOOLS 10: Technology of Object-oriented Languages and Systems* p.5-10.

34. **hiding that iconicity is harmful to students trying to learn mathematics:** Goguen p.5-10.

35. **Mathematics is syntax, and syntax is mathematics itself:** E. Nelson (2002) Syntax and semantics. Presented to the International Conference: *Foundations and the Ontological Quest. Prospects for the New Millennium* p.5. Online 8/18 at https://web.math.princeton.edu/~nelson/papers/s.pdf

36. **mathematics is simply formulas and proofs themselves, as strings of symbols:** Nelson p.6.

37. **and infer that there must therefore be an infinity of numbers:** P. Maddy (2014) A second philosophy of arithmetic. *The Review of Symbolic Logic* 7(2) p.234. Quoting P. Bloom (2000) *How Children Learn the Meanings of Words* p.238. Online 8/18 at http://www.socsci.uci.edu/~pjmaddy/bio/arithmetic%20 in%20RSL.pdf

Sets

The use of set theory as a foundation for mathematics
may be an historical aberration.[1]
— Nik Weaver (2009)

Postsymbolic math is intentionally connected to our senses and to our sensibility. In order to take the brazen step of developing formal mathematics for non-mathematicians, we will need to abandon the current foundations of a century ago and reintroduce the idea that math is not necessarily abstract. Platonic reality was imagined into existence 2500 years ago during attempts to conceptualize brand new philosophical ideas like logic, rhetoric, politics, ethics, physics, metaphysics and aesthetics. These ideas have permeated Western culture ever since. Then with the growth of science, skepticism, reason, constitutional government, books, universities, relativism, technology, atheism, household electronics, the internet and deep AI, the constructions of Greek antiquity weakened, leaving mathematics with, in Morris Kline's words, a *loss of certainty*. And now, like a toddler joyfully leveling a sand castle, we have the infant internet percolating structural change throughout all aspects of society. The established foundations of mathematics — set theory, logic and functions — have come under

increasing scrutiny. Neither the abstraction of the ancient
Greeks nor the abstraction of the early twentieth century
formalists incorporates ubiquitous computing. In moving
toward a postsymbolic basis for elementary mathematics,
this chapter reiterates contemporary dissatisfactions with
the theory of sets by comparing set theory to iconic math
and to the computational necessity of ultrafinitism. After
abstaining from the use of sets, in the next chapter we
will also abstain from the use of symbolic logic and the
functional way of thinking.

27.1 Doing without Sets

Sets collect together objects. Since containers provide the
same feature, a container-based system does not require
set theory. The idea of doing without set theory does
not mean that set theory cannot model James calculus.
It means that the structure of containers is sufficient to
replicate whatever we might need from a finite set theory.
The sections that follow briefly summarize several common objections to set theory. There are also other formal
systems that have achieved a divorce from set theory,
notably **mereology**, the study of whole/part relations.[2]

The original vision of the twentieth century was that
mathematics had a common ground, one without inherent contradiction. Contradiction was soon found to be
unavoidable, but the belief in a common ground persisted.
Mathematics philosopher David Corfield:

> By the 1920s, the extraordinary result had been
> established that this process [grounding in set
> theory] could be taken to such an extreme that any
> algebraic, analytic or geometric entity, any collec-
> tion of such entities, and any mapping between
> collections of such entities could be seen as the same
> kind of thing – a set. This finding cast a long shadow
> over the philosophy of mathematics for the rest of
> the century.[3]

Set theory arose out of Georg Cantor's work with one-to-one mappings. Cantor suggested the Well-Ordering Principle, intuitively that by some criterion there is a smallest member and therefore the rest of the members may be arranged one after the other. Cantor postulated that every set can be well-ordered, but this turned out to be quite tricky to prove. Zermelo provided a proof based upon the quite controversial Axiom of Choice during the first decade of the twentieth century, which was then elaborated two decades later by Abraham Fraenkel. The goal was to eliminate the paradoxes that plagued mathematical logic at the time. The central issue was a need to clarify what it means for a mathematical object to exist, as embodied within the Axiom of Choice which gives permission to construct a set from members of other sets. If the choice is specific, then what is chosen must exist, but if the choice is merely possible, then it is not clear that what is chosen could be demonstrated to exist. In contrast, existence proofs are not part of iconic arithmetic because we have anchored containers to a physical model.

Abraham Fraenkel
1891–1965

Set theory introduces one fundamental binary relation, $\in$, the **membership relation**. $A \in B$ means that object A is a member of set B.

$$A \in B \quad \textit{is} \quad \{A, \ldots\}_B \quad ☞ \quad \{A \ldots\}_B$$

The primary distinction made by sets is between an object and the set containing that object. Spencer Brown scholar Thomas McFarlane:

> Set theory thus supposes that $\{A\} \neq A$, rather than $\{A\} = A$. It supposes that A can actually be separated from itself. Set theory, and all of mathematics, arises from this fundamental assumption that a set can create a difference.[4]

Thus both sets and distinctions putatively have the same foundational perspective. Pure set theory has only one type of object, the *set*, similar to our single object type, the *container*. Set membership is analogous to the relation is-contained-by.[5] The primary and profound difference is that sets define properties while containers define relationships. Sets are object-oriented while containers are process-oriented.

Properties

The members of a particular set are determined by a communal property shared by all. The set of red hats is such because all hats in that set are red. All the red hats must also be *unique*, that is, different from one another. Since sets have unique members, every member is also co-dependent upon the others, sutured together by mutual *difference*. This effectively confounds the uniqueness of objects with our perceptual decision to ignore all but the color red. And the quality of hatness. To construct a set of objects that share the same property, we must ignore that property as a means to differentiate the members of the set. The property itself becomes global to all members, a characteristic of the environment holding those members together.[6] What is left, the uniqueness of the members, is that which is *not the property*. Thus an abstract set of objects that have only one property can have only one member. This type of set cannot support the concept of cardinality. The units in ensemble and tally arithmetics, in contrast, are identical and without properties, essentially indistinguishable but countable by virtue of existence.

Both sets and containers include a capability to label, to identify symbolically a particular set or particular container. Poincaré observed that no object in mathematics exists without a name.[7] Symbolic systems take advantage of free replication of labels to generate *expressions* that transcend physical reality. The capability of different sets to refer to the same object rests upon the generation of *replica indicators*, labels that refer to the same object but are not that object. Set theory thus addresses conceptual

$S_1 = \{a,b,c\}$
$S_2 = \{a,g,h\}$

symbols rather than actual objects. The set intersection operation is a clear example. An object can have two different properties, and thus participate conceptually in the two sets that identify separately objects having each property. The large black cat belongs both to the set of large cats and to the set of black cats, but there is only one cat. It is *indications* of an object that participate in set membership, not the objects themselves. *Properties* do not respect physical uniqueness, indeed properties are cognitive constructs that do not emanate directly from physical reality. The syntax/semantic barrier is a veil of illusion, allowing us to generate two types of reality, the actual and the abstract. Sets *cannot* collect objects, they collect fragments of conceptualizations of objects, abstracted properties that we are electing, at a particular time, to focus upon. It is not at all clear that properties of actual objects can be distinguished separately. The holistic perspective is that an object is precisely that because it is a unity, not an assembly of different facets. Separate properties are indications not of a thing but of a perceptual filter.

Labeled containers too can be cloned into multiple indications of the same form. ((A)(A B)) is a valid form, but we cannot construct a physical arrangement that includes container A in two separate locations. Yes it is strange to question the validity of symbolic labeling, but the point is that sets do not allow us to connect to the actual. Containers potentially do. At least containers make clear when we are locked into abstraction and when we have a physical model directly available. Iconic forms without replicated labels are *constructible*. In contrast, naive set theory has been shown to be inconsistent, while the assembly that is Zermelo-Fraenkel set theory is incoherent.

Equalness

How can we include the concept of *equality* without acknowledging both predicate calculus as a means to define how equality works and set theory to define how different structural forms can have the same value or meaning? The essential idea of **equivalence classes** is that classes are *disjoint*: no expression is a member of more than one class. In set theoretic terms, no equivalence classes intersect. In more pedestrian terms, we don't need to think about set intersection, all we really need is equivalence classes, not equivalence *sets*.

Similar to sets, containers with equal contents are equal. Sets and containers can both be nested, aligning the definitions of set equality and container equality. For two containers to be equal, the forms they contain also must have equal contents, and so on. In conventional definitions, nesting is treated as secondary, to be determined by a process of descent. For container forms, nesting is an inherent aspect of structure. The caution here is to avoid giving conceptual priority to juxtaposed rather than nested organization.

Countability

Implicit within the idea of a finite collection is the idea of being able to count the members, the idea of putting the members of a set in one-to-one correspondence with the natural numbers. The excitement about sets at the beginning of the twentieth century was that, in Thomas McFarlane's words, "For the first time, mathematicians were able to understand numbers in terms of a more fundamental 'sub-numeric' concept."[8] Number could be a property rather than the fundament.

The difficulty in counting elements of a set stems from the introduction by set theory of abstract "conceptual" objects. Have you ever tried to isolate and count the number of concepts in a thought? Perhaps Platonists could, but that line of thinking immediately removes us from the obvious embodiment of our thoughts within physical reality. Descartes' mind/body separation was a neat trick to separate Belief from Science, but hundreds of years later it is rather fantastic to build mathematics upon a belief system. There are no physical sets.

From her position of **realism** (mathematical concepts have objective existence due to their indispensable connection to Physics), Penelope Maddy asserts that numbers are a property of sets. "The von Neumann ordinals are nothing more than a measuring rod against which sets are compared for numerical size."[9] In comparison to sets, the contents of a container are independent, and thus are not inherently countable. The *number of contents* is a count of the containment relations that a particular labeled container is party to. It is *distinction* not sets that defines the elementary constituent of numbers. It is containment relations not structural forms that are mapped to natural numbers.

Fusion

Another significant difference between symbols and icons is the **fusion** model of addition described in Chapter 2. Adding ensembles of tally marks by fusion loses entirely any prior affiliation with initial collections. The *empty set* is a hinge point, it has always been a controversial object. When a set is considered to be a collection of unique individuals possessing a particular property, the possibility of a collection that has no qualifying individual cannot be avoided. Fusion of aggregates does not include the possibility of an empty collection. There can be no empty fusion since there is nothing being fused. The concept of fusion lets us treat nothing with legitimacy. Philosopher Michael Potter observes:

> And it was plainly fusions, not collections, that Dedekind had in mind...when he avoided the empty set and used the same symbol for membership and inclusion (1888, nos. 2-3) — two tell-tale signs of a mereological conception.[10]

Potter continues:

The theory of fusions has been almost totally neglected by mathematicians over the last century.... Very little investigation has been done into the adequacy of the theory of fusions as a foundations for mathematics. Indeed the collection-theoretic way of thinking is so entrenched among mathematicians that it is easy for them to forget how natural it is to think of a line, say, as the sum of its points rather than as the collection of them.[11]

27.2 Intelligibility

In attempting to provide a foundation for all of mathematics, set theory pays another price. Sets destroy rather than explain structure but it is pattern, structure, that human minds respond to. The collection of axioms that constitute Zermelo-Fraenkel set theory are ad hoc at best, assembled to eliminate the inherent logical contradictions of set theory identified by Russell. Philosopher of mathematics David Corfield remarks:

> The price to be paid for universality is unnaturalness. Instead of seeing mathematical entities and constructions merely as ultimately composed of set theoretic dust, we should take into account structural considerations, rather as the student of anatomy gains little by viewing the human skeleton merely as a deposit of calcium.[12]

A motivation to construct arithmetic without set theory comes from Morris Kline:

> The axioms of set theory are rather arbitrary and artificial. They were designed to avoid the paradoxes, but some are not natural or based on intuition. Why not then start with arithmetic itself since the logical principles are presupposed even by the set-theorists?[13]

Although sets are fundamental to advanced mathematics, they are not conceptually necessary *within* the James system. Modern systems such as category theory may even obsolete set theory itself. This still does not free us from sets. Sets become important when we refer to features of James forms, that is, in the metalanguage we use to characterize the James system. For example, there is a set of all James forms, the **language** of James algebra.[14]

Infinities

A more significant defect of set theory is that it introduces not only belief in non-existent properties, but also non-realizable concepts, the *hierarchy of infinite sets*. In order to avoid logical contradiction, set theory embraces an infinity of infinities, each infinitely more complex than the last. Sets are constructed in stages by forming power sets (via the Power Set axiom), but their passage to an infinity of sets (via the Infinite Set axiom) is by fiat. First, the countable infinity of whole numbers, then the uncountable infinity of the continuum, and next the incomprehensible infinity of an infinity that has no name and no models. And then the rest of them, although after passing the first countable infinity, *counting* itself is not possible.

The concept of an infinite language that describes *all* possible James forms is an imaginary imposition from outside, from our cultural belief in the infinite. All possible forms are not *within* James algebra because we will never come across an infinite number of forms. The language itself does not need to be infinite, it just needs to accommodate diversity as it arises. The idea of an infinite language is usually identified as a potential rather than an actual infinity, however this distinction itself is contaminated by thinking that whole numbers are an infinite collection in the first place. If we limit numbers to a finite collection, then the number of forms in the James language cannot be infinite.[15]

Penelope Maddy identifies the Axiom of Infinity as "perhaps *the* characteristic hypothesis of set theory".[16] She goes on to observe that there is no evidence in the developmental psychology literature to indicate that children understand the mathematical, as opposed to the linguistic, concept of infinite induction. Brian Rotman clearly calls for the removal of infinities from mathematics. "Endless prolongation of counting, of iteration in time, is no less problematic, no more necessarily 'true,' than unending extension of space."[17]

Various philosophers of mathematics since Cantor have invested infinite interest and effort in debating variants of types of justifiable infinity, climbing past the countable infinity into **transfinite ordinals** that are larger than infinite but not larger than the *absolute infinite* which is larger than anything imaginable. These excursions are justified by Hilbert's original program to disconnect mathematics from *reality*. Instead we will head in the other direction, to rest our efforts in feasible numbers.

Predicativism

Hilbert intended to justify the use of the countable infinite, such as the set of natural numbers, by calling upon only strictly finite, constructive methods of proof. Philosopher Curtis Franks identifies Hilbert's idea of *proof* as

> a finite sequence of formulas, each of which is either an axiom, a substitution instance...or the result of an application of modus ponens.[18]

The main idea is that sets must be built up from below, from sets that have already been shown to exist. Proof by contradiction was not permitted. An *impredicative* proof relies upon a set that contains the object being demonstrated, which is a type of circularity. The intent is to bring into question Cantor's definition of an infinite set that includes a subset of itself. A difficulty is that Peano's axioms of arithmetic include the infinite processes that set theory embraces as the existence of an infinite set of whole numbers. Another difficulty is that mathematical induction declaratively incorporates universal quantification.[19]

Predicativity places a finite restriction on the construction of sets: *there is no property common to all natural numbers*. Predicativism was supported and developed by Poincaré, Russell and Weyl as an attempt to eliminate the excesses of the infinite ladder of types of infinity proposed by Cantor. Acceptance of the natural numbers creates the solid ground. Individual real numbers are also accepted, but not the uncountable set of real numbers. The Power Set Axiom of set theory is rejected as being essentially circular. Mathematician Nic Weaver: "S is a set of natural numbers which only become available after we have all sets of natural numbers".[20] Feferman contributed an approach to provability that did not require ordinal numbers or a well-ordering principle, thus eliminating the Axiom of Choice. He demonstrated that this modestly *finitist arithmetic* is equivalent to Primitive Recursive Arithmetic as described in Chapter 23.

Predicativism and other finitist approaches have lead to severe criticism of both set theory and the principle of numeric induction. Feferman's reasons for eschewing set theory directly address the technical presumptions about mathematical reality that have been inherited from over two millenia of belief in Platonic absolutism. Feferman points to these (and other) failures:

(i) abstract entities are assumed to exist independently of any means of human definition or construction;

(ii) classical reasoning (leading to non-constructive existence results) is admitted;

(iii) completed infinite totalities and, in particular, the totality of all subsets of any infinite set are assumed to exist.[21]

The postsymbolic theme is that these indiscretions accompany *symbolic abstraction* which is itself the source of disconnection from our finite universe.

Finitism

Dedekind defined a **finite set** as one that does not contain itself as a subset. We do not need an infinity of possibilities to run into the conundrums and contradictions to which finitists object. Individual irrational numbers, for example, have infinite decimal expansions. Any single irrational number creates the same problems as an infinity of natural numbers. What does the symbolic expression $\sqrt{2}$ refer to? Yes it can be taken to be the diagonal of a unit square, but is it the *length* of that diagonal? The critical idea of measurement brings the meaning of $\sqrt{2}$ into physical reality, and thus excludes $\sqrt{2}$ as an infinite expansion. **Irrational numbers** can be categorized as algebraic, transcendental or lawless. Each category is infinite however lawless irrationals cannot be described. A **lawless number** has an infinity of digits in its decimal expansion and *no pattern*. Lawless irrationals are chaotic, beyond abstract description. Is an indescribable "number" still a number? From a more limited perspective of physical containment forms, infinite containment is also beyond description, beyond conceivable physical structure.

$\sqrt{2}$ ☞
$(([[oo]]<[oo]>))$

Wittgenstein agreed with Dedekind's definition that a real number is a **cut** (a *comparison* in Wittgenstein's vocabulary) between two rational numbers. A cut defines a process that will approach the irrational with arbitrary accuracy, but never generate the irrational. A form such as $(([[oo]]<[oo]>))$ can specify the comparative structure of an irrational, but not its infinite detail. Another criterion that Wittgenstein required for irrational numbers is that their expression be base-free. The computational rule that defines infinite detail must not depend upon the choice of a particular base. Wittgenstein:

Arithmetical operations only use the decimal system as a means to an end; that is, the rules for the operations are of such a kind that they can be translated into the language of any other number system, and do not have any of them as their subject matter.[22]

The idea of *base-free notation*, of course, is built into the James form directly. Computer Scientist Gregory Chaitin has taken Wittgenstein to an obvious conclusion.

The bits of a random real are maximally unknowable! ...with probability one, a specific real number chosen at random cannot even be named uniquely, we can't specify it somehow, constructively or not, we can't define it or even refer to it! So why should we believe that such an un-nameable real even exists?![23]

Gregory Chaitin
1947–

Emile Borel in 1927 deduced that if a real number were of infinite length, then it could encode an infinite amount of information, in effect embodying the answer to any binary (yes/no) question. Borel then concludes that belief in the existence of such a number is absurd, even though it does exist within the set of real numbers (were we to also believe in real numbers). Borel apparently did not make the analogous deduction that such a number must also exist within the infinite set of *whole* numbers since information itself is not infinite.

Emile Borel
1871–1956

Ultrafinitism

The computational perspective of **ultrafinitism** is a small step from here. Finitism short circuits the excursion to infinity by requiring that sets be constructed so that their cardinality has a basis for existence, even if that basis is an abstract mathematical formula such as a hyper-exponential function. Ultrafinitism places another restriction, that it must be possible to realize a number by some non-abstract physical criterion in order for it to exist. There are finite numbers so large that it would be impossible to record them or to state them. To an ultraf-initist these numbers also do not exist.[24] Ultrafinitism places numerics inside a realizable context, inside the boundary of a distinction rather than outside. This requires a contextualized concept to leave room on its outside for the environment it finds itself within. The *contents* of an environment then cannot be infinite.

Dehaene presents neurological evidence that people do not conceptualize numbers as equidistant. The further we go from 1, the smaller the distance between numbers. We do not think of the infinite, quite the contrary, we think of experience:

> When we think about numbers, or do arithmetic, we do not rely solely on a purified, ethereal, abstract concept of number. Our brain immediately links the abstract number to concrete notions of size, location and time.[25]

We already recognize the dissipative structure of counting in common language. Larger numbers become less exact in almost all conventional usage. The numeral 1,000,000 incorporates a completely different concept of 0. We almost never mean *exactly* one million. The chances of that are a million-to-one. The trailing zeros generate orders of magnitude, but they do not mean 0 rather than some other digit. They are as arbitrary as say 1,013,872, which in almost all cases also signifies one million. Further, cognitively we have no capability of distinguishing an exact one million, no way of verifying that "count", no way of justifying the effort necessary to verify such a count. The numeral 1,000,000 is not a counting number, nor is it a measurement. Rather it is a figure of speech.

Applied mathematician Mirco Mannucci has introduced the idea of a **dissipative proof**, basically the longer the proof the less likely it is to be valid.[26] Any definition or proof that calls upon, for example, an infinite series asks us to engage in an infinity of steps, in the process loosing all credibility.

SETS AND CONTAINERS

set theory	*boundaries*
set	container and interior
set delimiter	container boundary
set members	contents
membership relation	containment relation
subset	deep containment
union	fusion
intersection	*does not exist*
complement	context

Figure 27-1: *Set operations and containers*

27.3 Axioms

Figure 27-1 compares the operations of set theory to the computational structure of containers. Both systems are designed to collect members, but the Physicality constraint on containers eliminates both intersection and complement, while fusion of container contents eliminates union. The graph form of containment, which essentially converts intersecting labels to nodes with shared relations, is described in Chapter 29.

Transitivity

The reason that set inclusion is not containment is that inclusion does not address nested containers. When we say, for example, that rabbits are animals and that animals are living things, we conclude that rabbits are living things because the subset relation is transitive. The set of rabbits and the set of living things both consist of discrete, comparable abstractions. However, when we say that the rabbit ate the carrot, and the cat ate the rabbit, we do not conclude that the cat ate the carrot, even when the carrot remains undigested inside the rabbit.

Carrots and rabbits may be at the same level of nesting with regard to edibility, but carrots inside rabbits are not. We might say that the cat indirectly ate the carrot, in recognition that being eaten is the direct relationship. Set inclusion is transitive because it does not recognize these indirect relationships, however the idea of discrete nesting at deeper levels is central to transformation of containment structures.

To consider transitivity of containment, two types of containment need to be distinguished. **Deep containment** is transitive. If A contains B and B contains C, then A deepContains C. **Shallow containment** is not transitive. If A contains B and B contains C, then it is not the case that A shallowContains C. Container B intervenes. James containment is between an outer container and its direct content, so it is not transitive. As an example, being a parentOf a person is intransitive. Your father is not the father of your child. Being an ancestorOf a person is transitive. Your father is an ancestor of your child. Intransitive relations are common. A person is nourished by broccoli, for example, and broccoli is nourished by fertilizer, but that does not mean that a person is nourished by fertilizer. A bottle may contain water and the water may contain salt, but the bottle does not contain salt.

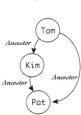

Although the shallowContains relation is not transitive, it is also not intransitive. However, violations of intransitivity will also be violations of the physicality constraint since a contradiction of intransitivity implies that there are at least two different containers that contain the same object.

Comparison of Axioms

Figure 27-2 compares the axioms of ZFC set theory[27] to James forms by informally mapping the contains relation to the set axioms. The notation in this figure is casual, intended to be a readable approximation of the formal set axioms as specified in predicate calculus.

	set theory	*James forms*
extensionality	$\forall x \; S_1 = S_2 \; iff \; x \in S_1 \Leftrightarrow x \in S_2$	A = B *iff* A <B> = *void*
separation	$S \Rightarrow Property(x \in S)$	x *is a container*
foundation	$\exists x \in y \; \{y \cap x\} = \{\;\}$	( ) ≠ *void*
replacement	$Function(x \in S) \Rightarrow S_{image}$	⟦A C E⟧ = E *iff* A = C
pair	$\forall x \forall y \exists S \; S = \{x, y\}$	*outermost container*
union	$S_1 \cup S_2 \Rightarrow S_3$	*composition*
empty set	$\{\;\}$ *exists*	*no it doesn't*
infinite set	$\{..\infty..\}$ *exists*	*no it doesn't*
power set	$S_{power} = \forall x \; x \subseteq S$	*not relevant*
choice	$S_1 \; X \; S_2$ *exists*	*not relevant*

Figure 27-2: *Associating set axioms with James forms*

The fundamental difference between classical set theory and James algebra is that both the Axiom of the Empty Set and the Axiom of Infinity have been eliminated. Alain Badiou states that

> The two axioms of the void and of the infinite structure the entire thinking of number. The pure void is that which supports *there being* number, and the infinite, that by which it is affirmed that number is the measure of all thinking in *every* situation.... So number will now manifest itself, without limit, as tyranny.[28]

It is important to distinguish *mathematical* metamathematics from *cultural* metamathematics. The former engages in maximum professional rigor, and for that endeavor, the more tools the better. The latter introduces a diversity of human interactions with applied math. Students and most professional mathematicians don't really care about the conceptual underpinnings of formal rigor. Math also has an *informal presence*. Informal math is not necessarily not formal, it is just not as technically and opaquely rigorous as our current descriptions of mathematical concepts on Wikipedia have become.

Finite Axioms

If we give up (or ignore) the possibility of an infinite variety of boundary configurations and settle instead for an assurance of a sufficiency for any finite purpose, then we can avoid the dominant complexity of set theory, that of infinite sets, and reduce set theory to three axioms. These three set axioms are sufficient to characterize both Robinson arithmetic and PRA that we explored in Chapter 23. These axioms also address the informal structural assumptions we have made for boundary forms. The three finite axioms are metaphors for simpler thoughts, thoughts not cluttered by objectified collections of properties associated with labels of an infinity of unique objects.

— **Adjunction (no reentry):** *New elements can be added to a set.* Initialization of the first set is supported by the Foundation axiom: *A new member can be put into a set.* This implies a minimal member. And yes, let's assume that we can construct forms.

— **Specification (property):** *A set exists for any identified property.*[29] In the case of a set with no members, the empty property is supported by the Empty Set axiom: *The empty set exists.*

— **Extension (equality):** *Sets are equal only when they contain the same members.* This axiom is also the definition of form equality.

Boundary forms have analogous axioms. To replace finite set theory we can provide one definition of the container domain and three finite axioms. Specific boundary systems such as James algebra are defined by specific structural axioms, however the following structural properties apply to any boundary math. Stated informally:

•• • ————————————————— • ••

Structural Principles of Finite Boundary Forms

Purity: Everything is a container.

Distinction: A container defines an inside and an outside.

Containment: Containers can be put inside one another.

Equivalence: Containers with equal contents are equal.

•• • ————————————————— • ••

Distinction serves the role of **Specification**, assuring that there are containers. Containment is analogous to **Adjunction**, assuring that there is an innermost container without requiring an empty set.

27.4 Remarks

Set theory has traveled a tumultuous path since its inception in the early twentieth century. Not only are it's axioms unintuitive, the consequences of these axioms are even more unintuitive. Perhaps the worst offense is the generation of hierarchies of infinities which have helped to project the foundations of mathematics into territories so far removed from common comprehension that they make the use of any physical metaphor completely inappropriate. The theory of infinities has cast us into fantasies beyond comprehension, while seducing the field of mathematics into out-of-body experiences.

Most relevant here is that iconic math is informed by set theoretic work on the nature of equality, existence and feedback. From our perspective, only the definition of equality has provided positive assistance. To continue, we will need to look underneath sets, to the language of predicate logic within which the theories of sets is expressed. In the next chapter we will explore the consequences of abstaining from logic too.

Endnotes

1. **opening quote:** N. Weaver (2009) Is set theory indispensible? p.2. Online 8/18 at https://arxiv.org/abs/0905.1680

It is also well known that Wittgenstein was extremely critical of set theory: "Mathematics is ridden through and through with the pernicious idioms of set theory," L. Wittgenstein (1953) *Philosophical Remarks* §173.

2. **mereology, the study of whole/part relations:** Coins in a piggy-bank, a herd of cattle, a bunch of grapes, a deck of cards and a pair of shoes, none are sets and none of the constituent components are elements of a set. A pair is a numeric measure, analogous to a half dozen. These objects are merelogical sums that can be located in physical space, whereas sets are abstract compositions of discrete elements. Sets also cannot describe fractions of wholes. For formal examples, see R. Casati & A. Varzi (1999) *Parts and Places*.

3. **a long shadow over the philosophy of mathematics for the rest of the century:** D. Corfield (2004) *Towards a Philosophy of Real Mathematics* p.238-9.

4. **arises from this fundamental assumption that a set can create a difference:** T. McFarlane (2007) Distinction and the foundation of arithmetic p.3. Online 8/18 at http://www.integralscience.org/distinctionarithmetic.pdf

5. **membership is analogous to the relation** is-contained-by**:** The curly brace is both the set theoretic container and the generic James container. Sets use commas to separate members, so there is little risk of confusion.

6. **a characteristic of the environment holding those members together:** A *cognitive* environment constructs indicators of objects having what we perceive to be the property of interest. The selected set is a product of our physical environment, our perception, our capabilities, predispositions, filters, motivations, objectives, and the like, that is, a densely connected network of personal distinctions.

7. **no object in mathematics exists without a name:** H. Poincaré (1908) *Science et Méthode*.

8. **understand numbers in terms of a more fundamental 'sub-numerical' concept:** McFarlane p.2.

9. a measuring rod against which sets are compared for numerical size:
P. Maddy (1993) *Realism in Mathematics*. Quoted in *Bulletin of the American Mathematical Society* **32**(1) (1995) p.142.

10. two tell-tale signs of a mereological conception: M. Potter (2004) *Set Theory and its Philosophy* p.23.

Potter's reference to Dedekind is his 1888 *Was sind und was sollen die Kahlen*, translated in W. Ewald (1996) *From Kant to Hilbert: A source book in the foundations of mathematics* p.787-832.

11. the sum of its points rather than as a collection of them: Potter p.32.

12. anatomy gains little by viewing the human skeleton merely as a deposit of calcium: Corfield p.31.

13. since the logical principles are presupposed even by the set-theorists: M. Kline (1980) *Mathematics: The loss of certainty* p.256.

14. the set of all James forms, the language of a James algebra: The technical idea of a *language* is not taught in elementary mathematics so much as assumed. Imagining a potential infinity of constructible forms may simply be laziness in identifying the systemic limits of a language. We could draw the line, for instance, at comprehensibility. An incomprehensible finite form clearly violates other formal standards such as the ability to identify transformation patterns or the possibility to verify consistency. The idea of associating meaningfulness with numbers arises from Peirce's *pragmaticism*.

15. the number of forms in the James language cannot be infinite: It may be tempting to default to an inability to imagine that numbers end, to default to a belief that a natural number can always be increased. This conundrum is no worse than trying to imagine an infinity of numbers directly. The difference is one of conceptual training not conceptual confusion. There is clearly a largest meaningful number M. Adding one to M changes its type, it is no longer meaningful. Mathematics *could* elect to respect an ultimate syntax/semantics barrier. Representations without any possible meaning are not semantically valid. Yes, modern physics relies on creatures such as infinite dimensional Hilbert spaces, but could this not be an error of immature understanding?

16. **perhaps *the* characteristic hypothesis of set theory:** P. Maddy (2014) A second philosophy of arithmetic. *The Review of Symbolic Logic.* **7**(2) p.222-249. (Footnote 6, p.223, emphasis in original.)

17. **no more necessarily 'true,' than unending extension of space:** B. Rotman (1993) *Ad Infinitum* p.120.

18. **or the result of an application of modus ponens:** C. Franks (2009) *The Autonomy of Mathematical Knowledge* p.74.

19. **mathematical induction declaratively incorporates as universal quantification:** S. Feferman & G. Hellman (1995) Predicative foundations of arithmetic. *Journal of Philosophical Logic* p.1-17. Online 8/18 at http://math. stanford.edu/~feferman/papers/predarith.pdf

20. **which only become available after we have all sets of natural numbers:** Weaver p.5.

21. **all subsets of any infinite set are assumed to exist:** S. Feferman (1992) Why a little bit goes a long way: Logical foundations of scientifically applicable mathematics. *Philosophy of Science Association* 1992 Vol. II. p.442-455. Online 8/18 at https://math.stanford.edu/~feferman/papers/psa1992.pdf

22. **and do not have any of them as their subject matter:** L. Wittgenstein (1953) *Philosophical Remarks* §188. p.36. Also see

V. Rodych (1999) Wittgenstein on irrationals and algorithmic decidability. *Synthese* 118 p.279-304.

23. **why should we believe that such an un-nameable real even exists:** G. Chaitin (2004) *Meta Math!* p.97-98.

24. **To an ultrafinitist these numbers also do not exist:** Different schools of mathematical philosophy adopt different canons which explicitly limit how that school sees the world. Computer scientists are commonly **ultrafinitists**, constructivists who professionally avoid both potential and actual infinities. Ultrafinitist thinking permeates commentary in these volumes. The computational capacity of the universe, for example, is limited to its storage capacity, which is somewhere around 10^{120} bits.

The computational storage capacity of the entire universe, as computed by Seth Lloyd of MIT, is about 2^{512} bits. (This is also about how many different chess games are possible.) Online 8/18 at `https://www.edge.org/conversation/seth_lloyd-the-computational-universe`. This example is meant to emphasize that we may have no idea what an arbitrary infinite real number might actually mean.

S. Lloyd (2002). Computational capacity of the universe. *Physical Review Letters* 88:237901.

A. Kornai (2003) Explicit finitism. *International Journal of Theoretical Physics* **42**(2) p.301-307.

Let's say that we could record a binary digit in the spin orientation of the smallest particle, say an electron. Let's say that we pack the entire universe solidly with these electrons and record the digits of a single number H on them, one digit per electron. Now lets imagine a digital language constructed by all the permutations of the digits of H. A larger number cannot by any realizable criterion be recorded. Roughly, 10^{86} cc for the volume of the universe and 10^{-39} cc for the volume of a proton gives us 10^{125} packed protons per universe. That's 10^{125}! (factorial, not amazement) possible arrangements, yielding approximately

$$H = 10^{10^{23500}}$$ possible universes.

We could certainly raise H to the power of H, H^H, but doing so is no less absurd than accepting a mathematics that is composed entirely of contradictions. What about a power tower of H exponents stacked H high? This finite number is still as far away from infinity as is a single unit.

25. **It tends to compress larger numbers into a smaller space:** S. Dehaene (2011) *The Number Sense: How the mind creates mathematics* p.246.

26. **the longer the proof the less likely it is to be valid:** M. Mannucci & R. Cherubin (2008) Model theory of ultrafinitism I: Fuzzy initial segments of arithmetic. Online 12/18 at `https://arxiv.org/pdf/cs/0611100v1.pdf`

27. **compares the axioms of ZFC set theory:** ZFC stands for Zermelo-Fraenkel set theory with Choice. Ernst Zermelo developed the axioms of set theory in 1908. A decade later (1922), Abraham Fraenkel (along with several other luminaries) refined Zermelo's axioms to accommodate the description of infinite cardinal numbers which were essential to Cantor's

original vision. Georg Cantor is credited with the invention of set theory in the 1880s. The Zermelo-Fraenkel axiomatization included a quite controversial axiom called the Axiom of Choice. Without it we have ZF set theory. There are many versions of the axiom of choice, essentially it states that the members of any set can be arranged in some well-determined order from first to last. This capability is essential for mathematical induction to work.

28. **number will now manifest itself, without limit, as tyranny:** A. Badiou (1990) *Number and Numbers* p.57. (Emphasis in original.)

29. **A set exists for any identified property:** The axioms of set theory are phrased as if sets were the only type of thing. A natural intuitive concept within one system often does not sound natural and intuitive when phrased in the vocabulary of sets. Replacement for example is stated colloquially as "Replacing equals with equals does not change the value of an expression." But to state the same idea as an axiom for sets, we need to claim that doing "replacement" generates another set. I've been relatively loose in phraseology within this section and here's why. The set theory Axiom of Replacement might be stated as:

Let S be a set and let $a \in b$ be an expression. If for all the elements in S, i.e. $\forall a \in S$, there is a unique set b so that $a \in b$ is TRUE, then there exists a set T such that $b \in T$ IF for some $a \in S$, $a \in b$ is TRUE.

That's how you say "substitute equals for equals" in set theory.

Chapter 28

Logic

We often think that when we have completed our study of
one we know all about two because "two" is "one and one".
We forget that we have still to make a study of "and".[1]
— *Arthur Eddington (1927)*

During the foundational period of the early twentieth century, sets triumphed over logic as the putative foundation of mathematics. It was a devil's agreement. The absolutism of logical Truth was exchanged for the incomprehensibility of esoteric axioms and a full embrace of infinity. Dichotomous thinking (which still dominates Western civilization) harbors irresolvable contradictions. Obviously. From a century later we can easily understand that knowledge is contextual. In this century, many folks prefer contradiction and constraint to absolutism, for example in the form of paraconsistent and linear logics.

28.1 Doing without Logic

Formal logic is anachronistic, providing particularly narrow and clumsy and inherently confusing constraints upon how we might chose to explore possible mathematical structures. Logic is also tricky, because throughout the history of Western civilization logic has been taken to be synonymous with *how people think*. Boole's book, which

George Boole
1815–1864

turned implicational logic into Boolean algebra, was entitled *The Laws of Thought*. We can safely ignore this historical predisposition. Today it is abundantly clear from neuro-physiology and from the irrationality of human behavior that nothing like logic goes on in our heads.

Truth

Truth is at the foundation of logic. Couturat's **Principle of Assertion** goes so far as to confound symbolic existence with Truth. "To say that a proposition A is true is to state the proposition itself."[2] This principle is at the core of void-equivalence as well.

$$(A = \text{TRUE}) \Rightarrow A \quad ☞ \quad (\ ) \neq void$$

Historically, logic and geometry came first, followed by algebraic thinking, followed by wide-spread use of arithmetic and very recently by computational thinking. So it is difficult not to regress, not to look for the presumed Truth underneath boundary forms. For our purposes, **truth** is strictly defined as *transformations that do not violate the structural axioms*. Iconic form does not require a separate semantics to determine truth. It does however require Existence to differentiate distinction from *void*.

existence

$(\ ) \neq void$

Truth also sneaks in when we make an assertion of equality. Two forms might be equal or not equal. From a computational perspective, abstract truth is not needed here as well, the challenge is *finding* a transformation path between the forms in question, not about proving that a path may exist. Even if there are two assertions that mutually lead to a contradiction, the question is not about truth, it is about consistency. Here boundary math weans us from the idea of logical truth, the kind of Truth that many folks believe is eternal.[3]

Implication

Propositional calculus gets weird when it comes to proofs, to the dynamics of manipulation of compound NOR relations. Logic introduces an *asymmetric* concept: implication can go in one direction but not back in the other direction to return to the starting point. Asymmetric implication differentiates logic from algebra. Implication imbues logic with stepwise directionality, with a sequential transformation structure.[4]

We do not need to stop thinking in the style of logic, since it is a direct interpretation of boundary structure. Calling upon the logical boundary, *implication is an interpretation of containment.*

$$A \; \textit{implies} \; B \quad ☞ \quad \langle A \rangle \; B$$

Classical Mathematics is reputed to describe how Physics works. This belief is one directional due to the biasing perspective of logical implication. The association is certainly not causal. We can equally as well say: Physics describes how Mathematics works.[5] Math is an *instrument* that we use to probe the workings of the world. Math is a result of human behavior. As a tool, it carries out our demands and returns feedback to our perceptions in terms of it effects. In neither direction is the association between Logic and Physics implicational. Mathematics *implies* only within its own sphere. We apply math to describe, to simplify, and to abstract the *actual*, never to imply it.

Here are some reasons why trying to constrain modeling and thinking to classical logical implication and Truth is not a good idea.

— Experience, observation and science are much more complex than logic.
— Logical foundations do not include the human processes of doing math. Logic lacks dynamics.
— Truth is contextual; proof is cultural.
— Mathematical logic is a branch of mathematics.
— Logic has recently fragmented into dozens of different types, such as modal, temporal,

concurrent, situated, fuzzy, linear, intuitionist, boundary, imaginary...

— Neuroscience has found no basis for the belief that logic and thinking are related.

Philosopher Carlo Cellucci nicely summarizes the objections to logical deduction:

> To claim that the logic of mathematics is deductive logic because theorems are justified by deductive inference, restricts mathematical experience to ways of reasoning found only in textbooks of mathematical logic, and neglects those that are really used in mathematical activity.[6]

Deconstruction

Logic provides an ancient and honored set of tools and principles and has recently been fully converted into an algebra. The **predicate** part of logic provides an infrastructure for domain theories. A **domain theory** consists of a set of labeled objects, and a collection of operations upon and relations between those labels. It is conventional to minimize the influence of labeling by calling the labels themselves "objects".

Quantification is a mechanism to attach variables to objects within some domain. OK, let's say that we have some domain of objects in mind. Constructive computation usually presumes **universal quantification**: a variable name can stand in place of any object within the established domain of discourse. *Computationally* we must, at some time, produce a direct representation of or pointer to that object.

$$\forall x \ Px$$
$$\exists x \ Px$$

If we begin with no *domain specific* objects or operations, then we are left with a predicate calculus consisting only of variables, quantification, and propositional logic.

A *variable* can be a **label** attached to some other form, or a **proxy** for one of any of the objects being considered, or a **hole** into which any structurally valid form can be put. Until we try to use it, however, a variable can just be an atom, like a unit, that does not interact with anything. Yes, there are technical details about how to connect variables to their referents but we can treat that question separately. The point is that there is some work we can do without knowing what a variable actually is. We can address the **structure** of a logic.

Existential quantification, the assertion that at least one of the objects described does exist, does not necessarily show us that object. Assertion of existence becomes unnecessary for a constructive approach in which the only way we have to refer to an object is to show it explicitly. Existential variables then are pointers to existent objects.[7]

When variables refer only to objects that can be constructed, we can convert any variable into a proposition, a statement that is clearly either TRUE or FALSE. Instead of actually constructing each relevant object, we can assert that if it becomes necessary, we can find what the variable is identifying. "The object you reference can be supplied upon request." Or more briefly, "Here." If the object cannot be located, then the variable is FALSE. In this case, predicate calculus degrades into **propositional calculus**. Variables then stand in place only of the idea of Truth or the idea of not-Truth. The "calculus" part of propositional logic is the connectives AND, OR, NOT and others that form expressions containing propositional variables. It turns out that these connectives are mutually redundant, we need *only one* for complete expressibility, the NOR or the NAND connective. We are left with **one binary relation**, a NOR b, upon which logic is constructed, together with the ideas of Truth and Label. We have rolled both Truth and Label into the real-time construction of presumed objects to fill the holes identified by a variable. This leaves

frames	☞	*relational expressions*
void inversion		
$([\ ]_A)_B$		$R(B,A)$ *and* $S(A,\ )$
dominion		
$(A\ [\ ]_B)_C$		$R(C,A)$ *and* $R(C,B)$ *and* $S(B,\ )$
generic frame		
$(A\ [B]_C)_D$		$R(D,A)$ *and* $R(D,C)$ *and* $S(C,B)$
arrangement		
$(A\ [B\ C]_D)_E$		$R(E,A)$ *and* $R(E,D)$ *and* $S(D,B)$ *and* $S(D,C)$

Figure 28-1: *Frames expressed as relations*

configurations of $NOR(a,b)$ relations to define the language and the structure of elementary logic.

A logic that uses equality as the primary connective is *algebraic*. The concept of Truth shifts from the value of a NOR expression to the correctness of an assertion that two forms have the same value, whatever that value is. Value itself is then defined by axioms and theorems that permit transformation of structure.

Not Logical Relations

Now let's consider predicate logic with containers as relations. Figure 28-1 shows the relational expressions for some James frames. The relations associated with each type of boundary are labeled R for the round-boundary, S for the square-boundary and N for the angle-boundary.

$R(1,2)$ ☞ $(2)_1$

$S(1,2)$ ☞ $[2]_1$

$N(1,2)$ ☞ $<2>_1$

$$(A\ B)_C\ ☞\ R(C,A) = TRUE\ and\ R(C,B) = TRUE$$

Unfortunately, the structure of logical relations is undermined by boundary transformations. Empty containers reduce relations to properties by reducing the number of *labeled form* ☞ *relational expression*

Inversion

$$([A]_C)_B = [(A)_B]_C = A$$

☞ $\{R(B,C), S(C,A)\} = \{S(C,B), R(B,A)\} = A$

Reflection

$$(\ldots A <A>_B \ldots)_G = (\ldots)_G$$

☞ $\{A, N(B,A), \ldots\} = \{\ldots\}$

Arrangement

$$(\ldots (A [B C]_D)_E \ldots)_G = (\ldots (A [B]_{D1})_{E1} (A [C]_{D2})_{E2} \ldots)_G$$

☞ $\{R(E,A), R(E,D), S(D,B), S(D,C)\}$
$= \{R(E1,A), R(E1,D1), S(D1,B), R(E2,A), R(E2,D2), S(D2,C)\}$

Figure 28-2: *James axioms as sets of relations*

arguments from two to one. A compound form requires extensive use of logical AND to collect the relations that compose it. Logical AND, in turn, requires that relations return a truth value rather than a structure. Elementary logic therefore provides no structural information about that which does exist.

The primary structural James template is the inversion frame, (A [B]). Paired boundaries are the norm. Here is an example of the nested function format for an inversion pair.

$(A [B]_C)_D$ ☞ R(D,A) *and* R(D,S(C,B))

And here is the same example in relational format.

$(A [B]_C)_D$ ☞ R(D,A) *and* R(D,C) *and* S(C,B)

Alternatively, logical AND can be replaced by a *set* of relations,

$(A [B]_C)_D$ ☞ $\{R(D,A), R(D,C), S(C,B)\}$

Figure 28-2 shows the James axioms expressed as sets of relations. Here we have exchanged the awkwardness of logical conjunction for the awkwardness of set membership. The relational representation in the figure hides the nesting of operations in multiple references to the same container. (Figure 28-2 mercifully omits the relational structures associated with the mandatory outermost boundary G.) Transformations defined by the axioms, though, change the internal argument structure of the relations that they map to. The James axioms

— change relations into properties and properties into grounds (i.e. objects)
— bring relations in and out of existence
— create new structures that replicate relations
— condense different relations into the same relation.

We are left with the observations that

— Deduction applies to labels rather than things.
— Implication and truth are not particularly good ideas for the organization of thought or computation.
— James transformations violate the structure of logical operators and relations.

28.2 Doing without Functions

A **function** is a type of relation that is restricted by two rules. The **existence** rule requires every member of the domain to participate in the function. The **uniqueness** rule requires that each member of the domain be associated with exactly one member of the co-domain. A common description of a function is as an *input/output* machine. We put a value into this machine and out comes a transformed value. The machine works for every different input value, and there is only one output value.

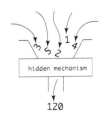

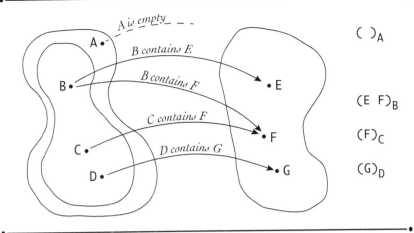

Figure 28-3: *Mapping the* contains *relation*

Functional thinking has been emphasized lately in education. Seeing the world as functional relations is conveniently simple, there is only one possible outcome for each beginning. But it completely misses the general relatedness of things. In particular, we can't build collections based on analogy, ambiguity or systemic interdependence. Disjunctive choices, the concept of OR, are difficult to manage. Functional thinking does not support constraint-based reasoning or reasoning by elimination. Nor are functions friendly to parametric reasoning over sample spaces. Neither is functional thinking natural for communication networks or cybernetic feedback. Functions combined with variable labels do provide representations of partial information and of possible intermediate states.

The two rules that constrain functions are incompatible with the conceptual structure of containers. Figure 28-3 shows the mapping of the contains relation from containers to contents. Containment is an *ordered relation* between two forms, not a function. The first form is the container, the second is the content form. Containers can be empty. There is no associated second object so the

functions

$(F)_B$

$(F)_C$

$(G)_D$

not functions

$(\ )_A$

$(E\ F)_B$

single boundary forms ☞	*functional terms*

the constants, grounds or units

$( )_B$ $[ ]_C$ $< >_D$ $R(B,)$ $S(C,)$ $N(D,)$

the containment forms

$(A)_B$ $[A]_C$ $<A>_D$ $R(B,A)$ $S(C,A)$ $N(D,A)$

$R(B,A)$ reads: *object* A is-contained-by *round boundary* B

Figure 28-4: *Boundaries expressed as* is-contained-by *functions*

one-to-many

$R(E,A)$
$R(E,B)$
$R(E,C)$
☞
$(A\ B\ C)_E$

existence constraint for functions is violated. Containers have unlimited capacity, they also violate the one-to-many uniqueness constraint of functions. As well, the many-to-one mapping of functions violates the physicality constraint of containers. We can do without functions because the basic structural relation between container objects, A contains B, is quite different than the limited type of relations defined by functions.

The inverse relation, B is-contained-by A, however, is functional *under the physical interpretation* of containers. Every object except the (sometimes implicit) global outermost container is-contained-by some object. And every object is-contained-by only one container. So James container structures do support functional thinking. Almost. In Chapter 29 we will explore the PUT function, which is a renaming of the is-contained-by relation as a function that emphasizes a process-oriented *construction* of forms rather than the object-oriented *description* of forms.

PUT **function** $(A)_B$ ☞ A ⊕ B   *put* A *into* B

PUT is not strictly substitution since it does not preserve equality, but PUT can be expressed roughly as a global substitution:

global substitution   *put* A *into* B ☞ $((A\ C)_B\ (C)_B\ (C)_B)$

---

labeled form ☞ *functional expression*

Inversion

$$([A]_C)_B = [(A)_B]_C = A$$

$$☞ \quad R(B,S(C,A)) = S(C,R(B,A)) = A$$

Reflection

$$(..A <A>_B..)_G = (...)_G$$

$$☞ \quad G(G,\{A, N(B,A),...\}) = G(G,\{...\})$$

Arrangement

$$(..(A [B C]_D)_E..)_G = (..(A [B]_{D1})_{E1} (A [C]_{D2})_{E2}..)_G$$

$$☞ \quad G(G,R(E,\{A, S(D,\{B,C\})\}))$$
$$= G(G, \{R(E1,\{A,S(D1,B)\}),R(E2,\{A,S(D2,C)\})\})$$

Figure 28-5: *James axioms as nested functions*

Functional Patterns

Figure 28-4 compares the notation of boundary forms to that of predicate calculus functions. Empty boundaries are conventionally identified as constants and we have been calling them that. The designation of a constant as a *ground* comes from the inductive/recursive model. However, from the perspective of is-contained-by, the empty boundary remains a function that identifies its outer container while not being the argument of any other is-contained-by function.

Figure 28-5 displays the James axioms as expressions composed of nested functions. Yes, the functional notation does get ugly! Part of that ugliness is that the language of **function composition** is inadequate for expressing boundary transformation patterns. When a labeled boundary has several content forms, several function calls are required.

Visualization of the functional form of James pattern rules is murky for several reasons. Boundaries have two

*not standard
notation*

$2_A +_1 4 +_2 6 +_3 2_B$

$((\cdot)_B \cdot)_A$ ☞

B is-contained-by A

available referential structures. In a pattern, *a boundary represents itself* as a universally quantified variable (a universal shape, a generic picture, …). We can also *label* each specific boundary in a pattern. In contrast, function notation is not indexical, it is unusual to label each occurrence of a function symbol, just like we do not usually uniquely identify each occurrence of the same variable or the same numeric constant. The *operational concepts* associated with boundary pattern-matching and function application are thus significantly different. Boundary forms themselves are discrete, so we often need a name for *each instance*. That name is associated with the unique outer container of each form.

Pattern transformation creates a great inconvenience for functional definitions, since pattern-based axioms specify a *constraint* on function composition, not the behavior of a specific function itself. Functions cannot represent the structure of boundary forms since they do not accommodate the concepts of

— a necessary outermost boundary,
— void-equivalent forms, and
— transformations that alter function structure

Functions still require logic or sets to express multiple arguments. Because of their **fixed arity** constraints, sets and functions are inextricably connected. Sets avoid calling upon logic by hiding the computational necessity to apply functions successively. Function nesting avoids the appearance that sets are necessary by constructing logical collections joined by AND. However, some definition or structure will eventually need to explain what AND means, as Eddington points out in the opening quote.

Not Nothing

Functions transgress upon a fundamental non-concept of container arithmetic, that of nothing, *void*. Clearly *void* cannot participate in the function is-contained-by B. The functional behavior of an empty boundary is the same as any other boundary, it identifies *its* outer container. However *void* is not contained because it is on both sides of every container.

The issue of absence also shows up for Reflection, which can reduce a form to *void*. Conventional notation handles empty containers differently. To accommodate absence of contents, we must create a symbolic object such as { } or 0, or define a function that can have any number of arguments. Functional thinking does not support creation of or operation upon the absence of a symbol.

void inversion

([ ]) = [( )] = *void*

There is also a ghost in this machinery. *Void-equivalent forms* constitute a background potential. They are everywhere available, and they can be used to construct desired patterns *de novo*. They are also inert. You can throw void-equivalent forms away (delete them) or add them in (create them) at any time without changing the structural intention or the interpretive meaning of an existent form. Void-equivalent forms can also be used as **catalysts** for transformation. This type of behavior is outside of functional behavior, and as it turns out, outside of conventional relational behavior as well.[8]

Multiple Arguments

Functions rely upon the propositional connective AND to reference multiple occurrences of the same function. The central question is how to describe two or more contents within the same boundary, for example

(A B)$_C$ ☞ A is-contained-by C *and* B is-contained-by C

In the James form, R(C,A) and R(C,B) are independent relations, there is no function or relation that provides a direct connection between A and B. From the perspective of the container, both are contained.

C contains A   *and*   C contains B

Do we necessarily need logical AND? Figure 28-5 uses the curly braces of set notation for multiple arguments to avoid calling upon logical connectives, such as in the Arrangement axiom.

$$[B\ C]_D \qquad ☞ \qquad S(D,\{B,C\})$$

Set functions take one argument, a set with unlimited members. We have replaced logical AND by a *collection*, the set contained-by C, but this significantly distorts the intention that the two contents are mutually independent. Although both B and C is-contained-by D, from the James perspective they do **not** share the property of being the contents of D. As an analogy, consider a function of two variables $f(x,y)$ where x and y are orthogonal (e.g. the standard Cartesian plane). The two variables x and y are mutually independent, it is the function f that specifies their relationship. Without the function f the only accorded relationship is orthogonality, which itself is induced by the coordinate system. Abandon the coordinate axes and the fractionalization of space into locations (points) and we begin to approach the interior of a container.

Non-functional Transformations

The most serious failure of functions to capture the patterns of boundary algebra is that the axioms of James algebra permit transformations that undermine the association between functions and their arguments. As a comparative example, Inversion is equivalent to canceling functional inverses, and can be expressed functionally as

$$([A]_C)_B = [(A)_B]_C = A \qquad ☞ \qquad f(f^{-1}(A)) = f^{-1}(f(A)) = A$$

A different circumstance exists for Reflection. The number of arguments of the G bracket is both 2 and 0.

$$(A\ <A>_N)_G = (\ )_G \qquad ☞ \qquad G(A,N(A)) = G(\ )$$

Now consider Arrangement. Simplifying the functional notation, eliminating labels, and permitting multiple arguments leaves

$$R(A,S(B,C)) = R(A,S(B)) \text{ } and \text{ } R(A,S(C))$$

The axiom converts one function application of R into two, while reducing the arity and changing the signature of the S function from binary to unary. When extended to multiple contents of the S boundary, the axiom permits construction of an S function with essentially arbitrary arity.

Incomprehensible Recursive Functions

Goodstein's Primitive Recursive Arithmetic provides an example of transferring the entire mechanism of logic over to the structure of recursive functions, apparently with only the slight problem that combining component equations requires the concept AND. But there is a deeper problem with a specific type of function: exponentials. A problem with our current interpretation of brackets, then, is a problem for James brackets in general. Here's the story.

Peano's axioms create a potential infinity of whole numbers by combining induction with the axiom that the successor of a number is also a number. But Peano does not allow for the possibility that there may be numbers other than those joined together by the ladder of succession.

The predicate is-a-number identifies one of what we are calling *all the numbers*. This predicate, or property, replaces the concept of set membership. Shortening is-a-number[...] to N[...], Peano's first two axioms are presented then in Figure 28-6 in three notations: words, sets and functions. Edward Nelson spent his career asserting that Peano arithmetic itself may be inconsistent due to its incorporation of potential infinities.[9] The recursive definitions of addition and multiplication both

words	*sets*	*functions*
one is a number	$1 \in N$	$N[1]$
every number has a successor	$n \in N \Rightarrow n+1 \in N$	$N[n] \Rightarrow N[n+1]$

Figure 28-6: *Generation of the numbers by Peano*

require the associative property, however exponentiation is not associative. Nelson observes that from this discontinuity, the arithmetic operations on two numbers {+ ,×, ∧} do not necessarily construct a number.

Figure 28-7 shows the self-similar tower of arithmetic functions, including hyper-exponentiation, symbolized by ⋏. Certainly taking an inductive step generates a valid number, but are there other numbers not reached by inductive steps? Nelson's suspicion is that induction and recursion conflate potential and actual infinities. We can apply the successor axiom to climb the ladder of induction, but that does not assure that exponentially larger steps still produce *every* number, even though exponentiation has a valid inductive definition.

There are also difficulties in formally defining exponentiation within a bounded arithmetic. Bernays observes that exponential power towers cannot be arithmetized without including function variables within the recursive definitions.[10] There is also the specter of proofs that are exponentially complex and thus out of reach of both humans and machines.

Predicativism accepts the natural numbers while seeking to keep axioms and the techniques of proof finite. Feferman has shown that Primitive Recursive Arithmetic is sufficient.[11] However Friedman and Nelson have exposed another deep issue. Not only might it be possible that whole numbers are not closed under exponentiation, exponentially recursive functions can grow so

words	base	recursion
tally	m + 0 = m	m + (0+1) = (m + 0) + 1
addition	m + 0 = m	m + (n+1) = (m + n) + 1
multiplication	m x 0 = 0	m x (n+1) = (m x n) + m
exponentiation	m ^ 0 = 1	m ^ (n+1) = (m ^ n) x m
hyper-exponentiation	m ⩘ 0 = m	m ⩘ (n+1) = (m ⩘ n) ^ m

Figure 28-7: *Self-similar tower of arithmetic functions*

exceedingly rapidly that they may lead us to *completely incomprehensible finite* "numbers".[12] Bluntly, exponentially increasing inductive steps might generate whole numbers that cannot be reached by the successor function. It does require a practiced cognitive flexibility to abandon the possibility that one-step-at-a-time is insufficient to achieve closure of N. The indoctrination of learning to count at the age of two or three is powerful. But it is an item of faith rather than definition that numbers remain countable as we approach thoroughly incomprehensible cardinality.

28.3 Remarks

In *Laws of Form* Spencer Brown reconceptualizes logic based on boundary forms.[13] This seminal text presents many of the distinction-based concepts incorporated within James arithmetic. Chapter 15 compares the axioms of boundary logic to those of James algebra, showing the deep structural similarities that unite logic and numerics. The iconic work of Peirce and Spencer Brown confirms that logic itself can be reduced to containment patterns and labels. Spencer Brown's iconic logic is *not isomorphic* with Boolean algebra. Rather it is a fundamental formal iconic system that provides conceptual grounding for a symbolically more verbose propositional logic.[14]

As soon as we step over the line that separates the three boundary logic axioms from conventional mathematical foundations, we inherit a tremendous amount of mechanism, the mechanism that this chapter seeks to abstain from using. Yes, all that mechanism is necessary for higher mathematics, for professional use by mathematicians, but it is a horrible idea to assert that all that mechanism is what school children should understand in math class. The usual argument for hiding the depth of math from kids is that it is premature to introduce complexity to school children. This deception, however, does not work because the mechanism of mathematics slips out as soon as a student begins to understand what math is (not to mention that the argument sadly misassesses the capabilities of children). Textbooks are kind enough, and deceptive enough, to assume that learners already know this mechanism and so students rarely learn how substitution or proof or logic or axiomatic relativity or comparative design decisions work.

In the next chapter we examine a natural iconic representation of boundary structure as networks of distinctions. The single binary PUT function suffices to construct any James form. Patterns of PUT functions are sufficient to specify the transformation axioms. Distinction networks (∂nets for short) embody PUT functions as links and boundaries as nodes, structurally eliminating the need for both labels and label replication.

Endnotes

1. **opening quote:** A. Eddington (1927) *The Nature of the Physical World: the Gifford Lectures* p.104-5. Online 8/18 at http://henry.pha.jhu.edu/Eddington.2008.pdf

2. **true is to state the proposition itself:** L. Couturat (1905) L. Robinson (trans. 1914) *The Algebra of Logic* p.71. Online 8/18 at http://www.gutenberg.org/ebooks/10836

3. **Truth that many folks believe is eternal:** In the twentieth century, logic became relativized or situated or contextual. Truth is a function of its interpretative context. $1 + 1 = 2$ except in the context of a binary system, in which case $1 + 1 = 0$. As an example of contextualized truth, Mathematician Thomas Etter has developed a three-valued equality operator, F(A=B), F *believes* A=B.

T. Etter (2006) Three-place identity. Online 12/18 via the Wayback Machine: https://web.archive.org/web/20130510223843/http://www.boundaryinstitute.org/bi/articles/Three-place_Identity.pdf

4. **stepwise directionality, with a sequential transformation structure:** The structure that makes reasoning sequential is

a IMPLIES b = ((a NOR FALSE) NOR b) NOR FALSE

In combination with FALSE, IMPLIES forms a basis for propositional calculus.

J. Łukasiewicz (1948) The shortest axiom of the implicational calculus of propositions. *Proceedings of the Royal Irish Academy* **52A**(3) p.25-33.

5. **Physics describes how Mathematics works:** In *A New Kind of Science* (2002), Stephen Wolfram reconstructs much of physical science from the distributed spatial formalism **cellular automata**, providing a proof in principle that Science does not necessarily depend upon symbolic mathematics.

6. **neglects those that are really used in mathematical activity:** C. Cellucci (2002) "Introduction" to *Filosofia e mathematica*. In R. Hersh (ed.) (2006) *18 Unconventional Essays on the Nature of Mathematics* p.27.

7. **pointers to existent objects:** T. Skolem (1928) On mathematical logic. In J. van Heijenoort (ed.) (1967) *From Frege to Gödel*. Skolem showed how to eliminate existential quantification using a function to identify an arbitrary object.

8. **outside of conventional relational behavior as well:** For further information on and examples of the use of void-equivalent forms as catalysts for computational

reduction of logic forms, see W. Bricken (2002) Generalized insertion. Online 11/18 at http://iconicmath.com/mypdfs/bl-general-insertion.020118.pdf

9. **may be inconsistent due to its incorporation of potential infinities:** E. Nelson (2015) *Elements*. Online 11/18 at https://arxiv.org/abs/1510.00369

10. **variables within the recursive definitions:** P. Bernays (1935) Hilbert's investigations into the foundations of arithmetic Dirk Schlimm (trans.). Online 12/18 at http://www.phil.cmu.edu/projects/bernays/Pdf/untersuchungen.pdf

For a technical discussion see S. Buss (1999) Bounded arithmetic, proof complexity and two papers by Parikh. Online at https://www.math.ucsd.edu/~s-buss/ResearchWeb/parikh/paper.pdf

11. **Primitive Recursive Arithmetic is sufficient:** S. Feferman & T. Strahm (2010) Unfolding finitist arithmetic. *Review of Symbolic Logic* **3**(4) p.665-689. Online 8/18 at https://math.stanford.edu/~feferman/papers/UnfoldFA.pdf

12. **completely incomprehensible finite "numbers":** One challenge game played by googologists is to identify the largest finite number that is clearly definable. Leaving functional definitions in the dust, Rayo's number, for example is "the smallest positive integer bigger than any finite positive integer named by an expression in the language of first order set theory with a googol symbols or less." A googol is 10^{100}. We could of course, in the spirit of Figure 21-1 Gödelize the description of Rayo's number. The reason for considering ultra-large numbers is that each of them is as far from infinity as the number 1. Online 8/18 at http://googology.wikia.com/wiki/Googology_Wiki

13. **Spencer Brown reconceptualized logic based on boundary forms:** G. Spencer Brown (1969) *Laws of Form*.

14. **for a symbolically more verbose propositional logic:** W. Bricken (2017) Distinction is Sufficient: Iconic and symbolic perspectives on *Laws of Form*. *Cybernetics and Human Knowing* **24**(3-4) p.29-74. Online 12/18 at http://iconicmath.com/new/distinctionissufficient/

This paper demonstrates that conjunctions and sets of relations *accidentally* introduce logic into Spencer Brown's boundary mathematics. The problem is the projection of *symbolic structure* onto an inherently iconic system. This volume makes the same arguments for the structure of our arithmetic of numbers. Iconic tallies are not isomorphic with the symbolic arithmetic of numbers.

Chapter 29

Containment

*The method of mathematics
is the study of diagrams or graphs.*[1]
— Charles Sanders Peirce (c1900)

Here's where we stand thus far. Boundary math is a collection of formal techniques for iconic notations. A boundary is a clearly delineated region, a cognitive distinction. Configurations of boundaries are *forms*. Selected axioms provide transformations that define equivalence classes of forms. These axioms are specifically chosen to provide a map between a boundary system and a conventional system. Many such maps are known, here we have been exploring the relationship between models of containment and models of numbers. The iconic form of containment defines an inside and an outside. Geometric boundaries (curves in a space of any dimension) are of two types, open and closed. We are exploring the iconic use of the closed variety.[2]

The distinction between bounded and unbounded goes back to the ancient Greek Parmenides, who took issue with the philosophy of the Pythagoreans. The school of Pythagoras taught that the interplay between Being (in the form of small natural numbers) and non-Being (as

*Parmenides
515-c.450 BCE*

the void) generated and limited what exists. Parmenides rejected the concept of the void. For his school what exists is absolute and spherical. (The spherical shape of the universe is a recurrent theme throughout European history.) The important consequence is that a spherical universe is necessarily bounded. The distinction between a bounded and an unbounded universe plays out throughout history as the contrast between finite and infinite.

Parmenides argued that we cannot think of the void, because *that which is not* does not exist. He conflated existence with thought, another theme running through Western philosophy. If thought cannot arise from nothing, if the universe cannot arise from nothing, then everything that is has always been. The world is eternal, there was no Big Bang. Essentially Parmenides rejected duality.

29.1 Containers

We have been portraying containers as forms that encompass other forms. The only relation between forms is that of containment. The dynamic model is the act of putting something into a container. In all cases we can represent the **containment relation** by two labels, one identifying the container and the other identifying the form that is contained. The curly brace here is our generic James container.

$$\text{A contains B} \quad \text{☞} \quad \{B\}_A$$

The inverse of the contains relation is the is-contained-by function, B is-contained-by A.

We have also introduced *types of containers*, encoded visually in the shape of typographic brackets. Figure 29-1 shows the textual and the 2D graph representations of some simple James forms. The graph representation is a **distinction network**, a *∂net* for short. Peirce considered these graphic representations to be the fundamental mathematical tool of description. For Peirce, the merit of

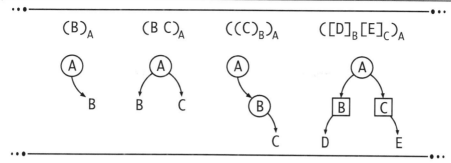

Figure 29-1: *Some simple distinction graphs*

graphical or diagrammatic representation "springs from its being veridically iconic, naturally analogous to the thing represented, and not a creation of conventions."[3]

A fundamental constructive property of **containment** is that the individual contents of any container are *mutually independent*. The only structural relationship defined by a container is that of containing a content form. Multiple contents require multiple containment relations. Each individual content form is itself a boundary around its own (contextually deeper) contents.

Formal Structure

It is possible to look just at shapes and the permitted transformations of shapes, without adding stories or concepts such as containers or counting. From a purely mathematical perspective, both containers and numbers are metaphors, models that make visualization easier. The logical content is one binary relation, R(A,B), with certain relational properties. Structure comes from restricted composition of different instances of this relation. But as was observed in Chapter 28, the containment relation is not a logical relation. It is an iconic boundary relation that differs from the relations of predicate calculus in its handling of outermost boundaries, *void*, multiple contents, and permissible transformations.

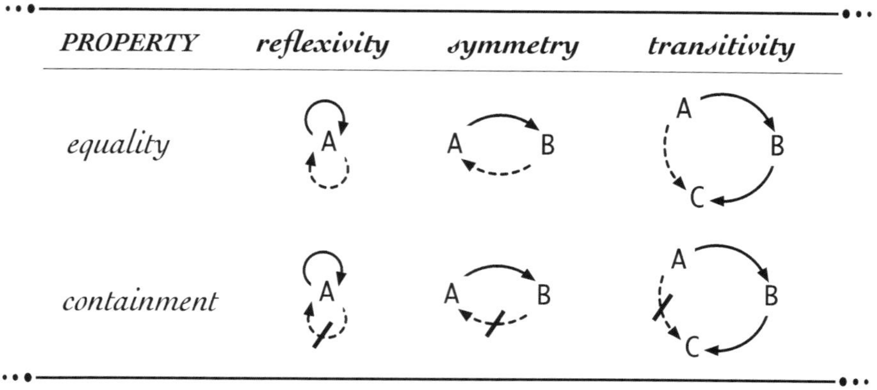

PROPERTY	reflexivity	symmetry	transitivity
equality			
containment			

Figure 29-2: *The relational structure of equality and containment*

Container equality is defined as having the same contents. Identical containers have identical contents. As well, some non-identical forms are equal by rule. The relation of equality for container forms, like all types of equality, is defined as being reflexive, symmetrical and transitive. In contrast, the relation of containment itself is based on difference, essentially the opposite of equality. The physical shallow containment relation is irreflexive, asymmetric and intransitive. Figure 29-2 shows this comparison.

The types of brackets (round, square, angle) could be viewed as defining three different relations, however the relational structure of each is the same. Bracket types matter only within the pattern-matching contexts of the axioms (and within the interpretation). The different types can therefore be seen to be extensions of the same single relation.[4]

The mechanism of constructing structure by composing relations, together with the idea that some structures are equal but not identical, leads naturally to questions about closure (are all constructions permitted?), consistency (can we create forms that are both unequal and equal?), completeness (can we construct all possible forms?) and convergence (do different sequences of transformation lead to the same results?).

Our culture has embraced the stories of logic and number and containment to such an extent that we believe them to be real. In a formal sense all that is real is relative structure defined by design rules. Containment and connection and contiguity are all the same relation with different nuances. Our theme is that number and logic are that same relation also, with different nuances created by small changes in design. To be able to see this semi-universal communality across basic mathematical ideas we need to go below and beyond them all, to the cognitive *ur-element*, the **distinction**. The journey is particularly difficult today because mathematics has evolved into a five-thousand-headed hydra, spewing esoteric symbols and incantations that assure it to be unreachable and unteachable without extensive professional training.[5] An equally valid description is that within the last sixty years mathematics has cross-connected its silos and subject categories into a densely woven matrix of relationships within which mathematicians are only now identifying the invariant structures.

the same (ish)

$R(A, B)$

$B \Rightarrow A$

B^A

Forms

A *form* is a specific, valid configuration of containers. From the conventional symbolic perspective, valid arrangements are identified by predicate calculus constraints on a universe of possible relational terms and formulas. From the iconic perspective, **valid containment forms** are constrained by construction, that is by putting forms into other forms. To display a form as a nesting of delimiting brackets that form must be physically constructible.

In iconic systems, logic becomes confounded with experience. The relational constraints of predicate calculus that would define valid *symbolic* James formulas are replaced by a representation of the *meaning* of the contains relation. Relations become bracket structure, which in turn becomes configurations of physical containers. James algebra dwells in physicality rather than in abstraction, while the semantic shift from symbol to icon to physical manifestation retains all of the abstraction inherent in the language of symbolic algebra.

Labels that identify specific forms can be replicated; replicas of labels permit multiple reference, potentially undermining physical containment while permitting transformations that do not violate intended equality. *Symbolic replicas* thus expand expressibility at the cost of physical semantics. The apparently minor change of the addition of arbitrary unique labels for structures permits symbolic construction of imaginary configurations of containment that in turn lead to arbitrary complexity. *Notation* itself forcefully reminds us when we shift from models of reality to pure abstraction. Labeling followed by replication of the labels marks that boundary.

29.2 Bracket Languages

Well-formed parentheses have been extensively studied, although usually as a trivial introduction to more complex systems, and rarely with the interpretation of containment. Textual brackets are also called *delimiters*.

Kleene's 1952 *Introduction to Metamathematics* provides some elementary theorems.[6] Parentheses are sufficient to unambiguously fix the order of operations in a mathematical expression. Kleene's three lemmas can be related directly to concepts within boundary algebra.

— *Brackets represent containment.* There is only one proper pairing for well-formed typographic parentheses, "(" and ")".
— *Containers nest.* Subsets of well-formed parentheses are well-formed.
— *Every form is grounded by a unit.* Well-formed parentheses have an innermost pair.

Languages composed solely of nested and concatenated brackets are called *bracket languages*, or more technically, *Dyck languages*. These languages extend to any number of types of brackets. Bracket languages always have an outermost container, so that ( )( ) is not a valid expression, but (( )( )) is. Bracket languages are also finite, which means that (...) does not imply infinite contents.[7] We have emphasized these necessary characteristics throughout. Unfortunately almost all study of bracket languages has been limited to string notation, which treats "(" as a different symbol than ")". From the perspective of containment this is of course nonsense driven by a fractured textual representation.

The most common use of bracket languages is in computer programming. In fact, the dominant language of the web, HTML, is a bracket language as are many high-level programming languages such as LISP and *Mathematica*. Perhaps the most relevant theoretical use for bracket languages to date is to define the difference between context-free and context-sensitive grammars.[8] Loosely, a *string language* is a structured sequence of words which themselves are structured sequences of characters, all given validity by the structural definitions and rules of the language. Context-free languages have transformation rules that are insensitive to the surrounding characters and words. In the case of the James language, we can apply the axioms regardless of other contents in a container and regardless of depth of nesting.

The Chomsky-Schutzenberger Representation Theorem combines a string language with a bracket language. The combined language is **context-free** only when the bracket language can be erased without creating an invalid expression. This concept can also be expressed through deletion of symbols. A language is context-free if all characters of the string language can be erased without creating an invalid expression in the bracket language. This theorem is important because it assures that parentheses can be added freely to establish operator precedence in string languages. For us, it manifests as the idea that variables can be deleted from any form without creating an invalid form. Again, an obvious result if we consider parentheses and variables to represent arbitrary containers.

In string bracket languages, erasing delimiters can result in ambiguity, for example

$$2 \times (3 + 4) = 14$$
$$2 \times 3 + 4 \quad \text{☞} \; \textit{ambiguous}$$

Erasing content and leaving delimiters in conventional string languages leaves well-formed containment structures that have no meaning.

The Representation Theorem highlights the central structural difference between string languages and bracket languages: *bracket structures require processing memory* to keep track of when a boundary has been crossed inwardly and when it has been exited.

In sequential computers, all processing is based on long strings of 0s and 1s. Often parts of these sequences need to be temporarily stored. *Pushdown automata* are abstract machines that store substrings on *stacks*. Bracket languages are fundamental to the control of a pushdown automata. Just like written words are separated by spaces, parentheses define grouping within strings, and thus specify when a stack is needed to store temporary results. When reading a string, it is straight-forward for a computer program to interpret "(" as *put on the stack* (push), and ")" as *take off the stack* (pop).

String languages with brackets are sufficient to define and compute all of the dominant types of mathematics today. The **Wolfram Language**, for example, is a premiere example of a comprehensive string processing bracket language capable of reading, computing and outputting *any* mathematical specifications, from numeric

type	name	purpose
(term)	*parentheses*	grouping
f[x]	*square brackets*	functions
{a,b,c}	*curly braces*	lists
m[[i,j]]	*double square brackets*	indices

Figure 29-3: *Formal delimiters in Mathematica*

arithmetic through advanced calculus and combinatorics.[9] The Wolfram language incorporates four types of delimiter listed in Figure 29-3.

29.3 Trees

Configurations of containment can also be expressed as **trees**, a computer science data structure of nodes and links that includes a single top node (the trunk) and empty bottom nodes (leaves) with each internal node having exactly one upper (parent) link. Trees have been exceptionally well-studied within computer science, they are one of the foundational data structures. We know that trees can be processed in parallel, that nodes can manage additions and deletions locally and independently, and that trees support object/operator confounding.

Trees map one-to-one with well-formed parenthesis structures. (Figure 29-5 provides an illustration.) The number of possible tree structures matches the number of possible parenthesis structures, with one nuance. Since parentheses are typographic, the order in which each symbol occurs matters. In contrast, the branches of a tree are unordered and ungrouped.[10]

different

$(( )_1( )_2)_3$
$(( )_2( )_1)_3$

not different

From a purely relational perspective, the top/bottom orientation of trees is unnecessary. There is a privileged node (the "top") that all links head toward, and empty nodes (the "bottom") that all links head away from. Or vice versa.

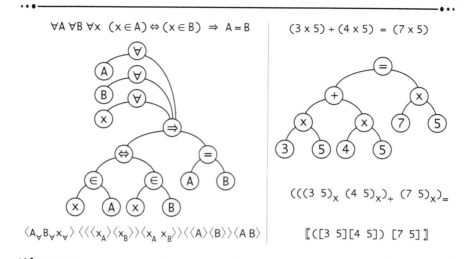

$$\forall A \, \forall B \, \forall x \; (x \in A) \Leftrightarrow (x \in B) \; \Rightarrow \; A = B$$

$$(3 \times 5) + (4 \times 5) = (7 \times 5)$$

$$\langle A_\forall B_\forall x_\forall \rangle \; \langle\langle\langle x_A \rangle \langle x_B \rangle\rangle \langle x_A \; x_B \rangle\rangle \langle\langle A \rangle \langle B \rangle\rangle \langle A \, B \rangle$$

$$(((3 \; 5)_x \; (4 \; 5)_x)_+ \; (7 \; 5)_x)_=$$

$$[\![\, ([3 \; 5][4 \; 5]) \; [7 \; 5] \,]\!]$$

Figure 29-4: *The tree structure of expressions*

It is straight-forward to express both formulas in predicate calculus and expressions in numeric arithmetic as tree structures. Figure 29-4 shows the graph representation of textual predicate calculus and textual arithmetic. The predicate calculus expression on the left asserts that two sets are equal if they have the same members. Universal quantification, ∀, is also a containment relation for which variable labels identify (contain) all the sets and elements within the domain of discourse. The boundary structure at the bottom of the logic graph in Figure 29-4 is hybrid. It uses the **logic boundary** to provide an impression of what set theory might look like in a boundary notation.

The arithmetic identity on the right side of Figure 29-4 converts fully to a boundary form. Underneath the conventional string expression are three spatial representations: the graph and two boundary versions. The version directly below the graph uses boundaries labeled by their functionality (+, ×, =). Although the structural elements are boundary forms, they are not James forms. Addition, for example, has its own type of boundary. In the bottommost form of the numeric example, labeled boundaries are exchanged for different bracket shapes: [ ] means x, ( ) means +, and ⟦ ⟧ means =. The James form of the arithmetic expression in the figure, for reference, is

$$([3][5])([4][5]) = ([7][5])$$

which is a specific instance of Arrangement. Here of course ( ) is interpreted as ∧ and [ ] is interpreted as log.

In the two examples, the predicate symbols for objects and operators are embedded within the nodes of the tree. Links are purely structural and carry no information other than which symbol is adjacent to which other symbol. James trees are fundamentally different in that they embed semantics, the meaning of containment, into the links of the tree. Nodes carry meaning in their diversity while special sequences of node types qualify the tree for reduction by structural pattern-matching.

Not Group Theoretic

A **rooted tree** has one outermost node; all James forms are thus rooted. Rooted trees do not have a preferential ordering of their branches. Ordering of content nodes is not a concept within the iconic notation, there is no structural information within the collection of links to support such a notion. The visual notation of equal orderings below distorts the spatial perspective to show linear permutations to be equal. The iconic display, in contrast, is invariant under rotation in three-dimensions.

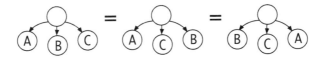

In the freedom of three dimensions, spatial transformation can be achieved by a greater diversity of methods, including two-dimensional spatial reflection, temporal network traversal and three-dimensional rotation. Traversal of a graph is a variety of being inside its form.

By permitting the reader to inhabit the three-dimensional space of representation, rotation can be expressed equivalently as the movement of the viewpoint of the reader. Symbolic notation limits a reader's viewpoint to outside the form, so relations such as commutativity must be expressed as a structural transformation of the representation. Iconic notation, in contrast, incorporates the concept of viewpoint, so that commutativity does not require restructuring the representation. Simply looking from a different perspective is sufficient.

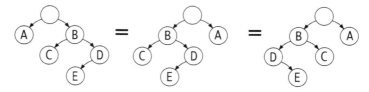

The two-dimensional page imposes accidental structure that forces the three-dimensional perspective into our imagination. Similarly the static accidental structure of the page suppresses dynamics such as moving one's perspective. We trade cognitive effort for physical display economy. The poverty of the page can be somewhat alleviated by attaching URL links to appropriate videos.

An associative string function is also a temporal sequence of accumulation. In a network, this accumulation over time can be represented by nodes that create additional depth in the representation.

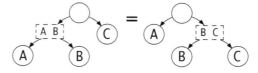

C.S. Peirce considers associativity to be a variety of commutativity. From the perspective of iconic patterns, both arranging and grouping the contents of a container (i.e. establishing an arity) violate the independence of those contents. Since containment itself is the iconic grouping operation, support of binary arity would require the

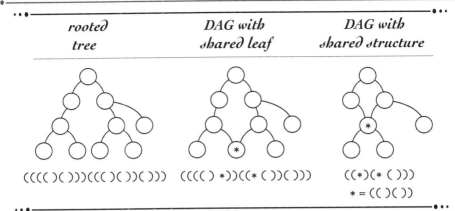

| rooted tree | DAG with shared leaf | DAG with shared structure |

(((( )( )))((( )( ))( )))   (((( ) *))((* ( ))( )))

((*)(* ( )))

* = (( )( ))

Figure 29-5: *Trees and directed acyclic graphs*

insertion of additional containers, in effect the creation of a new type of container. Although depth and breadth are different structurally, the network itself unifies these apparently different properties of string representations. Conceptually, all nodes can be processed, traversed, and/or viewed at the same time. Both commutativity and associativity are implementation details rather than fundamental properties. As accidents of representation they should not be considered to be "the rules of algebra".

Structure Sharing

Trees are a constrained type of **directed acyclic graph** (DAG) in which nodes have only one *upper* connection, one container. In general DAG nodes can have any number of upper connections. Trees are compared to DAGs in Figure 29-5. The figure also shows a linear parens notation for each DAG. The linear forms illustrate how multiple reference supports non-physical containment. The marked node in the center DAG is a *shared leaf* that has two upward paths or parent links, or in our case containers. Graph variables convert trees into directed acyclic graphs. The marked node in the rightmost DAG shows *shared structure* that has two paths upward and multiple paths downward.

Structure sharing is the process of using the same label to identify the same compound expression in different locations within a larger expression. In any pattern-matching implementation, or any implementation that uses symbolic labels, structure sharing is an essential tool to identify and store identical structures that may occur in multiple locations. Condensing a structure by using a label to identify identical substructures is necessary for addressing large problems, for instance, optimizing the routing of million gate silicon circuits.

structure sharing
dialects

Structure sharing in symbolic notations usually occurs through *explicit labeling of equivalent expressions*. Labeling is strictly controlled by assigning different labels to each different structure. Whenever two identical structures are identified, they can be assigned the same label. This label usually participates in transformation as a discrete object, with the implicit constraint that the transformation is restricted to operate on the label itself, and not on the compound form identified by the label. **Multiple reference** is the sole source of complexity in these formal structures.[11] Structure sharing in James forms does not necessarily violate the physicality constraint but it does require a dialect that supports multiple contacts. In almost all descriptions of symbolic transformation outside of computer science, though, structure sharing is not mentioned and is relegated to an implementation detail.

29.4 James Distinction Networks

((([B]] <[A]>))

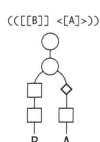

Figure 29-6 shows the dnet representation of the three James axioms.[12] Each James form has a single trunk (the outermost container). Branches stem from the trunk and from one another (nesting). Each branch ends in a leaf (an empty container or a label). We have three different types of bracket. Each tree node could be one of the three, so for a given tree with N nodes, there are 3^N James *arithmetic* forms prior to applying any reduction rules. Certainly Inversion and Reflection decrease this number significantly.

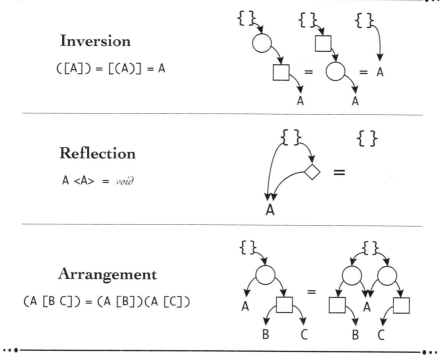

Inversion

([A]) = [(A)] = A

Reflection

A <A> = *void*

Arrangement

(A [B C]) = (A [B])(A [C])

Figure 29-6: *James axioms as distinction networks*

Network Constraints

The structural constraints on James forms can be represented abstractly as forbidden graph structures. Figure
29-7 expresses these constraints as relational concepts, as
symbols and as graphs. A bar across a link in the directed
graph indicates that the marked link is not permitted.

The **Existence Constraint** requires that every configuration of containers be bounded by some outer container.
Forms, like symbolic expressions, are singular objects.

The **Irreflexive Constraint** is a physical limitation on
containers. No container is inside itself.

The **Asymmetric Constraint** forbids reentrant containment graphs. The intention is to exclude cyclic

existence	irreflexivity	asymmetry	physicality
$\neg\{\ \}_{void}$	$\neg\{A\}_A$	$\{B\}_A \Leftrightarrow \neg\{A\}_B$	$\neg.\{C\}_A\ \&\ \{C\}_B$

no void	*no self containment*	*no reentry*	*no sharing*

Figure 29-7: *Symbolic and iconic constraints on James Onets*

chains of containment. Containment graphs are acyclic. Asymmetric relations are necessarily irreflexive.

The **Physicality Constraint** forbids a form to be the content of two different containers, because overlap (intersection) is not physically possible when container boundaries cannot be breached. Symbolically, however, the *label* of an object can be replicated and placed in different containers, in violation of the no overlap restriction. Replication of labels is a primary difference between symbolic and physical models of containment. A specific apple can be only in one bag, but a generic, abstract label of appleness can be in many bags. Physically though, when we say that there are apples in the bags, we mean that there are different apples in different bags.

arrangement

(A [B C]) =

(A [B]) (A [C])

Arrangement puts the replicated label A into two different containers. In Figure 29-8 the graph representation of Arrangement can incorporate either replicated labels or convergent links. Numeric structures require generation and replication of labels, as demonstrated in Chapter 6. It is this replication that maintains a tree structure which can then be recorded by a textual string. If we were to limit replication within a graph then the tree becomes a DAG. Replication is embedded in the links of the graph.

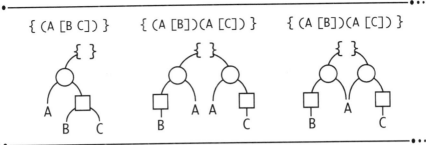

Figure 29-8: *Graphs of arrangement*

Both replication of labels and upward branching links indicate that we have stepped away from physical possibility into abstract structure supported by symbolic labels. It is precisely at this juncture that complexity of form and process enters.

29.5 PUT Functions

Containment is an asymmetric binary relation. The asymmetry can be described as non-commutativity.

A contains B ≠ B contains A   ☞ $\{B\}_A \neq \{A\}_B$

This relational description is both static and object-oriented. A *functional* description can be both dynamic and process-oriented: the function as an **input/output machine**. Rather than describing the end result that A contains B, we could describe the process of *putting* B *into* A. The PUT function could be written as put(B,A) or we could recruit an infix binary operator and give it a new symbol called *put*: B ⊕ A. The PUT function converts an achieved nesting such as ([A][B]) into the process of constructing the form.

([A][B])

Put A *into an empty square-bracket.*
Do the same for B.
Now put both into an empty round-bracket.

The domain of PUT is grounded by the two units: the empty square-bracket S, and the empty round-bracket

R. We will also need the outermost generic container G, whether explicitly or implicitly.

$$\text{PUT } R \textit{ into the top-level } G$$
$$R \oplus G \quad \text{☞} \quad \{ \; \} \Rightarrow \{ ( ) \}$$

G maintains a single outermost container, but it is *syntactic sugar*, a shorthand notation for one of the container types, R, S or N. The primary use of G is for putting the first object into *void*, that is, shifting from a conceptual to a representational mode. Once that is accomplished, G becomes superfluous.

PUT does not require labeled boundaries

The innermost *void* has no functional interpretation so we shift attention to the empty containers as ground objects. With PUT functions it is not necessary to label replicas of each type of boundary since the order in which we assemble configurations of boundaries is sufficient to distinguish one form from another. This converts labeling objects into sequencing transformation steps, while permitting unambiguous use of replicas to identify multiple occurrences of specific types of boundary. For example,

dots specify order of operations

$$\text{PUT } R \textit{ into } G \textit{ and do it again}$$
$$R \oplus . R \oplus G \quad \text{☞} \quad \{ ( )( ) \}$$

The *dot* is what people used before parentheses to specify **order of operations**.[13] We're using it because parentheses and other brackets are already in use. The above construction reads: First put R into G and then put another R into the result. The sequence of PUTs determines multiple use of the same boundary. Dots partition the string of boundary symbols into sequential pairs, with more deeply nested pairs partitioned by more dots. Alternatively, dots identify a construction sequence in which more dots identify later constructions. Here's another example for comparison.

$$\text{PUT } R \textit{ into } R \textit{ and PUT that into } G$$
$$R \oplus R . \oplus G \quad \text{☞} \quad \{ (( )) \}$$

In both cases, the two Rs refer to two different round-boundaries. Combining the two examples above,

PUT R *into* R, *do it again, then* PUT *that into* G

$$R \oplus .R \oplus R: \oplus \ G \ \text{☞} \ \{ \ ((\ )(\ )) \ \}$$

To help with reading the sequence of PUTs, there's a short-hand used in function notation: simply don't write the function symbol.

$\{( )( )\}$	☞ $R \oplus . R \oplus G$	☞	$R.RG$
$\{ (( )) \}$	☞ $R \oplus R .\oplus G$	☞	$RR.G$
$\{ (( )( )) \}$	☞ $R \oplus . R \oplus R : \oplus G$	☞	$R.RR:G$

One more simplification. The final .G is an instruction to put everything into G, the outermost inert container. The .G can be dropped, since every construction is, as a last function application, "PUT by itself" into its final resting space.

Figure 29-9 shows the James axioms expressed as PUT functions in both the explicit and abbreviated functional notations. These PUT functions are rather ugly,[14] requiring elaborate nesting that does not match the elegance of the boundary forms. The excess notation carries the sequential steps of construction, bringing attention to the imposition of another linear accident.

Commutativity

Usually a particular form can be constructed by many different PUT sequences, so there is another set of algebraic reduction rules to address invariants of sequential construction. The description of structure using sequentially ordered pairs of symbols has computational and conceptual overhead. It is here, for example, that rules of commutativity must be introduced.

$$(a \ b) \ \text{☞} \ b \oplus . \ a \oplus R \ \text{☞} \ b.aR$$
$$(a \ b) \ \text{☞} \ a \oplus . \ b \oplus R \ \text{☞} \ a.bR$$

This suggests a "put into container C in any order" rule. Potentially concurrent construction can be expressed as an invariance over sequential steps.

$$X.YC = Y.XC$$

James form	☞ *PUT function*	*unwritten* ⊕

Inversion

([A]) = [(A)] = A

☞ A ⊕ S.⊕ R = A ⊕ R.⊕ S = A   AS.R = AR.S = A

Reflection

A <A> = *void*

☞ A ⊕:A ⊕ N.⊕ G = G   A:AN.G = G

Arrangement

(A [B C]) = (A [B])(A [C])

☞ A⊕:B⊕.C⊕S:⊕R⊕::G = A⊕:B⊕S.⊕R::A⊕:C⊕S.⊕R⊕:G

A:B.CS:R::G = A:BS.R::A:CS.R:G

Figure 29-9: *James axioms as* PUT *functions*

PUT Graphs

The binary PUT function is neither associative nor commutative. Changing the grouping of objects to PUT changes its meaning (i.e. the resulting construction), as does exchanging the forms being PUT *in* with forms being PUT *into*. PUT with dots is just a linear notation for a spatial containment *graph*. By moving the notation into two dimensions, dots can be eliminated as an accident of typography. The clarity of function composition benefits from a spatial display. Figure 29-10 compares the PUT function graphs (on the left) to the more natural distinction networks (on the right) for the three James axioms. The figure is a bit of an overstatement to make an essential point. Both the awkward notation and the sequential composition of the typographic PUT functions are accidents due to communication using a string of symbols. The textual notation encourages us to see steps as one at a time. It is not inherent in the semantics of PUT functions that they be composed

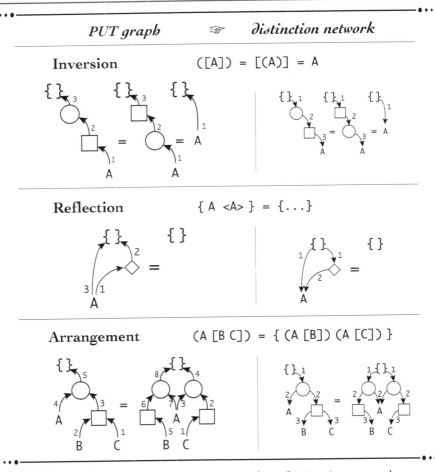

PUT graph	☞	distinction network

Inversion   ([A]) = [(A)] = A

Reflection   { A <A> } = {...}

Arrangement   (A [B C]) = { (A [B]) (A [C]) }

Figure 29-10: *Comparing* PUT *graphs to distinction networks*

in sequence. That illusion is a residual from how we think about function composition as taking sequential steps.

Figure 29-10 includes numbered steps annotated beside the PUT graph and the dnet links. The PUT sequence is taken from the linear specification of PUT compositions in Figure 29-9. In the case of Inversion, the sequence is natural, we are embedding and then embedding again. The dnet also shows three steps. In the case of Reflection, A can be embedded concurrently (step 1 in the dnet), the PUT sequence is accidental. Finally, in the case of

Arrangement, the PUT graph and the linear specification suggest the availability of concurrent construction. The PUT specification, A:BS.R::A:CS.R:G, includes initial constructions BS and CS which are *not* expressed as linearly dependent by grouping dots. The three sequential steps within the dnet provide structural evidence that the linear specification is confounding sequential and parallel composition. Both the PUT graphs and the distinction networks show clearly that the number of necessary sequential composition steps is identical to the depth of nesting. Even this linear dependence is an accident. With the appropriate resources and access, all PUTs can be implemented at the same time.

29.6 Remarks

We have traced the various attempts to represent containment structure in symbolic terms. These include

- label replication
- set membership
- argument positioning
- logical conjunction and
- function nesting.

We have also been using two iconic representations, containers (as represented by typographic delimiters) and networks. Both adequately represent the physical circumstance of putting containers into other containers. Two other iconic representations are also widely in use: Spencer Brown's LoF crosses and Peirce's circles.

Symbolic expressions cannot do justice to iconic concepts. One insight is that structure, in both breadth and depth, should be apparent rather than abstracted. Another primary insight is that typographic expressions require many structural techniques that compensate for the lack of expressibility caused by the linearity of string expressions. These artifacts have significantly degraded the mathematical ideas they are meant to represent.

Endnotes

1. **opening quote:** C.S. Peirce (1931-35) *Collected Papers of Charles Sanders Peirce*. C. Hartshorne & P. Weiss (eds.) Volume 3 § 556.

2. **the fundamental properties of the closed variety:** Abstractly, any curve can be viewed intrinsically as temporal motion along a given spatial trajectory. The spatial and temporal locations corresponding to each point on a curve can then be expressed as a collection of space-time coordinates. Instead of viewing a curve as a trajectory with x and y coordinates relative to an external origin, we view the curve as a single *relationship* between a space coordinate and a time coordinate, independent of origin. Since the space-time points can be mapped isomorphically, all curves are identical. The space-time perspective (the *phase space*) describes two general classes of curves: those for which each space-time point has one label (open curves), and those for which the two end points of an open curve are defined to be the same spatial point.

3. **naturally analogous to the thing represented, and not a creation of conventions:** C.S. Peirce 4.368.

4. **be seen to be extensions of the same single relation:** In predicate calculus we would say that the containment relation is the first-order theory, while different types of containment lay the groundwork for a second order theory.

5. **unreachable and unteachable without extensive professional training:** There are about 5000 different subtopics in the Mathematics Subject Classification maintained by the American Mathematical Society. When I was a graduate student at Stanford, I would go into the Math Library and select a volume at random, to see how far I could read with understanding. The great majority of the time I left disillusioned, having been stopped at the very first page. C.N. Yang, Nobel Prize winner in Physics has commented

> There are only two kinds of math books. Those you cannot read beyond the first sentence, and those you cannot read beyond the first page.

6. **provides some elementary theorems:** S. Kleene (1952) *Introduction to Metamathematics* p.23.

7. **does not imply infinite contents:** We have used the ellipsis, "...", only with the implication of a finite number of forms.

8. context-free and context-sensitive grammars: M. Davis, R. Sigal & E. Weyuker (1994) *Computability, Complexity, and Languages 2nd ed.* p.308.

9. numeric arithmetic through advanced calculus and combinatorics: S. Wolfram (2017) *An Elementary Introduction to the Wolfram Language 2nd ed.*

10. the branches of a tree are unordered and ungrouped: When spatial ordering of containers is included, the number of bracket structures for a given number of brackets is the well-known *Catalan numbers*. In our case, when order does not matter and there is always an outermost container, this sequence is the *rooted trees* (Online Encyclopedia of Integer Sequences A000081).

11. sole source of complexity in these formal structures: Labeling is not strictly necessary for most data structures that can be easily recorded in strings (examples include lists, sets, trees and arrays). Purely functional languages, for example, replace all labels by function nesting. Multiple reference is achieved by recomputing functions. However graphs may require labels when multiple links connect the same node. This complexity was a significant obstacle during the development of object-oriented programming languages with inheritance in the late 1980s, and may help to explain the relatively late incorporation of graphs and networks into mathematical notation.

12. the graph representation of the three James axioms: These graphs do not fully express the structural constraints defined by each axiom. For example each node may have links other than those depicted. For a complete description of the representation needed for pattern-matching dnets, see W. Bricken (2017) Distinction is Sufficient: Iconic and symbolic perspectives on *Laws of Form. Cybernetics and Human Knowing* **24**(3-4) p.29-74. Online 12/18 at http://iconicmath.com/new/distinctionissufficient/

13. used before parentheses to specify order of operations: A. Whitehead & B. Russell (1910) *Principia Mathematica*. Online 8/18 at https://archive.org/details/PrincipiaMathematicaVolumeI

Russell and Whitehead popularized this method of expressing nesting. They credit Peano for the invention (p.4). "The general principle is that a larger number of dots indicates an outside bracket, a smaller number indicates an inside bracket." (p.9).

14. These PUT functions are rather ugly: I did not intend for this section to sound like a satire of functional notation.

Chapter 30

Connection

We live in an era of number's despotism:
thought yields to the law of denumerable multiplicities;
and yet...we have at our disposal no recent,
active idea of what number is.[1]
— Alain Badiou (2008)

Volume I presents two iconic approaches to the representation of the formal structure of arithmetic. It also serves as an introduction to a different way of thinking about formality. This volume compares the iconic concepts embodied in James algebra to those of string-based numerics. As we will see in the next volume, James forms also include structures that behave like imaginary numbers and those that behave like infinity. These forms arise naturally out of the three James axioms and require no additional transformational mechanism, with the exception that we will need to add a fourth axiom to be able to reduce the many forms that act like infinity.

Postsymbolism introduces *representational freedom* without the loss of formality or expressibility. Iconic form permits many new families of representation that allow us to directly see and interact with the abstract concepts of logic and arithmetic. These new ways of thinking are intended to greatly simplify elementary mathematics. Our audience is grade school students.[2] However the iconic innovations are very unfamiliar, a barrier unlikely to be torn down due to the universal acceptance of textual expressions as vehicles for the formal concepts described in Chapter 24. Iconic formalism is making progress in calculus since many of the concepts within calculus have traditionally been associated with Cartesian graphs, surfaces and objects of rotation, visualizations of trajectory and flow, and other physical applications. Although *void* is identified as a valuable tool for solving equations in Chapters 17 and 18, I cannot over-emphasize the impact of void-equivalent forms. Within our culture *void* is abhorred by religion, Nature and typography. And yet it is this absent foundation that permits iconic form to flourish, as exemplified in Chapter 20.

30.1 Cognition

Our endeavor is guided by two fundamental perspectives about the nature of reality, that nothing is not something and that all things are unique unless we have elected explicitly to ignore differences. Our entire exploration centers around the nature of difference. And difference is not within the physical realm, it is purely mind stuff. Gregory Bateson delineates the essential characteristics of difference:[3]

— Difference is not material and cannot be localized.

— Difference cannot be placed in time.

— Difference is not a quantity. It is dimensionless and, for sense organs, digital.

— Information is news of difference. It is not energy.

We harness abstraction by making it concrete, only to discover that concrete form itself is a difference that our perceptions impose in support of abstract thought.

Containers are a physical envisionment of *cognitive distinctions*. A distinction constructs a difference. Since difference is not a physical quality, distinction is a purely cognitive act. Difference is the way that our senses construct order out of an essentially undifferentiated reality.[4]

Cognitive distinction constructs boundaries to create forms. The boundary can be as simple as a label, as categoric as an arbitrary property or as physical as a tree. Identifying a label or a property or an apparently discrete physical object creates a relation between the labeler and the labeled. The relation we have been calling *containment* is between object and environment, not between objects within a shared environment. Containers themselves cannot be separated from their inside and their outside. The One comes only as Three. It is our choice of perspective that defines what is inside and what is outside.

The concept we have been calling *distinction* is a recognition that it is difference that counts, and that what we consider to be the same is our unique personal choice. The mathematical language of axioms and theorems and transformations is a rigorously structured microcosm that allows us to practice with safety what is truly real. Postsymbolism seeks to explicitly enrich that microcosm.

An individual's world is the dynamic network of distinctions that person is constructing at the time. **Distinction network** *(∂net)* then is both the name of the graphic display of containment relations and the name of the cognitive construction that the containment relations represent. The primary difference is one of degree of interconnectivity. The dnets used herein to describe arithmetic are a tiny slice of a cognitive perspective. In a sense, mathematical philosophy is an exploration of different slices of our cognitive dnets, networks that have already be radically partitioned by the agreed upon distinctions that define mathematics. *There is a Platonic reality, but it is unique to each individual.* Although mathematical formalism seeks to greatly constrain that uniqueness, it is apparent that there is little agreement within mathematical philosophy about which constraints are appropriate. However, so long as mathematics embraces disembodiment it is isolating itself from the roots of its creation and thus embracing an unintelligible philosophy.

30.2 Last Century

From a formal perspective, what we believe to be numbers and arithmetic was established during the early twentieth century, as presented in Chapter 22. But as the opening quotes from John Bell in Chapter 23, from Bertrand Russell in Chapter 24, from Carl Sandburg in Chapter 25 and from Alain Badiou in this chapter testify, we are still very far from understanding what number and its arithmetic is.

design choices depend upon notation

In this volume, we have explored many of the founding concepts and strategies employed to define formal numerics. We have deconstructed equality, induction, set theory, logic, functional thinking and symbolic representation in an attempt to identify how and why iconic arithmetic is different. A minor objective in this effort is to dissuade conventional mathematics from its predilection of degrading iconic form to an isomorphism with linguistic expressions. It is a startlingly narrow perspective to insist that representation is independent of meaning, and worse, independent of formal thinking. One great learning over the last fifty years is that *concept* is **embodied**, it does not exist separate from *homo sapiens*. We have met our ideas and they are us. This is not to suggest that concept is anchored to physical manifestation. But we no longer need to project great thoughts outward to an unknown and unknowable Agent in the sky. Here is cybernetician Francisco Varela:

> The proper units of knowledge are primarily *concrete*, embodied, incorporated, lived.... The concrete is not a step toward something else; it is both where we are and how we get to where we will be.

The structure of mathematics is inseparable from the structure of our cognitive distinctions. Both are non-physical and both are irrevocably anchored to experience.

30.3 Computational Perspective

Chapter 25 declares that the perspective of James algebra is *computational*, specifically Hilbert's ideas that mathematics is both structural and operationally finite (Chapter 21). A more modern perspective, which is expressed in Chapter 27, is *ultrafinitism*, that the type of mathematics that is meaningful to a computer scientist is that which can be done using an algorithmic strategy with time constraints limited to the life of the universe. Another description of this position is **computational pragmatism**.

Chapter 23 introduces Primitive Recursive Arithmetic (PRA), a minimalist foundation that is supported by Friedman and Feferman as sufficient for pragmatic mathematics. In the late 1930s, prior to the domination of silicon computers, several different academic cultures converged in understanding that they each had been addressing the *same* formal concepts from different perspectives. This understanding is the **Church-Turing Thesis**. Kurt Gödel and Jacques Herbrand pioneered what later became PRA. Herbrand, following closely in Hilbert's footsteps, developed the equational formulation of PRA. Alonzo Church and Stephen Kleene developed the *lambda calculus*, a system based on substitution and abstraction. Alan Turing developed Turing machines, a formal specification of what a computer can do. And Emil Post demonstrated that string rewriting systems too were equivalent to PRA, lambda-calculus and Turing machines.

Church-Turing Thesis

All reasonable formulations of the intuitive notion of effective computability are equivalent.

This convergence then guided the development of software programming languages which provide formal specifications of what is computable.

The most recent advocacy of the computational perspective is Stephen Wolfram's fundamental theorem in 2002, which arose from his study of **cellular automata**, a vastly different computational approach with strong local fine-grained parallelism and with simple accumulation rules determined by the state of adjacent neighbors within an unlimited discrete array. The distinction networks described in Chapter 29 are, by design, similar but with containment relations defining the meaning of adjacency between neighbors.

Principle of Computational Equivalence

Almost all processes that are not obviously simple can be viewed as computations of equivalent sophistication.[6]

The Principle of Computational Equivalence widens the Church-Turing Thesis beyond computation to laws and processes of Nature across all varieties of machines and brains. Stephen Wolfram:

> No system can ever carry out explicit computations that are more sophisticated than those carried out by systems like cellular automata and Turing machines.[7]

The implication is that formal processes, those that we understand as embodied in computers and thoughts, are *universal*. The gauntlet thus thrown is that infinite mathematics, the kind used by almost all pure mathematicians, is not realizable. This certainly does not suggest that the concept of infinity is not valuable or worthwhile, in developing approximate models for example and in explaining how some models break down. But to be *useful*, for measurement in particular, infinite models need to be scaled to conform with what we have been describing as ultrafinitism. Specifically to qualify as science, mathematical theories should be bounded, local and determinate.[8] Areas of mathematics that do not qualify as computable include real numbers, infinity, ZFC set theory, existence proofs and *void*. Even comfortable transcendental concepts such as π and e do not qualify as exact numbers. In Volume III we will be able to identify the specific structures within James algebra that step outside of computability. Iconic mathematics can embrace both computable and non-computable structures and clearly identify which is which.

Modern study of the *non-computable* came hand-in-hand with the Church-Turing thesis. It is relatively easy to identify what a computer cannot do. The archetype is the **Halting Problem**: a computer cannot tell you when it will finish a computation. Obviously neither can another computer observing that computation. Both cellular automata and dynamic systems have exposed deterministic processes that are *immune to abstraction*. These **chaotic processes** are formal but cannot be simplified or predicted. The only way to know what will happen next is to carry out the process. And yet they are simple iterative algorithmic processes that fall well within PRA. These processes are reversible, include nothing random or probabilistic, and are not knowable but through experience. There are a plethora of examples for which a computation cannot tell us about upcoming results except by taking all of the steps to reach those results. Applied to human experience, Tor Norretranders observes

> There are no principal universal logical rules that tell us anything we did not already know. The Church-Turing thesis and Turing's halting problem tell us that we can learn nothing unless it is through experience.[9]

Bluntly, knowledge *must* be embodied. Iconic math merely attempts to provide a more consistent formal representation, one that aligns with the structure of cognition. In this volume, distinction networks have converged with whole numbers to provide what Charles Peirce identifies as *the form of formal thought*.

30.4 Beyond Arithmetic

As we will see in Volume III, we can call a container "infinity" and still manipulate it directly, even though we are associating a concrete object with a very abstract concept. This finesse has an unexpected consequence. We may find that what we believe to be abstract is actually within reach. The creations of our imagination may indeed be unreachable, but for entirely different reasons other than their abstraction. Infinity can be as concrete as One.

For whatever reasons, we have designed here a numeric arithmetic that accumulates while insisting that only numeric forms can accumulate. Infinity can exist but cannot accumulate, while accumulating *void* is an absurdity. Thus both [ ] and *void* are non-numeric. We have accepted two types of existence (round and square) and constrained their interaction with three axioms or beliefs. Given this belief structure, we rigorously limited our conceptual and structural tools to those permitted by the axioms. Well, and one additional tool, the idea of equality abstracted as the Composition Principle and implemented as pattern-matching and substitution. Some forms may look different but we construct *beliefs* that define them to be the same. Thus axioms guide us into complexity by expanding identity into equality. A *pattern-matcher* can provide search and recognition, but not construction. For that we need a *substitution-engine* that must perform exacting surgery on existent forms and thus create permitted structural variety without creating monster forms that change their equivalence class.

We have pursued two themes that do not negate our understanding of arithmetic but rather that attempt to expand its conceptualization. To embrace an unified reality, to see interaction, connectivity and feedback as essential to an understanding of numbers, *concurrency* as described in Chapter 19 is mandatory. Dedekind and

Badiou envision our numbers as a unified whole, not as separate objects. To do so requires seeing them all at the same time, not visiting them one by one as encouraged by Peano's successor function and by today's fragmentary preschool educational practices described as "learning to count". Children need to learn first the cybernetic unity required for an appreciation not only of ecologies but also of social interaction. To combat prejudice we need to practice defining our world not by the properties of objects but by the network of connectivity that unifies object and environment.

The second theme is to reunite cognition with our bodies. What Chapter 26 calls postsymbolism is more than a visual and experiential approach to numbers, it is also an attempt to develop a deeper respect for the human being as constituted within a human body. The abstinence from sets and logic and functions described in Chapter 27 and Chapter 28 is based not only on coming to understand arithmetic better, it is also coming to understand social and cultural reality better by appreciating *uniqueness* rather than by collecting reality into sets defined by the properties of objects; by embracing *contradiction and context* rather than fabricating the dream that people should be rational; and by seeing feedback and evolution as the source of what we identify as structure rather than encouraging our senses to fracture cybernetic networks into input/output processes that distort both time and place.

30.5 Structure in Volume III

The content of Volume III has been mentioned incidentally many times. One reason for this is that the content grew beyond the space available in this volume. Although not disconnected from the ongoing exploration, three major aspects of James arithmetic have been exiled into Volume III.

AXIOMS

[ ]   [ ] ⇒ [ ]   **unify**

<[ ]><[ ]> ⇒ <[ ]>   **unify II**

[ ] <[ ]> ⇒ *indeterminate*   **indeterminacy**

(<[[ ]]>) ≠ *void*   **infinitesimal**

HYBRID AXIOM

(<[ ]>) = <[ ]> = [<[ ]>]   **infinite interpretation**

THEOREMS

(A [ ]) = ([ ]) = *void*   **dominion**

(A <[ ]>) = (<[ ]>)   **dominion II**

(A [[ ]]) =   [ ]   **dominion III**

[[ ]] = J <[ ]>   **double-square**

Figure 30-1: *Theorems of* [ ] *and* <[ ]> *(Figure 41-2)*

Infinite Forms

The James form (<[ ]>) is stable and can be interpreted as 1/0. Stable forms are grounds that are the constants of a formal system. Embedded within the James notation are forms of what might be called infinity, although that description relies upon our interpretation of these forms. It is a comfortable description because throughout history 1/0 has been associated with ∞. The empty square-bracket, [ ], is a non-accumulating, non-numeric unit that lies within the deepest level of all existent non-numeric James forms. (Void-equivalent forms are also non-numeric and rely upon a completely different mechanism: they are non-numeric *and* non-existent.) We will explore the unifying influence that [ ] has upon many of the infinite, banned and exceptional expressions within symbolic arithmetic. From our new perspective, infinite and indeterminate expressions can be identified by specific James structures and integrated within numeric arithmetic to eliminate the confusion currently associated

name	derivative	☞	interpretation
constant	dc $\;=$ void		dc $\quad\;\; = 0$
variable	dx $= o$		dx $\quad\; = 1$
power	d(u) $=$ (u [du])		d#^{u} $\quad = $ #^{u} (ln #) du
logarithm	d[u] $=$ (<[u]>[du])		d(log$_\#$ u) $= 1/$(u ln #) du
inverse	d<u> $=$ <du>		d(-u) $\quad = -$du
sum	d(u v) $=$ (du dv)		d(u+v) $\; = $ du + dv

Figure 30-2: *Derivatives of James boundaries (Figure 37-2)*

with computational exceptions. Figure 30-1 shows the structural forms and transformations in Volume III that derive from forms containing [ ] after reduction. We will be able to explore not only infinite expressions but other exotics such as infinite powers, infinitesimals, indeterminate variables, unresolvable forms, and logarithms with base 1, 0 and ∞.

Differential Forms

Closely connected to infinite expressions are the topics of limit theory and the calculus of derivatives. Volume III takes our first excursion past algebra to explore elementary differential calculus. Figure 30-2 shows the structure of the derivatives of James boundaries. As is typical of each of our James explorations, some remarkable structural regularities emerge.

Imaginary Forms

One of the most remarkable contributions of the study of James algebra is the stable form [<( )>], named J, which can be interpreted as log$_\#$-1. J is structurally numeric, as can be seen by the innermost round-bracket. It cycles in value with a phase of 2. When two J forms

J THEOREMS

J = [<o>]	**definition of** J
<A> = (J [A])	**J-conversion**
J J = *void*	**J-void object**
[<(J)>] = *void*	**J-void process**
([J][oo]) = *void*	**J-void tally**
J = <J>	**J-self-inverse**
[<(A)>] = A J	**J-transparency**
A (J [A]) = *void*	**J-occlusion**
J (J [J]) = *void*	**J-self-occlusion**
J = <[A]>[<A>]	**J-invariant**
[<J>] = J [J]	**J-absorption**
<(J/2)> = (<J/2>)	**J/2-toggle**

COMPLEX NUMBERS

i	☞	(J/2 [o])	*form of* i
π	☞	(J/2 [J])	*form of* π
a + bi	☞	a (J/2 [b])	*form of complex numbers*

Figure 30-3: J *patterns and transformations (Figure 34-2)*

accumulate, they return to *void*. The imaginary unit i has four phases in exponential space. As a logarithm J shares this exponential space with i. In Volume III we'll show that i can be decomposed into J. That is, i is *not* the fundamental imaginary unit, it is one-half of J. The precise relation is

$$i \quad ☞ \quad (J/2) = ((\ [J]<[2]>))$$
$$J \quad = \quad ([[i]][2]\ ) \ = [i][i]$$

J is the *sum* of two logarithms of i.[10] To express this in exotic symbolism

$$\log_{\#} -1 = \log_{\#} i \ + \ \log_{\#} i$$

Thus J provides a third variety of accumulation.

$$( )( ) \neq ( ) \qquad \textit{numeric accumulation}$$
$$[ ][ ] \Rightarrow [ ] \qquad \textit{unification}$$
$$J \quad J \ = \textit{void} \qquad \textit{cyclic accumulation}$$

Figure 30-3 shows what to expect from the exploration of the structural relations of J. Since J is within numeric James algebra, there are no new axioms, just several new theorems that with familiarity provide an entirely different perspective on imaginary numbers. As an operator, J also provides a new perspective on the operations of arithmetic, since any form with an angle-bracket can be expressed as a J-form. For example,

$$i^2 = -1 \qquad \text{☞} \qquad <o>$$
$$([<o>]) \qquad\qquad\qquad \text{enfold}$$
$$(\quad J \quad) \qquad \text{☞} \quad \#^J \qquad \text{substitute}$$

It is −1 that is the mother of imaginary numbers, not i and not J. The broadly useful angle-bracket that stands in place of conventional inverse functions can itself be replaced by the single constant J. James algebra then consists of two mutually canceling bracket types and a constant.

One final example. Euler's famous equation, $e^{i\pi} + 1 = 0$, is reputed to be mysterious yet we can derive it directly in a *base-free* form from −1 and the theorems in Figure 30-3. We first demonstrate that J = −iπ. In mixed notation,

$$<J> = (\qquad\quad J \qquad\qquad [J] \quad) \qquad \text{J-conversion}$$
$$(\quad J/2 \qquad\quad J/2 \ [J] \quad) \qquad \text{substitute}$$
$$([[(J/2 \ [o])] \ [(J/2 \ [J])]) \quad \text{☞} \ i\pi \qquad \text{enfold}$$

From above,

$$-1 = \#^J = \#^{-i\pi}$$
$$\#^{-i\pi} + 1 = 0$$

let # = 1/e
$$e^{\,i\pi} + 1 = 0$$

30.6 Remarks

Spencer Brown's book *Laws of Form* is seminal for grounding the formal theory of distinctions. He presented an iconic form for logic, as did Peirce. Here we have presented a possible iconic form for numbers. We next step into the deep end of this pool of thought, to explore the non-numeric and imaginary James forms. Volume III provides the structure and interpretation of forms that redefine Accumulation to generate imaginaries, indeterminates and infinities. These unexpected forms are entirely natural, arising solely from the three *numeric* James axioms. There is nothing more but to explore the consequences.

Endnotes

1. **opening quote:** A. Badiou (2008) *Number and Numbers* p.1.

2. **Our audience is grade school students:** Several pilot projects are under-way to introduce iconic thinking into the classroom. Past second grade, though, the utter dominance of textual form both in required curriculum and in the training of mathematics teachers makes traction nearly impos-sible. Even Euclidean geometry is being removed from the curriculum in the United States, both by suppressing visualization techniques and by converting geometry into exercises in symbolic logic proofs. Only a few experimental high school instructors who manage to mix "art" with "math" have succeeded in introducing symmetry, fractals, cellular automata, and information visualization into their math classrooms.

For pioneering work introducing Spencer Brown's *Laws of Form* and iconic algebra into the classroom, see

W. Bricken (1987) *Analyzing Errors in Elementary Mathematics*. Doctoral dis-sertation, Stanford School of Education.

W. Winn & W. Bricken (1992) Designing Virtual Worlds for Use in Mathematics Education: The Example of Experiential Algebra. *Educational Technology* **32**(12) p.12-19. Online 12/18 at http://wbricken.com/pdfs/03words/03ed-ucation/03iconic-math/07worlds-for-math.pdf

W. Bricken (2007) *Presentation at WSMC07*. Online 12/18 at http://wbricken.com/htmls/03words/0303ed/030305spacearith.html

M. Klein & O. Pelz (2018) No Box Today. Online 12/18 at https://www.noboxtoday.com/

3. **delineates the essential characteristics of difference:** G. Bateson (1991) *A Sacred Unity* p.219. Online 8/18 at https://monoskop.org/images/c/c3/Bateson_Gregory_Mind_and_Nature.pdf

4. **our senses construct order out of an essentially undifferentiated real-ity:** When I look outside my window I see the yard covered in grass and an apparently different object, a tree. They are different because I have made cognitive distinctions to see them as different. They are the same when I make the distinction "where I live". They are also the same underground, out-of-sight where roots entwine to share water and nutrients. Tree and grass belong to the same Plant kingdom, we differentiate them both from

creatures that change location within the time frame of our perceptions. Trees and plants do travel by a different mechanism, that of spreading seeds. The mycelial networks that connect the roots of trees to one another abolish the difference not only between what we see as individual trees, but also what we believe to be the different kingdoms of life. Plants and fungi are literally One. Reality is undifferentiated until we construct differences and then ignore them into similarities.

The cybernetic concept is **umwelt**, loosely the coupling between world and cognition that is the source of distinction. The distinctions we make are coupled to our physical capabilities. The dog in the yard is making fundamentally different distinctions based on his superb ability to smell. The honey bee differentiates flowers, not plants. The hummingbird is not bound by gravity. What *is* is what physiology and cognition construct as relevant differences.

5. **and how we get to where we will be:** F. Varela (1992) *Ethical Know-How: Action, Wisdom, and Cognition* p.7. (Emphasis in original.) Online 8/18 at https://www.heartoftheart.org/wp-content/uploads/2017/08/Varela-F.-J.-1999-Ethical-know-how.-Action-wisdom-and-cognition-2119.pdf

6. **viewed as computations of equivalent sophistication:** S. Wolfram (2002) *A New Kind of Science* p.716-717. Online 8/18 at https://www.wolframscience.com/nks/

7. **by systems like cellular automata and Turing machines:** Wolfram p.720.

8. **mathematical theories should be bounded, local, and determinate:** The ultrafinitist perspective would be that the use of infinite tools just identifies an immature science. In physics *renormalization* techniques have been developed to eliminate infinite "quantities" that arise during calculation. We do still have, though, *singularities* such as black holes that appear to step outside of boundedness. Again the ultrafinitist position would be that these are phenomena that we can describe only approximately, via an infinite model that is necessary due to a lack of complete understanding.

9. **we can learn nothing unless it is through experience:** T. Norretranders (1998) *The User Illusion* p.57.

10. **J is the sum of two logarithms of i:** This observation leads to an interesting math problem: Find the value of x in this equation. x is *not* zero.

$$x + x = 0$$

Bibliography

All entries in the bibliography are from the chapter endnotes.

K. Appel & W. Haken (1977) Solution of the four color map problem. *Scientific American* **237**(4) p.108-121.

Aristotle (c. 350 BCE) *Metaphysics* 1022a. Online 8/18 at http://classics.mit.edu/Aristotle/metaphysics.html

_____ (c. 350 BCE) *Physics* Book IV. R. Hardie & R. Gaye (trans.) Online 11/18 at http://classics.mit.edu/Aristotle/physics.html

A. Badiou (1990) *Number and Numbers.*

J. Baez & J. Dolan (2001) From finite sets to Feynman diagrams. In B. Engquist & W. Schmid (eds.) *Mathematics Unlimited — 2001 and Beyond.*

G. Bateson (1972) Redundancy and coding. *Steps to an Ecology of Mind* Online 8/18 at http://shifter-magazine.com/wp-content/uploads/2015/11/gregory-bateson-steps-to-an-ecology-of-mind-1.pdf

_____ (1979) *Mind and Nature: A necessary unity.* Online 8/18 at https://monoskop.org/images/c/c3/Bateson_Gregory_Mind_and_Nature.pdf

_____ (1991) *A Sacred Unity.*

J. Bell (1999) *The Art of the Intelligible: An elementary survey of mathematics in its conceptual development.*

P. Benacerraf (1965) What numbers could not be. In P. Benacerraf & H. Putnam (eds.) (1983) *Philosophy of Mathematics 2nd ed.* p.272-294.

P. Bernays (1922) On Hilbert's ideas for the foundation of arithmetic. P. Mancosu (trans.) Online 12/18 at http://www.phil.cmu.edu/projects/bernays/Pdf/bernays02_2003-05-18.pdf

_____ (1930) The philosophy of mathematics and Hilbert's proof theory. P. Mancosu & I. Mueller (trans.) Online 12/18 at http://www.phil.cmu.edu/projects/bernays/Pdf/philmath.pdf

_____ (1935) Hilbert's investigations into the foundations of arithmetic D. Schlimm (trans.) Online 12/18 at http://www.phil.cmu.edu/projects/bernays/Pdf/untersuchungen.pdf

P. Bloom (2000) *How Children Learn the Meanings of Words.*

A. Borovik (2007) *Mathematics under the Microscope: Notes on cognitive aspects of mathematical practice.* Online 8/18 at http://eprints.ma.man.ac.uk/844/1/covered/MIMS_ep2007_112.pdf

W. Bricken (1987) *Analyzing Errors in Elementary Mathematics.* Doctoral dissertation, Stanford University School of Education.

_____ (1995) Distinction networks. In I. Wachsmuth, C. Rollinger & W. Brauer (eds.) *KI-95: Advances in Artificial Intelligence* p.35-48. Online 8/18 at http://wbricken.com/pdfs/01bm/05arch/01dnets/04distinction-networks.pdf

_____ (2002) Generalized insertion. Online 11/18 at http://iconicmath.com/mypdfs/bl-general-insertion.020118.pdf

_____ (2007) *Presentation at WSCC07.* Online 12/18 at http://wbricken.com/htmls/03words/0303ed/030305spacearith.html

_____ (2008) Simplicity rather than knowledge *AI Magazine* **29**(2).

_____ (2017) Distinction is sufficient: Iconic and symbolic perspectives on *Laws of Form. Cybernetics and Human Knowing* **24**(3-4) p.29-74. Online 12/18 at http://iconicmath.com/new/distinctionissufficient/

W. Bricken & G. Coco (1995) VEOS: The virtual environment operating shell. In W. Barfield & T. Furness (eds.), *Virtual Environments and Advanced Interface Design* p.102-142. Online 8/18 at http://wbricken.com/pdfs/03words/02vr/02veos/01describe/04veos-proj-book.pdf

M. Burns (1998) *Math: Facing an American Phobia.*

S. Buss (1999) Bounded arithmetic, proof complexity and two papers by Parikh. Online 8/18 at https://www.math.ucsd.edu/~sbuss/ResearchWeb/parikh/paper.pdf

R. Casati & A. Varzi (1999) *Parts and Places.*

C. Cellucci (2002) "Introduction" to *Filosofia e mathematica.* In R. Hersh (ed.) (2006) *18 Unconventional Essays on the Nature of Mathematics.*

G. Chaitin (2004) *Meta Math!*

D. Clements (1999) Concrete manipulatives, concrete ideas. *Contemporary Issues in Early Childhood* **1**(1) p.45-60. Online 8/18 at http://www.gse.buffalo.edu/org/buildingblocks/Newsletters/Concrete_Yelland.htm

A. Collings (2017) The Brown-4 indicational calculus. *Cybernetics and Human Knowing* **24**(3-4) p.75-101.

A. Connes (2010) A view of mathematics. Online 11/18 at http://www.alainconnes.org/en/downloads.php

J. Conway (1976) *On Numbers and Games.*

J. Conway & R. Guy (1996) *The Book of Numbers.*

D. Corfield (2004) *Towards a Philosophy of Real Mathematics.*

L. Couturat (1901) *The Logic of Leibniz.* Online 8/18 (in French) at https://babel.hathitrust.org/cgi/pt?id=ien.35556036601318;view=1up;seq=1

_____ (1905) *The Algebra of Logic* L. Robinson (trans.) (1914) Online 8/18 at http://www.gutenberg.org/ebooks/10836

R. Cummings (1922) *The Girl in the Golden Atom.*

T. Danzig (1930) *Number: The language of science.* J. Mazur (ed.) (2005). Online 8/18 at http://www.engineering108.com/Data/Engineering/Maths/Number_the_language_of_science_by_Joseph-Mazur_and_Barry-Mazur.pdf

M. Davis, R. Sigal & E. Weyuker (1994) *Computability, Complexity, and Languages 2nd ed.*

R. Dedekind (1901) *Essays on the Theory of Numbers* W. Beman (trans.). Online 8/18 at https://www.gutenberg.org/files/21016/21016-pdf.pdf

S. Dehaene (2011) *The Number Sense: How the mind creates mathematics.*

_____ (2014) *Consciousness and the Brain.*

A. DeMorgan (1849) *Trigonometry and Double Algebra.* Online 8/18 at https://archive.org/details/trigonometrydoub00demoiala/page/n8

J. Derbyshire (2006) *Unknown Quantity.*

K. Devlin (2006) The useful and reliable illusion of reality in mathematics. *Toward a New Epistemology of Mathematics Workshop* GAP.6 Conference 2006. Online 8/18 at https://web.stanford.edu/~kdevlin/Papers/Berlin06.pdf

R. Dipert (1995) Peirce's underestimated place in the history of logic: A response to Quine. In K. Ketner (ed.) *Peirce and Contemporary Thought: Philosophical Inquiries.*

M. Donovan & J. Bransford (eds.) (2005) *How Students Learn Mathematics in the Classroom.*

A. Eddington (1927) *The Nature of the Physical World: The Gifford Lectures.* Online 8/18 at http://henry.pha.jhu.edu/Eddington.2008.pdf

Encyclopedia Britannica, 1771 edition Volume 2 "Logic".

T. Etter (2006) Three-place identity. Online 12/18 via the Wayback Machine: https://web.archive.org/web/20130510223843/http://www.boundaryinstitute.org/bi/articles/Three-place_Identity.pdf

Euclid (c. 300 BCE) *The Elements*. Online 12/18 at https://mathcs.clarku.edu/~djoyce/java/elements/toc.html

W. Ewald (1996) *From Kant to Hilbert: A source book in the foundations of mathematics* p.787-832.

S. Feferman (1992) Why a little bit goes a long way: Logical foundations of scientifically applicable mathematics. *Philosophy of Science Association* 1992 Vol. II p.442-455. Online 8/18 at https://math.stanford.edu/~feferman/papers/psa1992.pdf

_____ (1997) Does mathematics need new axioms? Online 4/18 at https://web.archive.org/web/20170911031521/http://math.stanford.edu/~feferman/papers.html

S. Feferman & G. Hellman (1995) Predicative foundations of arithmetic. *Journal of Philosophical Logic* p.1-17. Online 8/18 at http://math.stanford.edu/~feferman/papers/predarith.pdf

S. Feferman & T. Strahm (2010) Unfolding finitist arithmetic. *Review of Symbolic Logic* **3**(4) p.665-689. Online 8/18 at https://math.stanford.edu/~feferman/papers/UnfoldFA.pdf

K. François (2007) The untouchable and frightening status of mathematics. In K. François & J. van Bendegem (eds.) (2007) *Philosophical Dimensions in Mathematics Education*.

C. Franks (2009) *The Autonomy of Mathematical Knowledge*.

G. Frege (1884/1950) *The Foundations of Arithmetic*. Online 8/18 at http://www.naturalthinker.net/trl/texts/Frege,Gottlob/Frege,%20Gottlob%20-%20The%20Foundations%20of%20Arithmetic%20(1953)%202Ed_%207.0-2.5%20LotB.pdf

_____ (1903) *The Fundamental Laws of Arithmetic Vol. II*.

H. Friedman (2013) Concrete mathematical incompleteness. Online 8/18 at http://cage.ugent.be/programFriedman/slides/MathInc083113.pdf

J. Goguen (1988) What is unification? Online 8/18 at http://citeseerx.ist.psu.edu/viewdoc/summary?doi=10.1.1.16.9221

_____ (1993) On notation. In. B. Magnusson, B. Meyer & J-F. Perrot (eds.) *TOOLS 10: Technology of Object-oriented Languages and Systems* p.5-10.

R. Goodstein (1954) Logic-free formalizations of recursive arithmetic. *Mathematica Scandinavica* **2** p.247-261.

I. Grattan-Guinness (1997) *The Rainbow of Mathematics.*

M. Greaves (2002) *The Philosophical Status of Diagrams.*

J. Greeno & R. Hall (1997) Practicing representation: learning with and about representational forms. *Phi Delta Kappan* 78 p.1-24. Online 4/18 at http://www.pdkintl.org/kappan/kgreeno.htm

T. Hales (2007) The Jordan curve theorem, formally and informally. *The Mathematical Association of America Monthly* 114. Online 8/18 at https://pdfs.semanticscholar.org/70ab/0431a8d59e1cd9147b54c5e99883a54190a1.pdf

A. Heeffer (2007) Learning concepts through the history of mathematics. In K. François & J. van Bendegem (eds.) (2007) *Philosophical Dimensions in Mathematics Education.*

H. Hellman (2006) *Great Feuds in Mathematics.*

A. Heyting (1971) Disputations. In P. Benacerraf & H. Putnam (1983) *Philosophy of Mathematics 2ed.*

V. Huber-Dyson (1998) On the nature of mathematical concepts: Why and how do mathematicians jump to conclusions? EDGE conversation 2/15/98. Online 8/18 at https://www.edge.org/conversation/verena_huber_dyson-on-the-nature-of-mathematical-concepts-why-and-how-do-mathematicians

D. Kahneman (2013) *Thinking, Fast and Slow.*

J. Kaput (1987) Representation systems and mathematics. In C. Janvier (ed.) *Problems of Representation in the Teaching and Learning of Mathematics* p.19-26.

L. Kauffman (1995) Arithmetic in the form. *Cybernetics and Systems: An International Journal* **26**(1) p.1-57. Online 8/18 at http://homepages.math.uic.edu/~kauffman/ArithForm.pdf

_____ (2017 in process) *Laws of Form — An Exploration in Mathematics and Foundations* (rough draft) Online 2/17 at http://homepages.math.uic.edu/~kauffman/Laws.pdf

L. Kauffman & F. Varela (1980) Form dynamics. *Journal of Social and Biological Structures* **3**. Online 8/18 at http://homepages.math.uic.edu/~kauffman/FormDynamics.pdf

C. Kieran (1981) Concepts associated with the equality symbol. *Educational Studies in Mathematics* **12** p.317-326. Online 8/18 at https://oak.ucc.nau.edu/smg224/401pdfs/algebrareadings/kieran1.pdf

J. Kilpatrick, J. Swalford & B. Findell (eds.) (2001) *Adding It Up: Helping children learn mathematics.*

S. Kleene (1952) *Introduction to Metamathematics.*

I. Kleiner (1991) Rigor and proof in mathematics: A historical perspective. *Mathematics Magazine* 64 p.291-314. Online 8/18 at https://www.maa.org/sites/default/files/pdf/upload_library/22/Allendoerfer/1992/0025570x.di021172.02p0031c.pdf

M. Klein & O. Pelz (2018) No Box Today. Online 12/18 at https://www.nobox-today.com/

M. Kline (1972) *Mathematical Thought from Ancient to Modern Times.*

_____ (1980) *Mathematics: The loss of certainty.*

D. Knuth (1976) Mathematics and computer science: Coping with finiteness. *Science* **194**(4271) p.1235-1242.

E. Knuth et al (2006) Does understanding the equal sign matter? Evidence from solving equations. *Journal for Research in Mathematics Education* **37**(4) p.297-312. Online 8/18 at http://www.sciacchitano.it/Spazio/Coping%20with%20Finiteness.pdf

A. Kornai (2003) Explicit finitism. *International Journal of Theoretical Physics* **42**(2) p.301-307.

G. Lakoff & R. Núñez (2000) *Where Mathematics Comes From.*

J. Lanier (1989) Communication without symbols. *Whole Earth Review* 64 p.118-119. Online 8/18 at http://www.jaronlanier.com/jaron%20whole%20earth%20review.pdf

_____ (2017) *Dawn of the New Everything.*

F. Lawvere & S. Schanuel (2009) *Conceptual Mathematics 2nd ed.*

J. Leach (2010) *Mathematics and Religion.*

M. Leng (2010) *Mathematics and Reality.*

T. Lenoir (2008) Machinic bodies, ghosts, and paraselves: confronting the singularity with Brian Rotman. Foreword to B. Rotman (2008) *Becoming Beside Ourselves.*

B. Lewin (2018) *Enthusiastic Mathematics.*

S. Lloyd (2002) Computational capacity of the universe. *Physical Review Letters* 88:237901.

P. Lockhart (2017) *Arithmetic.*

J. Łukasiewicz (1948) The shortest axiom of the implicational calculus of propositions. *Proceedings of the Royal Irish Academy* **52A**(3) p.25-33.

P. Maddy (1993) *Realism in Mathematics.*

_____ (2008) How applied mathematics became pure. *The Review of Symbolic Logic* **1**(1) p.16-41.

_____ (2014) A second philosophy of arithmetic. *The Review of Symbolic Logic* **7**(2) p.222-249. Online 8/18 at http://www.socsci.uci.edu/~pjmaddy/bio/arithmetic%20in%20RSL.pdf

M. Mannucci & R. Cherubin (2008) Model theory of ultrafinitism I: Fuzzy initial segments of arithmetic. Online 12/18 at https://arxiv.org/pdf/cs/0611100v1.pdf

A. Mathias (2002) A term length of 4,523,659,424,929. *Synthese* 133 p.75-86.

B. Mazur (2007) When is one thing equal to some other thing? Online 4/18 at http://www.math.harvard.edu/~mazur/preprints/when_is_one.pdf

T. McFarlane (2007) Distinction and the foundation of arithmetic. Online 8/18 at http://www.integralscience.org/distinctionarithmetic.pdf

J. Misra (1994) Powerlist: A structure for parallel recursion. *ACM Transactions on Programming Languages and Systems* **16**(6) p.1737-1767.

R. Munroe xkcd *cartoon* "⊂". Online 8/18 at https://xkcd.com/859/

P. Moyer, J. Bolyard & M. Spikell (2002) What are virtual manipulatives? *Teaching Children Mathematics* **8**(6).

T. Needham (1999) *Visual Complex Analysis.*

E. Nelson (2015) *Elements.* Online 11/18 at https://arxiv.org/abs/1510.00369

_____ (2002) Syntax and semantics. *Foundations and the Ontological Quest. Prospects for the New Millennium.* Online 8/18 at https://web.math.princeton.edu/~nelson/papers/s.pdf

T. Nelson (1974) *Computer Lib/Dream Machines.*

R. Netz (1999) *The Shaping of Deduction in Greek Mathematics.*

T. Norretranders (1998) *The User Illusion.*

J. Paris & L. Harrington (1977) A mathematical incompleteness in Peano arithmetic. In J. Barwise (ed.) (1982) *Handbook of Mathematical Logic.* Online 8/18 at https://www.karlin.mff.cuni.cz/~krajicek/ph.pdf

G. Peano (1889) The principles of arithmetic presented by a new method. In J. van Heijenoort (ed.) (1967) *From Frege to Gödel: A sourcebook in mathematical logic, 1879-1931*.

C. S. Peirce (1909) MS 514 Existential graphs.

_____ (1931-35) *Collected Papers of Charles Sanders Peirce*. C. Hartshorne & P. Weiss (eds.).

R. Penrose (2004) *The Road to Reality*.

R. Plasmeijer & M. van Eekelen (1993) *Functional Programming and Parallel Graph Rewriting*.

H. Poincaré (1908) *Science et Méthode*. G. Halstead (trans.) (1913) *The Foundations of Science*. Online 8/18 at https://www.gutenberg.org/files/39713/39713-h/39713-h.htm

M. Potter (2004) *Set Theory and its Philosophy*.

S. Powell (2012) Equations and the equal sign in elementary mathematics textbooks. *Elementary School Journal* **112**(4) p.627-648.

F. Ramsey (1922) Truth and simplicity. *British Journal for the Philosophy of Science* (2007) **58** p.379-386.

A. Robinson (1974) *Non-Standard Analysis*.

R. Robinson (1950) An essentially undecidable axiom system. *Proceedings of the International Congress of Mathematics 1950* p.729-730.

V. Rodych (1999) Wittgenstein on irrationals and algorithmic decidability. *Synthese* 118 p.279-304.

_____ Wittgenstein's philosophy of mathematics, *Stanford Encyclopedia of Philosophy*. Online 3/17 at https://plato.stanford.edu/entries/wittgenstein-mathematics/

B. Rotman (1993) *Ad Infinitum*.

_____ (2000) *Mathematics as Sign: writing imagining counting*.

_____ (2008) *Becoming Beside Ourselves: the alphabet, ghosts, and distributed human being*.

B. Russell (1918) *Mysticism and Logic and Other Essays*. Online 8/18 at https://www.gutenberg.org/files/25447/25447-h/25447-h.htm

_____ (1920) *Introduction to Mathematical Philosophy*. Online 4/18 at https://people.umass.edu/klement/imp/imp.html

C. Sandburg (1993) *Arithmetic.*

D. Schmandt-Besserat (1999) *The Evolution of Writing.* Online 4/18 at https:// sites.utexas.edu/dsb/tokens/the-evolution-of-writing/

G. Spencer Brown (1969) *Laws of Form.* Online 8/18 at http://www.manuelugarte. org/modulos/biblioteca/b/G-Spencer-Brown-Laws-of-Form.pdf.

_____ (1969) *Laws of Form* Bohmeier Verlag Edition (2009) Appendix 4: *An algebra for the natural numbers* (1961).

R. Stansifer (1984) Presburger's article on integer arithmetic: remarks and translation. Technical Report 84-639. Dept. of Computer Science, Cornell University.

L. Stebbing (1931) *A Modern Introduction to Logic.* Online 8/18 at http://www. naturalthinker.net/trl/texts/Stebbing,LSusan/PostulationalSystems.html

W. Tait (1981) Finitism. In W. Tait (2005) *The Provenance of Pure Reason* p. 21-42.

A. Tarski (1953) Undecidable theories. *Studies in Logic and the Foundations of Mathematics.*

S. Tobias (1993) *Overcoming Math Anxiety.*

Utah State University (1999) National library of virtual manipulatives. Online 4/18 at http://nlvm.usu.edu/en/nav/index.html

J. van Heijenoort (ed.) (1967) *From Frege to Gödel: A sourcebook in mathematical logic, 1879-1931.*

F. Varela (1992) *Ethical Know-How: Action, wisdom, and cognition.* Online 8/18 at https://www.heartoftheart.org/wp-content/uploads/2017/08/Varela-F.-J.-1999-Ethical-know-how.-Action-wisdom-and-cognition-2119.pdf

U. Vishkin (2011) Using simple abstraction to reinvent computing for parallelism. *Communications of the ACM* **54**(1) p.75-85.

M. Walicki (1995) The origin of mathematics. Online 8/18 at https://www.ii.uib. no/~michal/phil/om/om.pdf

N. Weaver (2009) Is set theory indispensible? Online 8/18 at https://arxiv.org/ abs/0905.1680

H. Weyl (1941) *The Mathematical Way of Thinking.*

J. Wheeler (1990) *Complexity, Entropy, and the Physics of Information.* Online 8/18 at https://archive.org/details/ComplexityEntropyAndThePhysicsOfInformation

A. Whitehead & B. Russell (1910) *Principia Mathematica*. Online 8/18 at https://archive.org/details/PrincipiaMathematicaVolumeI

N. Wildberger (2005) Set theory: should you believe? Online 10/18 at http://web.maths.unsw.edu.au/~norman/views2.htm

W. Winn & W. Bricken (1992) Designing virtual worlds for use in mathematics education: The example of experiential algebra. *Educational Technology* **32**(12) p.12-19. Online 12/18 at http://wbricken.com/pdfs/03words/03education/03iconic-math/07worlds-for-math.pdf

L. Wittgenstein (1921) *Tractatus Logico-Philosophicus*. Online 8/18 at https://www.gutenberg.org/files/5740/5740-pdf.pdf

_____ (1929-30) *Philosophical Remarks*.

S. Wolfram (2002) *A New Kind of Science*. Online 8/18 at https://www.wolframscience.com/nks/

_____ (2016) *Idea Makers*.

_____ (2017) *An Elementary Introduction to the Wolfram Language 2nd ed.*

F. Zalamea (2009) *Synthetic Philosophy of Contemporary Mathematics*.

Index to the Index

The index is organized by concept and by content. Keywords are associated with each index category.

As a suggestion, decide first what kind of things you are looking for: *person, concept, pattern* or *iconic system*. Then look under the appropriate category for page and figure locations. Figures are listed by page number followed by the figure number in bold italics, for example: 124 *5-2*. Boldface page numbers indicate primary definitions and content emphasis.

The five **Primary Reference Figures** summarize the structural forms of James algebra and have been isolated from the alphabetical Index as globally applicable.

PEOPLE

SYMBOLIC CONCEPTS
mathematics and logic
number and arithmetic
computer science
education and other
acronyms
symbols and icons

ICONIC CONCEPTS

JAMES ALGEBRA
containers and delimiters
patterns and principles

VOLUMES
volume I
volume II
volume III
volumes I, II and III

PRIMARY REFERENCE FIGURES

TYPOGRAPHIC DELIMITERS

BUMPER STICKERS

COVER
cover words

WEBSITES

Index

Index

Symbolic Concepts

emphasis in bold
figure numbers follow their
page number in *bold italic*

Index

NUMBER AND ARITHMETIC

Index

COMPUTER SCIENCE

Index

SYMBOLS AND ICONS

ICONIC CONCEPTS

JAMES ALGEBRA

Figure 16-1 summarizes the axioms and theorems of James algebra

Figure 16-2 summarizes the concepts of James Algebra

Figure 21-1 summarizes James Algebra for whole number arithmetic

CONTAINERS AND DELIMITERS

PATTERNS AND PRINCIPLES

VOLUMES

Primary Reference Figures

Typographic Delimiters

bracket	*name*	*use*	*chapters*
James Algebra			
o, ( )	round	numeric, exponential	all
[ ]	square	non-numeric, logarithmic	all
< >	angle	reflection, inverse	all
( )	shell	void-equivalent outermost	18, 20, 28
{ }	curly	generic boundary	18, 24, 27, 29
(( ))	double shell	substitution operator	16, 18, 23-**25**, 27, 28
⟨ ⟩	large angle	logic, not numeric	28, 29
⟦ ⟧	double square	two-boundary system	20
Textual Mathematics			
( )	parenthesis	textual scoping	all
[ ]	bracket	function arguments	19, 23
{ }	brace	set delimiter	16-17, 20, 22, 26, 27
⟪ ⟫	double angle	equivalence class	17, 24
Incidental			*page*
⌐	cross, mark	LoF distinction	xxvi
⟪ ⟫	large double angle	two-boundary alternative	124
( )	shell	semantic oscillation	125-126
" "	quotation mark	string expression	191
⟦ ⟧	double bracket	equality	350

BUMPER STICKERS

COVER

COVER WORDS

Symbolic arithmetic is a belief system.

The arithmetic we are taught was designed
before film, before TV, before music videos, before smart phones.

Our media are coupled to how we think and what we do.
Symbolic abstraction is too detached for this century.

Postsymbolism reintegrates our bodies and our minds.

Sets and logic and functional thinking
need to evolve to incorporate
global unity and ecological diversity.

Concept is embodied, concrete, incorporated, lived.
Meaning comes from experience.

Arithmetic is multisensory pattern.

Index

WEBSITES

Printed in Great Britain
by Amazon